Other books by Rutherford Platt

THE RIVER OF LIFE

AMERICAN TREES, A BOOK OF DISCOVERY

THE WOODS OF TIME

THIS GREEN WORLD

1001 Questions Answered About Trees

The forest is a peculiar organism of unlimited kindness and benevolence that makes no demands for its sustenance and extends generously the products of its life activity; it provides protection to all beings, offering shade even to the axeman who destroys it.

GAUTAMA BUDDHA
Founder of the
Buddhist religion
circa 525 B.C.

1001 Questions Answered About Trees

§§§§§§§§§§§§§§§§§§§§§§§

BY RUTHERFORD PLATT

ILLUSTRATED WITH DRAWINGS
AND WITH PHOTOGRAPHS BY THE AUTHOR

DODD, MEAD & COMPANY

NEW YORK **1959**

LIBRARY OF CONGRESS CATALOG CARD NUMBER: 59-6900

PRINTED IN THE UNITED STATES OF AMERICA

BY VAIL-BALLOU PRESS, INC., BINGHAMTON, N. Y.

2256

To
Arthur H. Graves, Hester M. Rusk,
and the Brooklyn Botanic Garden
for first opening my eyes to trees

I am grateful to Shirley Sarnoff for the help she has given in the preparation of this book.

R. P.

CONTENTS

CONTENTS

PHOTOGRAPHS

(Following page 144)

Beech bark is elastic, so it does not crack and break

Sycamore, or plane tree, has bark like a patchwork quilt

Paper birch bark is famous as the material used to make Indian birch bark canoes

Eucalyptus has bark that strips off with a play of many colors

A fossil stump of solid stone from the dawn-seed fern tree that flourished on earth more than 300 million years ago

The fluted trunk of horsetail

1001 Questions
Answered
About
Trees

I. HISTORY AND FACTS

1. What is a tree? A tree is a perennial woody plant with three basic characteristics that distinguish it from all other plants. 1. *Size:* In maturity it is much bigger than all other plants. 2. *Form:* A typical tree has a single stem which bears branches a distance above the ground. 3. *Way of life:* Under natural conditions trees grow in stands (forests) which dominate their area of land. By the wood of their trunks, their fruits, and the special kind of environment they create, trees influence life on earth more than any other kind of plant.

2. How long have trees been growing on earth? The first definite evidence of trees on earth goes back 300 million years, to a time which geologists call the Devonian Period.

3. What is the record of the earliest known tree life on earth? A flash flood struck in the western Catskill Mountains, in upper New York State, in 1869, uprooting trees, carrying away bridges, causing the banks of Schoharie Creek to cave in. This exposed in the bed of the creek some tree stumps made of solid rock which aroused great curiosity. Later, while building the Gilboa Dam for the New York City water supply excavation penetrated deeper into the hillsides of the same area, and turned up many mysterious stumps.

4. What kind were those first trees on earth? They were unlike any types of tree growing on earth today. Each tree was a composition of a fern that had taken the form of a large tree, and a tree which bore a strange kind of seed. Thus, these first trees known to have grown on earth are called *Eospermatopteris,* a Greek word which says in English: Dawn-seed-fern.

5. How big were those first trees? The trunks averaged two feet in diameter and the trees were about 40 feet tall.

6. Where are the Eospermatopteris stumps to be seen? Some of them are in a roadside exhibit at Gilboa, New York. Others are in the New York State Museum at Albany.

1

7. When did trees like some on earth today first appear? Some 60 million years after the *Eospermatopteris,* forests of the Coal Age were luxurious and worldwide, and contained a number of different kinds of trees, with similarities to trees in our world. That was 240 million years ago.

8. How did we find out about the trees of the Coal Age? Lumps of coal and rock dug out of coal mines reveal countless impressions of parts of trees and other plants, such as leaves, stems, seeds, roots.

9. Would those trees of the Coal Age look familiar to us? Yes, in part. Some of the types have survived to our day but not as large trees. Some of those earlier types were trees with tall, straight, fluted trunks like columns of a Greek temple—related to the little horsetail plants of our day. Others were stocky with thick trunks covered with overlapping scales instead of bark—related to our clubmosses. The tallest tree of the Coal Age forests, although greatly outnumbered by the horsetail and clubmoss trees, was the most exciting innovation because it had real wood. It is named *Cordaites* from the Latin word for heart. The other trees did not have solid wood trunks; they were hollow or pithy, while *Cordaites* had wood and features like *Auracaria,* often seen as a house plant. It was probably the ancestor of the true pines.

10. Are any trees now living on earth the same kind as trees which grew in the Coal Age more than 200 million years ago? Near the close of the Coal Age two seed trees appeared, which we call cycad and gingko. The cycad is a palm-like tree which grows in Florida where it is known as comfort root and coontie, but it is more prominent in the southern hemisphere. A cycad can be seen in botanical gardens where it is known as sago palm. The gingko is a familiar tree of our big city streets and parks. (See Question 127.)

11. Did the Coal Age forests have any animal inhabitants? Yes. The principal inhabitants were giant salamanders and crocodiles, dragon flies with a 29-inch wing spread, enormous scorpions, spiders, and cockroaches 4 inches long.

12. How long have trees like those in the woods of eastern United States been growing on earth? Some hundred million years ago (in what geologists call the Upper Cretaceous period) a forest was growing on the west coast of Greenland with many trees like those of New England today.

13. What kind of trees grew in that Greenland forest? Sycamore heads the list. We can honor the name of sycamore as an original pioneer of the world's hardwood trees, according to the evidence. While some 30 million years slid by, the Greenland forest was enriched by poplar, willow, tulip tree, elm, hawthorn, hornbeam, sweet gum, juniper, sassafras, hickory and walnut.

14. Did our kind of trees first appear on earth in Greenland? No. That is only the earliest record that has turned up. There is a valid theory that the familiar trees of northeastern United States such as elm, maple, oak, poplar were originally associated in woodlands in what is now northeastern India, near Darjeeling. During unknown millions of years they traveled from there across China, the Bering Straits, and formed a great circumpolar forest around the Arctic Ocean. From there they spread southward into Europe and America. Their fossils, discovered in Greenland, are those of trees in the midst of their travels through the ages.

15. Where and when did our familiar trees first grow in the United States? The first record comes from the Potomac Valley, in Arundel County, Maryland. There a remarkable forest was growing 95 million years ago. That was only 5 million years after the sycamores in Greenland.

16. What trees were among these first families of Maryland? Most of the woods consisted of cycads, giant ferns, and the old *Auracaria,* the ancestor of the pines, but about 25 percent consisted of something sensationally new in trees. These were willow, poplar, oak, elm, sassafras, plus familiar accompaniments such as Virginia creeper, grape vines, and climbing bittersweet.

17. Did people live among those trees? No. *Homo sapiens* was not destined to appear on earth until about 94 million years after those trees were making the landscape lovely in Maryland. Those willows, poplars, and oaks were growing in this country even before the Rocky Mountains had been pushed up.

18. How much of the United States was covered by trees when the Pilgrims landed? There were 937 million acres of superb virgin forest. That included all territory except the Great Plains and some western desert areas.

19. What is "virgin forest?" Primeval forest unchanged by man.

20. How much is left today of the original forest that was here when the first settlers came? About 5.4 percent. Most of that is in the National Park system.

21. What happened to the other 94.6 percent of the original forest? Man cut down and burned the virgin forest for homesteading and farming, and later for forest products. This stimulated forest fires, insects and pest attacks which quickened the destruction.

22. When did land clearing take place in the United States? The greatest period was in the 18th and 19th centuries, but it is not quite finished in our northwestern states. There the last remnants (containing Douglas fir, western hemlock, redwood, ponderosa pine) of the virgin forest outside of the National Parks are being felled today.

23. Does forest clearing stop at the United States–Canadian border? No. Roadbuilding and railroad extensions into the hitherto inaccessible forests of western Canada and Alaska are going on at a feverish rate, and the last of the incredibly tall virgin forests of North America are doomed, except those with government protection.

24. What is left of the virgin forests east of the Mississippi? Only a few specimens of old patriarchs of long-lived trees such as tulip tree and white oak. The forests of Indian and colonial days live only in legends and history.

25. What was the final chapter in the deforestation of the eastern states? The transformation of the wonderfully forested states of Ohio and Indiana into farmland during the 19th century.

26. What were the first cargoes of tree products exported from America? Sassafras bark collected along the coasts of Maine and Massachusetts was shipped to England in 1603 by a man named Martin Pring, Captain George Weymouth, in 1605, took to England a load of white pine logs which he cut in Maine along the Penobscot and Kennebec Rivers.

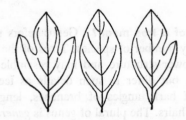

Sassafras leaves come in three shapes

27. Is the loss of our original American forests a human tragedy? Not in the sense of what happened in China, eastern Mediterranean, and what is happening in large areas of Africa today. This country had statesmanlike leadership in the nick of time to preserve much of the sentimental, scenic, and wildlife value of our finest trees in the National Parks and to control the use of trees in our national forests. The largest users of trees, the timber, paper, and wood-products companies, are taking the leadership in sound forestry practices to insure a supply of trees for future generations. Both government and private conservation movements are gaining momentum by leaps and bounds, with the result that forest areas may be increasing today. Nevertheless, for spiritual assets, for wildlife and the enchantment of the wilderness, efforts should be relentless to leave every last one of the superb giants in the Northwest still standing. Nature took hundreds and even thousands of years to create them, and a little man with his terrible mechanical power can destroy one of these marvels of life in minutes. Now that we have learned how to grow trees like crops, we should be compelled to raise the wood and to stimulate new growth to supply all our necessities for tree products, and leave those last forests of old giants unharmed.

28. What does "species" of tree mean? It means the individual kind of tree. Trees of the same species have the same characteristics of bark, leaf, flower, seed, etc., and present the same general appearance. The word *species* is both singular and plural.

29. How many species of trees are there in the United States? 1,182 species grow naturally in our country, and many more have been introduced.

30. How does our number of species compare with other countries? Ours is a far greater tree treasury than Europe's. Only India has more species.

31. What does the "genus" of a tree mean? Genus refers to the class of a tree and includes any number of species. Trees of the same genus have the same basic flower structure and may resemble each other in outward appearance, but differ in such details as teeth of leaf, style of acorn, color of bark, angles of branches, length of thorns, presence or absence of hairs. The plural of genus is *genera*.

32. How are genus and species indicated in the name of a tree? In everyday language the species is named first when it is named at all; for example, white oak, black walnut, sugar maple. In scientific language the genus is named first and the species second, so these three trees would be, respectively, *Quercus alba, Juglans nigra, Acer saccharum*.

33. What tree genus has the greatest number of species? Hawthorn with 165 species. Some of these species are so complicated that an expert would have trouble identifying them. The average person can enjoy hawthorns by knowing four of the commonest: cockspur thorn, white thorn, Washington thorn, and English hawthorn.

34. What large forest tree genus has the greatest number of species? Oak, with some 60 species. Of these 9 are common in northeastern United States, 8 in the South, 3 in the Northwest, and 5 in California. These are all that one would have to know to enjoy oaks most likely to be encountered. Recognizing different kinds of trees is a simple puzzle and not a scientific project. (See Question 192.)

35. What area has the most species of trees? Eastern United States, particularly the southern Appalachian Mountains, which was a natural sanctuary from which trees radiated after the Ice Age. Florida and California with trees imported from all over the world also have many different kinds of trees.

36. What is meant by hardwood and softwood trees? The hardwoods are trees with broad leaves, usually dropping in winter. The softwoods are trees with needles, typically evergreen and bearing cones.

37. Is the wood of the hardwoods actually harder than the wood of the softwoods? Yes, generally, and from the viewpoint of the lumber man who thinks in terms of the hardwoods—oak, hickory, walnut, versus the softwoods—pine, fir, redwood. Actually, some hardwoods such as poplar, and willow (and the phenomenal balsa which is the softest, lightest wood in the world), are much softer than some softwoods such as red cedar and bald cypress. (See Question 999.)

38. What is meant by deciduous and coniferous? Deciduous means leaf-dropping, and is another word for hardwood. Coniferous means cone bearing, and is another word for softwood.

Redwood cone

39. What is the tallest tree? A redwood sequoia in Big Tree National Park, on Redwood Highway, California, is 300 feet high. This tree has a circumference of 65 feet at 4 feet. Claims that this is the tallest tree in the world are disputed by a eucalyptus in Australia said to be 326 feet high. (See Question 169.)

40. How large do pine cones grow? Cones of the sugar pine are longer than 20 inches.

41. What tree has the largest leaves? The American hardwood with the largest single blade is large-leafed cucumber tree, *Magnolia macrophylla*. This magnolia with 30-inch leaves grows in limestone valleys of North Carolina in protected spots where it avoids tearing its huge sail-like leaves in the wind. Banana leaves reach 12 feet, and always have a tattered appearance. The date palm has leaves 15 feet long, not in single blades but consisting of leaflets along an axis. The largest true leaf is Hercules' club (*Aralia spinosa*) with blades two feet wide and three feet long—but these are double compound with leaflets so they can be mistaken for small leaves. This is a southern tree but it is often planted in the north.

Hercules' club—largest
multiple leaf

42. What leaves turn what colors in the fall? Sugar maple, sumac: flame red and orange. Red maple, dogwood, sassafras, scarlet oak: dark, rich red. Poplar, birch, tulip tree, willow: yellow. Ash: plum purple. Oak, beech (often streaked with yellow along the veins), larch, elm, hickory, sycamore: tan or brown. The locust retains its green until the leaves drop. The black walnut, butternut drop leaves so fast they don't have time to turn. (See Question 221.)

43. Why do chips of birch sink when they leap from your axe into the brook? Birch has a high proportion of green wood, that is, cells filled with sap instead of air.

44. What tree produces the hardest wood? Desert ironwood of the Southwest has wood as heavy as stone that blunts tools and can hardly be cut with a saw. In our eastern woodland blue beech (*Carpinus caroliniana*) and hop hornbeam (*Ostrya virginiana*) are extremely hard and also go by the name of ironwood.

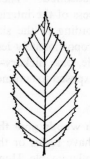  

Hop hornbeam leaf and cluster of fruits   Blue beech seed attached to wing

45. What is the difference between a plane tree and a sycamore? These names are interchangeable in the United States. In England the tree we call sycamore is called plane tree. The sycamore in England is a species of maple.

46. What is the difference between larch and tamarack? Tamarack is an alternative name for the eastern larch (*Larix americana*). The tall western larch and European larch are not, strictly speaking, tamarack. Tamarack should not be confused with tamarisk, a small tree with grayish, juniper-like leaves from Mediterranean countries.

47. What makes white birch so flexible? A slender trunk, with fine straight grain and elastic bark. Also, there is a high proportion of green wood in white birch, with cell walls soft and flexible.

48. How do branches "marry" and grow together? Friction wears off the outer bark, and when the living cells of the inner bark (cambian) are pressed together they merge into one structure. This usually occurs when the branches are young and the bark is tender. This is the same process as grafting.

49. What woods burn well when green?   Ash, because its wood contains inflammable oleic acid. This is a fatty acid constituent of olive oil, and the ash tree belongs to the olive family. Also, wood of the pine family burns when green due to resin in the wood.

50. How long should the principal firewoods be seasoned?   There is no rule of thumb. Seasoning is a drying-out process of the interior cells of the wood. The length of time varies according to the size of the log, its age when cut (older trees having proportionately less sap wood), and climate. A medium-size log of apple, oak, hickory— excellent firewoods—will season in one year, or, if exposed to summer sun, in a few months.

51. What are sluggish burning woods and which woods give the best coals?   Willow and butternut woods do not have resins or the fatty acids and oils which make other woods more inflammable. However, slow-burning willow makes good charcoal. Any dry hardwoods like oak, birch, maple and fruit trees are the best for cooking, but pine trees—especially hemlock—snap sparks.

52. Why does seasoned pine last so well in air but disintegrate rapidly in the ground?   Pine wood does not have essential oils that give the distinctive colors to hardwoods like walnut or the red color and fragrance to cedar wood, and which, locked in them, preserves them from decay. Pine resin is an oxidation formed near the surface of the log, not in the interior. This is dispersed underground, and unresisted decay then proceeds.

53. Why do some woods split more easily than others when you drive in a nail?   Hardwoods, such as oak and walnut, have their fibers woven together by bands of tissue that radiate out from the center, called pith rays or flakes. These are seen as whitish swirls and waves that add beauty to the wood grain. Straight-grain woods, such as pine and poplar, lack this binding and the fibers are apt to split when the nail is driven lengthwise between them, wedging them apart. Also, wood that is overdry and without its natural oils loses its resiliency and is more susceptible to splitting. This happens to the backs of bureau drawers and other unpainted and unwaxed wood that has stood for years in a heated house. A crooked-grained wood, such as hemlock, splinters badly when it is brittle dry.

54. Why do mushrooms grow better on some trees than on others? Mushrooms appear from cottony threads of a fungus hidden in the wood, especially when the air is cool. This condition is most common in a northern or mountain woodland. Thus the dead wood of northern trees, such as spruce, fir, birch, poplar, produce the most mushrooms. It would be hard to find a twig or log lying on the ground in a damp forest that is not invaded by fungus. It is not the kind of wood but weather conditions that bring forth mushrooms. (See Questions 1040 and 1043.)

55. Are any trees poisonous to human beings? No large tree commonly encountered is poisonous to touch. Poison sumac is a slender shrub-like tree of wooded swamps east of the Rockies whose leaves, berries, and bark scald the skin viciously with a waxy, acid element. This tree is extra dangerous because its bright red fall foliage attracts the eye. Coral sumac or black poison wood (*Metopium toxiferum*) is a good sized tree of the Florida Keys with exquisite smooth red bark that is very poisonous to touch. Farther south in the West Indies and British Honduras black poison wood (*Cameria*) has highly poisonous sap that badly burns the skin. However, many fine and common trees can wound cruelly without poisoning, such as the thorns on the locust and hawthorns, and the daggers on Osage orange and the Hercules' club.

56. What about poison oak and poison hemlock? Despite their names these are not trees. Poison oak is a form of poison ivy growing as a low shrub chiefly on the west coast. Poison hemlock is a biennial herb, related to Queen Anne's lace, with sap that is deadly to people and livestock. This weed is the hemlock that Socrates drank, and that was used to kill criminals in ancient Greece.

57. What is the difference between an arboretum and a nursery? An arboretum is a place for the cultivation, study, and enjoyment of trees. A nursery is a place for raising trees to use elsewhere in landscaping and forestry.

58. What purposes do arboretums serve? Two general purposes. 1. A laboratory for developing new varieties of trees and shrubs of special beauty, or faster growth, or resistance to pests and diseases, and to experiment with trees from foreign lands to discover their uses and adaptability to our climate. 2. A living museum where people can see and learn about trees and a place of beauty at every season.

59. What and where are the leading arboretums of the United States?

Name	*Location*
Arnold Arboretum	Boston, Mass.
Boyce Thompson Southwestern Arboretum	Superior, Ariz.
Brooklyn Botanic Garden	Brooklyn, N.Y.
Desmond Arboretum	Newburgh, N.Y.
Fairchild Tropical Garden	Coral Gables, Fla.
Highland and Durand-Eastman Park Arboretum	Rochester, N.Y.
Huntington Botanical Garden	San Marino, Cal.
Kingwood Center	Mansfield, Ohio
Longwood Gardens	Kennett Square, Pa.
Los Angeles State and County Arboretum	Arcadia, Cal.
Missouri Botanical Garden	St. Louis, Mo.
Morris Arboretum	Philadelphia, Pa.
Morton Arboretum	Lisle, Ill.
National Arboretum	Washington, D.C.
New York Botanical Garden	New York, N.Y.
University of Washington Arboretum	Seattle, Wash.

60. What is the fastest growing tree? Paulownia or princess tree (named after Anna Paulowna, princess of Holland) is the fastest growing commercial wood tree in America. A seedling can raise 20 feet of height in one growing season. Sumac and ailanthus (the tree of city backyards) compete with paulownia in speed of lengthening, but they are weed trees with pithy trunks. Catalpa is also in the race for growing good wood fast. It can add an inch-wide ring to its wood in one summer.

61. What is our most valuable tree? The wood-products industry would name Douglas fir. This tree has the greatest standing volume and the greatest variety of valuable uses. Until this century white oak was the most valuable. After these there is no one most valuable tree. Paper men would consider red spruce their most valuable tree in terms of investment. Furniture people might name black walnut for its market value. Landscapers would nominate a different kind of tree in each area of the country.

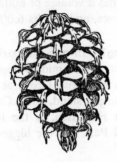

Douglas fir cone

62. What tree has the most beautiful flowers? The answer depends on locality and personal taste. In eastern United States flowering dogwood is the most popular decorative tree of spring with white flowers in undulating horizontal planes. Later in the same area horse chestnut becomes a dome of upstanding candelabra of white flowers with yellow and red spots and long yellow stamens that curve far out of the flower tubes. This is followed a month later by another tall superb flowering tree, catalpa, on which, in late June, flowers pile up in ten-inch towers. Petals are scalloped and ruffled, white with purple spots and two gold stripes. Northerly, apple and cherry trees are loved for their flowers. Georgia boasts of its peach trees. In the South, southern magnolia is the most aristocratic of American flowering trees, with flowers simulating waterlilies among dark polished leaves. Both Florida and California have adopted trees from more tropical climates for the bright Spanish hues of their flowers —acacia and crepe myrtle are outstanding examples. Royal poinciana is the world's showiest tree with huge clusters of flame-red flowers. Its splendor is heightened by a color combination of four scarlet petals and one white petal with orange spots in each flower. In the Midwest the popular redbud tree is the only wild American tree with bright purple-red flowers. Jacaranda of southern California is both beautiful and exciting. Eye-catching 2-inch flowers in big blue or lavender clusters are more luxurious, and last three times longer than the flowers of the catalpa.

63. What is the biggest tree? It is actually named "big tree," *Sequoiadendron gigantea.* Big tree reaches 272 feet in height, has a circumference of 101½ feet at its base, and its bark is two feet thick. One big tree (General Sherman) has a volume of 600,000 board feet, enough to build 80 five-room houses, and weighs 6,000 tons.

64. Where are big trees growing? In national parks (where they are protected from commercial use) on the middle slopes of the Sierra Nevada Mountains in California. Mariposa Grove at the south end of Yosemite National Park is the largest stand. South Calaveras Grove, a few hours eastward from San Francisco, is the least despoiled. Giant Forest in Sequoia National Park has the biggest trees.

65. Can big tree be grown in other parts of the country? Flourishing big trees are growing in the eastern states. There is one at the Clayton Pinetum, Roslyn, Long Island, New York, and another 100 feet tall at Bristol, Rhode Island.

66. Do big trees have any commercial value? Only as an awe-inspiring sight. There are few left, and the wood is brittle.

67. When were big trees first discovered? About 1853 hunters in the Sierras brought back tall tales which nobody believed. (That was before the days of cameras.) Finally men with P. T. Barnum instincts went to look. After that the first big tree was felled when four men working 22 days bored holes and upset the tree with wedges. Then a double bowling alley was built on the prone log and gold prospectors and their friends from Sacramento and San Francisco rode out on horseback to be awed and have fun.

68. What is the future of big tree? They are seeding well and young big trees are coming along. Also, they transplant well. But they live in a time cycle different from ours, and who is going to wait several thousand years to see the felled giants replaced by fresh giants? We are lucky to see the remnant before they are all cut down, or big tree would be as legendary as *Brontosaurus*. Even though we raise them, no one will know how they keep on growing while nations rise and fall.

69. How old is big tree before it produces fertile seeds? About 150 years old. After that it will keep on producing fertile seed for perhaps 4,000 years.

70. Where are seeds produced on a big tree? They are locked in cones hundreds of feet above the ground, and held there for about three years while the cones are drying out. Then the cone segments separate and the seeds fall out and are scattered in the wind.

71. Are the big tree seeds huge compared to other kinds? No. Each cone holds some 3,000 seeds. The kernel which contains all the potentials for creating another giant is less than ¾ inch long, and 3,000 weigh only an ounce or so.

72. Do old trees look different from young ones? Yes, the form of the old giant does not resemble that of the young one. When it is around 150 years old, the lower boughs drop off and limbs very high up become irregular and heavy and tend to point up.

73. What kind of a root system does the big tree have? It starts out with a tap root like other trees. After eight years this stops functioning as a tap root and leader of the system and runs out horizontally. Eventually a huge horizontal root mat is formed that does not penetrate the ground more than eight feet, but the roots of a single tree may occupy three acres. The diameter of some root runners may be as big as the trunk of an elm or oak.

74. What is the chief reason for the big tree's survival through the ages? The bark is one to two feet thick and as it lacks resin, it is practically fireproof.

75. Is big tree the same kind of tree as redwood sequoia? No.
The needles are different, cones are different sizes, and the type of
location is different, so that the two never grow together.

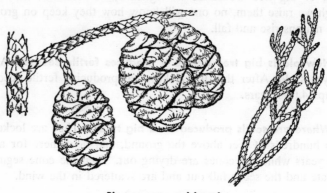

Big tree cones and branch

**76. What are the specific differences between redwood and big
tree?** Redwood needles are about ¾ inch long, flat, sharp-pointed
and stand out stiffly on each side of the twig, making a flat spray.
Cones are small, egg-shaped, less than an inch long. The trunk is
slender in proportion to its height, although these great trees may
have trunks 20 feet in diameter. Redwood grows in the twilight of
damp valleys of the Coast Range where it gets some 55 inches of

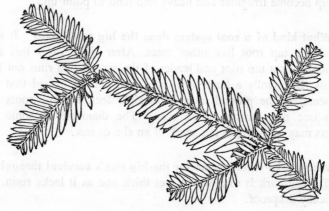

Redwood branch

rainfall each year, lots of fog and cool nights. Big tree needles are small overlapping scales lying close against the twig. The cones are fat, egg-shaped and two to three inches long. The trunk is massive. Big tree grows a mile high in the Sierra Nevada where winter snows are deep and summer sun is drying. One should never confuse the two sequoias because they grow in such widely separated places.

77. Are any trees still living in the eastern states which were growing when the Pilgrims landed from the Mayflower in 1620? A few old bald cypress trees in deep coastal river swamps from the Carolinas to Florida. Some post oaks and possibly an old sassafras, some white oaks, one of which would be the Wye Oak on the eastern shore of Maryland, reputed to be America's biggest white oak, although California white oaks in the San Bernardino Valley are our country's tallest white oaks.

78. Are bald cypress and oak the oldest trees in America? No. We are considering a period of only about 350 years for those trees. Near the Pacific coast, Douglas fir, sugar pine, ponderosa pine, western hemlock, and junipers have been growing in the same locations for 500 to 1,000 years. Sequoias have been growing for 2,000 and 3,000 years. Three bristlecone pines are over 4,000 years old. These are in the White Mountains along the southern California-Nevada border.

79. Is bristlecone pine the oldest tree in the world? Yes, the bristlecone pines are the world's oldest living things. They were growing in the very same place before the Greek and Roman Empires; long before Alexander the Great; 1,000 years before David and Solomon; in their youth Hammurabi founded the first Babylonian Empire.

80. Are there any trees living planted by George Washington? Trees at his home in Mount Vernon designated as having been planted by George Washington, or under his direction, are tulip trees, buckeyes, elms, pecans, hollies, lindens, hemlocks, and mulberries. Two pecan trees, the oldest standing on the estate, were grown from nuts given to Washington by Thomas Jefferson. The two men were kindred spirits in the enjoyment of trees.

81. What is the story of the Washington Elm that stood near the Senate wing of the U.S. Capitol until 1948? The first President was said to have stood under it repeatedly as a favorite spot to watch the construction of the Capitol.

82. What is the story of the Washington Elm in Cambridge, Massachusetts? This famous elm was so called because under these branches Washington took command of the Continental Army on July 3, 1775. It was thought to be a survivor of the primeval forest. A large branch fell from the elm in 1872 and the wood was used to make a pulpit for a nearby church. After that came more troubles with insects and decay, at a time when tree surgery was not perfected, until what was left of the Washington Elm finally vanished in the early 1920s.

83. What is the history of the Washington Live Oak at Charlestown, South Carolina? On his tour through the South in 1791, George Washington was a breakfast guest at the Pinckney estate. He overheard the mistress tell her gardener to cut down the oak as it obstructed a view from a new terrace. Washington expressed the wish that the tree be spared, and it was.

84. What is the Charter Oak? This was a real-life legend. The superb white oak was standing on the present site of Hartford, Connecticut, when white settlers first moved in. Indians begged that it be spared because it had been the guide "of our ancestors for hundreds of years, telling us when to plant the corn. When the leaves are the size of a mouse's ear, then it is time to put the seed in the ground." In 1687, the charter of the State of Connecticut was hidden in a hollow of the trunk of that same oak when it was demanded by the English Governor of New England. Later the charter was ruled to be still in force because it had never been surrendered. When a storm finally destroyed the Charter Oak in 1856, it was mourned by tolling bells in the city of Hartford. Pieces of its wood were made into gavels, picture frames, and chairs, one of which stands in the Senate chamber of the State Capitol.

85. What is the story of the Liberty Tree? This is a huge old poplar that stood on the campus of St. John's College, Annapolis,

Maryland. A treaty was made under it between white settlers and the Susquehannah Indians in 1652. LaFayette held a reception under the Liberty Tree when he visited Annapolis in 1824. It became so hollow that ten people could stand inside the tree. Then fifty tons of cement were poured into it and the branches were supported by iron rods. What is left today is just about enough to hold a bronze tablet commemorating its history.

86. What kind of trees are in the Petrified Forest of Arizona?
They are Auracarian trees. The scientific name (there is no popular name except petrified tree) is *Araucarioxylon*. This type does not grow in the northern hemisphere today, but related trees are the *Auracaria,* the Norfolk Island Pine, and the monkey puzzle tree of Australia. (See Question 168.)

87. Who was "Douglas" of Douglas fir fame?   An intrepid Scotch botanist, David Douglas, who in 1823–1827 explored the Northwest for plants and seeds for gardens in England. His most important find was the Douglas fir, most valuable commercial evergreen of our day.

88. Who was Paul Bunyan?   A legendary giant who personified the fabulous lumberjack era with his strength. The fable goes that in addition to inventing the lumber industry, he dug Puget Sound and built Niagara Falls for his shower bath. Paul sharpened his axe by rolling boulders down hillsides, and the batter for his flapjacks was mixed in cement mixers. By hitching his blue ox, named Babe, to his camp, he moved it 3,000 miles a day.

89. Who was Johnny Appleseed?   A man named John Chapman, who deserves to be the patron saint of the Humane Society and the Society for the Prevention of Cruelty to Animals. He purchased any animal he saw ill-treated and found homes for worn-out horses turned away to starve. Those that recovered he lent or gave away for a promise of kind treatment. A friend of every living creature, he would journey thirty miles through the forest to get help for a neighbor, and give up a night's shelter in a hollow log rather than disturb a squirrel family that inhabited it.

Johnny Appleseed was eloquent on the virtues of apples. He established his first apple nursery at Lagrange, Ohio, and from 1806 to 1830 went from county to county, preceding the original settlers, planting apple trees so that they could have the fruit when they arrived. He sought fertile soil and planted near streams, giving his tender shoots protection with brush fences. Later he returned, traveling hundreds of miles, to prune and care for his trees. He brought the seeds for his nurseries from fine bearing trees in Pennsylvania. Although a fanatic, Johnny Appleseed was a practical benefactor and was loved by the settlers who were too busy wresting a livelihood from the wilderness and fighting the Indians to raise apple trees from seed.

90. What are the State trees?

State	Tree
Alabama	Slash pine, *Pinus caribaea*
Alaska	(not yet designated)
Arizona	Mesquite, *Prosopis juliflora*
Arkansas	Shortleaf pine, *Pinus echinata*
California	Redwood, *Sequoia sempervirens*
Colorado	Blue spruce, *Picea pungens*
Connecticut	White oak, *Quercus alba*
Delaware	American holly, *Ilex opaca*
Florida	Palmetto, *Sabal palmetto*
Georgia	Longleaf pine, *Pinus palustris*
Idaho	Western white pine, *Pinus monticola*
Illinois	Bur oak, *Quercus macrocarpa*
Indiana	Tulip tree, also called yellow poplar, *Liriodendron tulipifera*
Iowa	Black walnut, *Juglans nigra*
Kansas	Cottonwood, *Populus deltoides*
Kentucky	Tulip tree, also called yellow poplar, *Liriodendron tulipifera*
Louisiana	Southern magnolia, *Magnolia grandiflora*
Maine	White pine (no species officially named; Maine is popularly known as the Pine Tree State)
Maryland	White oak, *Quercus alba*
Massachusetts	American elm, *Ulmus americana*
Michigan	Apple, *Malus pumila*

State	Tree
Minnesota	Eastern white pine, *Pinus strobus*
Mississippi	Southern magnolia, *Magnolia grandiflora*
Missouri	Engelmann hawthorn, *Crataegus engelmanni*
Montana	Ponderosa pine, *Pinus ponderosa*
Nebraska	Cottonwood, *Populus deltoides*
Nevada	Oneleaf pinyon, *Pinus monophylla*
New Hampshire	Yellow birch, *Betula lutea*
New Jersey	White cedar, *Chamaecyparis thyoides*
New Mexico	Pinyon pine, *Pinus edulis*
New York	Sugar maple, *Acer saccharum*
North Carolina	Flowering dogwood, *Cornus florida*
North Dakota	American elm, *Ulmus americana*
Ohio	Buckeye, *Aesculus glabra*
Oklahoma	Redbud, also called Judas tree, *Cercis canadensis*
Oregon	Douglas fir, *Pseudotsuga taxifolia*
Pennsylvania	Hemlock, *Tsuga canadensis*
Rhode Island	Maple, *Acer saccharum*
South Carolina	Palmetto, *Sabal palmetto*
South Dakota	Cottonwood, *Populus deltoides*
Tennessee	Eastern red cedar, *Juniperus virginiana*
Texas	Pecan, *Carya pecan*
Utah	Blue spruce, *Picea pungens*
Vermont	Sugar maple, *Acer saccharum*
Virginia	Flowering dogwood, *Cornus florida*
Washington	Western hemlock, *Tsuga heterophylla*
West Virginia	White oak, *Quercus alba*
Wisconsin	Sugar maple, *Acer saccharum*
Wyoming	Lodgepole pine, *Pinus contorta*

91. What trees have been featured on U.S. stamps? Spruce, 1937; Fir, 1934; Oak, 1925, 1935; Sycamore, 1932; Apple, 1922–23; Willow, 1928; Pine, three stamps in 1934.

This is surprisingly few. Conspicuous omissions are maple, popular, walnut, hickory, dogwood, bald cypress, sequoia, Douglas fir, Joshua tree, saguaro. These are some of the tree landmarks of our country with worldwide fame. (For trees featured on stamps of foreign countries see Question 181.)

92. What is the origin of the word sequoia? The name honors the great Cherokee Indian chief, Sequoyah. This distinguished chief made an alphabet for his people and his statue stands in the rotunda of the Capitol at Washington.

93. What big country is named after a tree? Brazil takes its name from brazilwood (*Guilandina echinata*), a tree that may reach 100 feet, 3 feet in diameter, free of branches to 50 feet. Bright red heartwood was formerly an important source of commercial dye. Since the days of Marco Polo, 1260, the word Brazil or Brésil has been used for Far Eastern plants producing red dyes. In 1500, a tree of the same group, brazilwood, was discovered in South America and the area where it was found was named Brazil after the oriental trees.

Today brazilwood is used also for violin bows and goes by the name of Pernambuco in the violin trade. (See Question 810.)

94. What is the tree referred to in Longfellow's poem that begins "Under the spreading chestnut tree the village smithy stands"? This was not the native American chestnut but the horsechestnut, commonly planted in New England by colonial settlers. By Longfellow's time fine old specimens were features of the village streets. Horsechestnut is a native of eastern Asia but has long been considered the handsomest tree in Europe, whence it was brought to America. The American chestnut was not apt to be seen in coastal New England towns; it stood on higher, hilly ground, inland and westward. (See Question 141.)

95. What is the scythe tree? A balm of Gilead poplar near Waterloo, New York, in which about six inches of the blade of a scythe protrudes from the bark. The rest is buried in the tree where it was impacted by a farmer when he went to war in 1861 and never returned. In 1917 two more farmers hung their scythes in the tree, and they returned.

96. What mythological character turned into a tree? Daphne, as celebrated in these lines by James Russell Lowell:

> Phoebus, sitting one day in a laurel-tree's shade,
> Was reminded of Daphne, of whom it was made,

For the god being one day too warm in his wooing,
She took to the tree to escape his pursuing;
Be the cause what it might, from his offers she shrunk,
And, Ginevra-like, shut up herself in a trunk.

97. What are some memorable poems about trees? Trees have inspired countless poems. Every reader of this book would probably name different favorites. The author suggests the following:

A Ballad of Trees and the Master

Sidney Lanier

Into the woods my Master went,
Clean forspent, forspent.
Into the woods my Master came,
Forspent with love and shame.
But the olives they were not blind to Him;
The little gray leaves were kind to Him;
The thorn-tree had a mind to Him;
When into the woods He came.
Out of the woods my Master went,
And He was well content.
Out of the woods my Master came,
Content with death and shame.
When Death and Shame would woo Him last,
From under the trees they drew Him last:
'Twas on a tree they slew Him—last
When out of the woods He came.

Under the Greenwood Tree

William Shakespeare

Under the greenwood tree,
Who loves to lie with me,
And turn his merry note
Unto the sweet bird's throat,
Come hither, come hither, come hither:
Here shall he see
No enemy
But winter and rough weather.

The Oak
Vergil

Jove's own tree,
That holds the woods in awful sovereignty,
Requires a depth of loding in the ground,
And next the lower skies a bed profound:
High as his topmost boughs to heaven ascend,
So low his roots to hell's dominions tend.
Therefore nor winds nor winter's rage o'erthrows
His bulky body, but unmoved he grows.
For length of ages lasts his happy reign,
And lines of mortal men contend in vain.
Full in the midst of his own strength he stands,
Stretching his brawny arms and leafy hands;
His shade protects the plains; his head the hills commands.

The Resurrection of Mr. Jasper Gray
Rutherford Platt

*The massive roots of an ancient colossal elm in Old Lyme, Connecticut,
are deflected by a tombstone like a river flowing around a rock. This
bears the inscription "Here Lies Mr. Jasper Gray Who Died May 2, 1728
at Ye 55th Year of His Age." The tree was apparently planted as a sapling
at the head of the grave.*

Sturdy his house and heart, patient and wise
In simple ways; his popularity
Confined to half a dozen neighboring ties,
Without romance, without diversity.
Yet held his star a subtle destiny,
For when entombed within the hill he lay,
Crept from that ground the immortality
Spawned in the humble mould of Jasper Gray.

When silence fell the mould began to rise,
The stirring sapling grew into a tree
Until a monument that time defies,
A lofty, elemental canopy,
Within whose vault a heavenly symphony
Born of the winds, the mighty branches sway,
A glistening, tossing, emerald jubilee
Transformed the humble mould of Jasper Gray.

The honeysuckle's kissed by butterflies,
(Perfume invites such gentle larceny),
Bob White answers Bob White with liquid cries,
And heartily hums a busy little bee.
These are the vassals of serenity.
These with the fireflies and their night display,
The stars' and moon's perpetual pageantry
Exalt the humble mould of Jasper Gray.

Behold how struggle and intensity
And all the fever of a fleeting day
Fade in this vision of eternity,
Before the miracle of Jasper Gray!

TREE FEELINGS

Charlotte Perkins Stetson

I wonder if they like it—being trees?
I suppose they do.
It must feel so good to have the ground so flat,
And feel yourself stand straight up like that.
So stiff in the middle, and then branch at ease,
Big boughs that arch, small ones that bend and blow,
And all those fringy leaves that flutter so.
You'd think they'd break off at the lower end
When the wind fills them and their great boughs bend,
But when you think of all the roots they drop,
As much on the bottom as there is on top,
A double tree, widespread in earth and air,
Like a reflection on the water there.

WHAT DO WE PLANT?

Henry Abbey

What do we plant when we plant the tree?
We plant the ship, which will cross the sea.
We plant the mast to carry the sails;
We plant the plank to withstand the gales,
The keel, the keelson, and beam and knee;
We plant the ship when we plant the tree.

What do we plant when we plant the tree?
We plant the houses for you and me.

We plant the rafters, the shingles, the floors,
We plant the studding, the lath, the doors,
The beams and sidings, all parts that be:
We plant the house when we plant the tree.

What do we plant when we plant the tree?
A thousand things that we daily see;
We plant the spire that out-towers the crag,
We plant the staff for our country's flag,
We plant the shade, from the hot sun free;
We plant all these when we plant the tree.

WOODMAN, SPARE THAT TREE

George F. Morris

Woodman, spare that tree!
Touch not a single bough!
In youth it sheltered me,
And I'll protect it now.
'Twas my forefather's hand
That placed it near his cot;
There, woodman, let it stand;
Thy axe shall harm it not!

That old familiar tree,
Whose glory and renown
Are spread o'er land and sea—
And would'st thou hack it down?
Woodman, forbear thy stroke!
Cut not its earth-bound ties;
O spare that aged oak,
Now towering to the skies!

When but an idle boy
I sought its grateful shade;
In all their gushing joy,
Here, too, my sisters played.
My mother kissed me here;
My father pressed my hand—
Forgive the foolish tear,
But let that old oak stand.

My heartstrings round thee cling,
Close as thy bark, old friend;
Here shall the wild bird sing,
And still thy branches bend.
Old tree! The storm still brave!
And, woodman, leave the spot,
While I've a hand to save,
Thy axe shall harm it not.

From EVANGELINE

Henry Wadsworth Longfellow

This is the forest primeval. The murmur-
ing pines and the hemlocks,
Bearded with moss, and in garments green,
indistinct in the twilight,
Stand like Druids of eld, with voices sad
and prophetic,
Stand like harpers hoar, with beards that
rest on their bosoms.
Loud from its rocky caverns, the deep-
voiced neighboring ocean
Speaks, and in accents disconsolate answers
the wail of the forest.

THE OAK

Alfred Tennyson

Live thy Life,
Young and old,
Like yon oak,
Bright in spring,
Living gold;

Summer-rich
Then; and then
Autumn-changed,
Soberer-hued
Gold again

All his leaves
Fall'n at length,
Look, he stands,
Trunk and bough,
Naked strength.

From A Shropshire Lad

A. E. Housman

Loveliest of trees, the cherry now
Is hung with bloom along the bough,
And stands about the woodland ride
Wearing white for Eastertide.
Now, of my threescore years and ten,
Twenty will not come again,
And take from seventy springs a score,
It only leaves me fifty more.
And since to look at things in bloom
Fifty springs are little room,
About the woodlands I will go
To see the cherry hung with snow.

BIRCHES

Robert Frost

When I see birches bend to left and right
Across the line of straighter darker trees,
I like to think some boy's been swinging them.
But swinging doesn't bend them down to stay.
Ice-storms do that. Often you must have seen them
Loaded with ice a sunny winter morning
After a rain. They click upon themselves
As the breeze rises, and turn many-colored
As the stir cracks and crazes their enamel.
Soon the sun's warmth makes them shed crystal shells
Shattering and avalanching on the snow-crust—

Such heaps of broken glass to sweep away
You'd think the inner dome of heaven had fallen.
They are dragged to the withered bracken by the load,
And they seem not to break; though once they are bowed
So low for long, they never right themselves:
You may see their trunks arching in the woods

Years afterwards, trailing their leaves on the ground
Like girls on hands and knees that throw their hair
Before them over their heads to dry in the sun.
But I was going to say when Truth broke in
With all her matter-of-fact about the ice-storm
I should prefer to have some boy bend them
As he went out and in to fetch the cows—
Some boy too far from town to learn baseball,
Whose only play was what he found himself,
Summer or winter, and could play alone.
One by one he subdued his father's trees
By riding them down over and over again
Until he took the stiffness out of them,
And not one but hung limp, not one was left
For him to conquer. He learned all there was
To learn about not launching out too soon
And so not carrying the tree away
Clear to the ground. He always kept his poise
To the top branches, climbing carefully
With the same pains you use to fill a cup
Up to the brim, and even above the brim.
Then he flung outward, feet first, with a swish,
Kicking his way down through the air to the ground.

So was I once myself a swinger of birches;
And so I dream of going back to be.
It's when I'm weary of considerations,
And life is too much like a pathless wood
Where your face burns and tickles with the cobwebs
Broken across it, and one eye is weeping
From a twig's having lashed across it open.
I'd like to get away from earth awhile
And then come back to it and begin over.
May no fate willfully misunderstand me
And half grant what I wish and snatch me away
Not to return. Earth's the right place for love:
I don't know where it's likely to go better.
I'd like to go by climbing a birch tree,
And climb black branches up a snow-white trunk
Toward heaven, till the tree could bear no more,
But dipped its top and set me down again.
That would be good both going and coming back.
One could do worse than be a swinger of birches.

98. What trees are mentioned in the Bible? Some fifty different kinds of trees, besides a wealth of many other plants. Biblical history and legend are closely identified with trees. Olive is mentioned sixty times; fig, fifty-seven times; date palm, forty-two times. Others frequently mentioned are cypress, cedar, acacia, sandalwood, oak, pomegranate and tamarisk.

99. Are these trees still growing in Palestine? A few of them grow there sparsely, but in contrast to the richly wooded land of Biblical times the area is almost bare of trees.

100. When did Palestine lose its trees? First the Romans conquered the country, exiled its inhabitants and felled trees recklessly. Later came other invasions that culminated when the Arabs conquered the country and brought with them herds of goats and camels. These animals are enemies of woodlands because they eat seedling trees and sprouts. Finally the Ottoman Turks took the land and finished the destruction of the forests descended from Biblical times. Just before the Western Allies drove the Turks from Palestine, the Turkish government cut down the few trees that remained for timber in the emergency. When the Israelis returned to their ancient homeland, they found it treeless.

101. What is being done to reforest Palestine? When Israel became an independent state in 1948, the government set up one of its most important agencies for reforestation. From the Bible they knew the kinds of trees that used to grow in different parts of the country. For example, in King David's day, cypress and oak flourished on the hillsides, and Abraham used to plant tamarisks in the arid south. The army is used to plant trees, and planting contributions are received by the Jewish National Fund from friends of Israel all over the world. In the first seven years of Israel's independence twenty-five million trees were planted. A ten-year program calls for planting a quarter of a billion. Today the land of the Bible is regaining fertility, and beauty and shade are returning.

102. What kind of wood was used to build the Ark of the Tabernacle? The Book of Exodus calls it shittim wood, out of which many important things were built in those days. Harold N. Moldenke in *Plants of the Bible* identifies this as probably the acacia which was the largest and commonest tree on the deserts of Arabia where the Israelites wandered for forty years.

103. What kind of apple did Adam and Eve sample? Dr. Moldenke thinks this was an apricot tree, *Prunus armeniaca.* There were no apple trees as we know them in Palestine.

104. Was the sycamore which the short man Zacharias climbed into to see over the heads of crowd like ours? No, the sycamore of the Bible was a kind of fig, *Ficus sycomorus,* heavy trunked, widespread, easy to climb. It is abundant in Egypt today, evergreen, and a great shade tree.

105. Do figs still grow on Mount Olivet? Yes. They are cared for in the Garden there.

106. What was Noah's Ark made of? According to the Bible, gopher wood. This is identified as cypress, *Cupressus sempervirens,* one of the most durable woods in the world. The doors of St. Peter's in Rome are made of this cypress and show no signs of disintegration after 1,200 years.

107. What kind of tree is supposed to have supplied the Crown of Thorns? The weight of evidence is that this was a buckthorn tree, *Paliurus spinachristi.*

108. What was the Cross of Christ made of? According to authoritative legend, the upright beam was cedar, the cross arm cypress, and the title above was olive.

109. What tree does manna come from? Manna is a product of tamarisk. Young stems punctured by an insect exude a honey-like fluid. This hardens and drops to the ground, where it is picked up and eaten as a great delicacy.

110. What trees were used by the American Indians for their bows and arrows?   Osage orange and hickory for bows; tulip poplar and ash for arrows.

111. What was the Tree of Life?   Probably the date palm. It is still a tree of life because it is the food tree of the desert and helps to feed millions of people.

112. Are there any cedars of Lebanon still growing in the grove where Solomon got the timber for the Temple?   Yes, just barely. The grove now consists of about ten trees from three to twelve feet in diameter. No seedlings are coming along. The grove is situated in a valley in the Lebanon Mountains about a mile high, close to the village of Becharre, and looks like a black speck on a vast snowfield because of the undulating expanse of white sand where there is no vegetation today except these timeless old trees.

113. What is a druid?   A member of a religious order concerned with the worship of the oak tree and the miraculous properties of mistletoe which grows upon the oak. Druids originated in ancient Gaul, and carried their arts to the Celts in Britain and Ireland. James G. Frazer in *The Golden Bough* tells of hideous rites practiced by druids in which human and animal sacrifices were burned in wicker baskets to exorcise witch spells and restore fertility to the soil. (See Question 144.)

114. What is a climax forest?   A climax is reached after a succession of plant populations has become established and stabilized around a ruling class that cannot be overthrown without a revolution. Thus, a climax forest will continue indefinitely without changing its character, unless there is a fundamental change in climate, water supply, or change of light intensity by fire or felling. There are four major plant climaxes in North America of which two are forests: 1. Eastern climax forest dominated by beech, maple, oak. 2. Prairie climax dominated by grasses. 3. North transcontinental dominated by spruce and fir. 4. Tundra dominated by black crowberry, sphagnum moss and heath. Each climax is the product of a particular climate.

There are many local climaxes such as the redwood and Douglas fir areas, and on mountaintops. The everglades of Florida is another example of a climax, dominated by pond cypress.

115. What is tree succession?   This is a progressive change of the dominant trees of an area due principally to the different responses to shade of various kinds of seedling trees. For example, white birch must have plenty of sunlight shining on its seedlings for them to survive, so white birch may be the first trees to occupy a sunny place. For this reason white birch is familiar by the side of lakes and on the outer edge of the woods. Beech and sugar maple will grow in low illumination and as their canopy gets more dense and shades the ground the birch seedlings surrender their places to the beech and sugar maple seedlings which like the shade. Among the evergreens, hemlock is very tolerant of shade, and where its seeds are cast it may succeed as the dominant tree.

116. How can trees grow out of rocks?   Tree roots cannot penetrate solid rock, but when seeds fall on the face of the rock they may be washed into a crack. If this is in a sunwarmed cliff or boulder and the opening contains damp sand and fertile humus, it is an excellent place for a tree seed to germinate. Eventually the power of expanding roots and ice may widen the crack; the tree grows big and strong, and puts forth more roots which pour over the face of the rock to reach deeper soil.

117. What is a clone?   Trees grown by cuttings, buds, or suckers from the same individual stock are members of a clone. Such groups are most frequently found among horticultural varieties and brand-name fruit trees. The basis of a clone is nonsexual reproduction, in contrast to trees produced by seeds. There is no rejuvenation in a clone, as the members are an extension of the life of an individual. Its advantages lie in holding characteristics of flower or fruit.

118. Where are the biggest specimens of some outstanding American trees?   The following nominations have been made to the American Forestry Association. There is no guarantee that bigger ones may not be found.

Tree	Circumference (in feet)	Height (in feet)	Spread (in feet)	Location of Tree
Arbor vitae (northern white cedar) *Thuja occidentalis*	15½	125	50	Natural Bridge, Va.
Ash, white *Fraxinus americana*	22	80	82	Glenn Mills, Pa.
Bald cypress *Taxodium distichum*	39⅔	122½	47	Obion River, Weakley County, Tenn.
Birch *Betula nigra*	12⅓	98	72	Near Odenton, Md.
Buckeye *Aesculus glabra*	8	90	60	Cascade Park, Elyria, O.
Cherry *Prunus serotina*	18⅓	64	77	Near Worton, Md.
Douglas fir *Pseudotsuga taxifolia*	53⅓	221	61	Olympic National Park, Wash.
Elm * *Ulmus americana*	24½	160	147	Trigonia, Blount County, Tenn.
Fir, noble *Abies nobilis*	22⅔	260	35	Mt. Ranier National Park, Wash.
Hemlock *Tsuga canadensis*	19¾	98	69	Great Smoky Mts. National Park, Tenn.
Hemlock *Tsuga heterophylla*	27	125	47½	Olympic National Park, Wash.
Hickory, bitternut *Carya cordiformis*	12½	171	?	West Feliciana Parish, La.
Hickory, shagbark *Carya ovata*	10⅓	101	62	Near Easton, Md.
Holly *Ilex opaca*	11	72	45	Pamlico County, N.C.
Larch, eastern *Larix laricina*	11½	60	60	Chaplin, Conn.
Larch, western *Larix occidentalis*	24	120	36⅔	Near Kootenai National Forest, Mont.
Linden (basswood) *Tilia americana*	17	98	103	Queenstown, Md.
Locust *Robinia pseudoacacia*	16	85	60	Near Jefferson, Ind.
Magnolia (cucumber tree) *Magnolia acuminata*	18⅓	125	60	Great Smoky Mts. National Park, Tenn.
Maple *Acer saccharum*	19¾	116	75	Garret County, Md.
Oak, live *Quercus virginiana*	35	78	168	Near Hahnville, La.

Tree	Circumference (in feet)	Height (in feet)	Spread (in feet)	Location of Tree
Oak, southern red *Quercus shumardi*	17½	140	100	Near Keensburg, Wabash County, Ill.
Oak, white *Quercus alba*	27⅔	95	165	Wye Mills, Md.
Palm, royal *Roystonea regia*	4¾	100	12	Collier Seminole State Park, Naples, Fla.
Pecan *Carya illinoensis*	21⅓	135	145	Assumption Parish, La.
Pine, eastern white *Pinus strobus*	17	140	56	Near Newald, Wis.
Pine, ponderosa *Pinus ponderosa*	27	162	?	Near Lapine, Ore.
Pine, sugar *Pinus lambertiana*	32⅔	220	61	Stanislau National Forest, Cal.
Pine, western *Pinus monticola*	21¼	219	36	Near Elk River, Idaho
Poplar *Populus grandidentata*	10	90	75	Rocks, Md.
Poplar (cottonwood) *Populus deltoides*	21½	124	115	Near Geneva, N.Y.
Red cedar *Juniperus virginiana*	13⅓	62	42	Cumberstone, Md.
Sassafras *Sassafras variifolium*	16	88½	68	Owensboro, Ky.
Sequoia (big tree) *Sequoiadendron gigantea*	101½ (at base)	272	90	Sequoia National Park, Cal.
Sequoia (redwood) ** *Sequoia sempervirens*	65¾	300	?	Redwood Highway, Big Tree National Park, Cal.
Spruce, blue *Picea pungens*	11¾	123	?	Bunnison National Forest, Colo.
Spruce, Sitka *Picea sitchensis*	51½	180	50	Olympic National Park, Wash.
Sweetgum *Liquidamber styraciflua*	16½	112	71	New Madrid, Mo.
Sycamore (planetree) *Platanus occidentalis*	26	114	79	Wakefield, Md.
Tulip tree (yellow poplar) *Liriodendron tulipifera*	26½	83	98	Annapolis, Md.
Tupelo *Nyssa aquatica*	18	110	65	Near Camden, S.C.

Tree	Circumference (in feet)	Height (in feet)	Spread (in feet)	Location of Tree
Walnut, black *Juglans nigra*	20¼	108	128	Anne Arundel County, Md.
Willow, black *Salix nigra*	19½	85	50	Near Woodville, O.

* Another elm at Framingham, Mass., with greater base and spread lays claim to the title, but it appears to be two trees growing together at the base.

** The tallest tree is the redwood sequoia at 300 feet, with big-tree sequoia runner-up at 272 feet, and noble fir not far behind at 260 feet. The tallest western trees are two and three times taller than the loftiest eastern trees. For massiveness, the big-tree sequoia wins with its tremendous base and spread. The live oak in Louisiana has by far the greatest spread with 168 feet. (See Questions 39 and 63)

119. Do any trees bloom in winter in the northern states? Witch hazel blooms in late fall, and its petals, like yellow ribbons dangling on the tree, may be seen when snow is on the ground. Sequoias and pines of the western mountains bloom in the bright sun of late winter, showering yellow pollen on the snow. No tree blooms out-doors when the temperature is below freezing in mid-winter.

120. Is fog a good substitute for rain as a water supply? As trees get their sap water entirely through their roots, fog is only a substitute for rain when it condenses and drips to the ground. In certain localities this may be the chief reliance of trees. A fine example is the summer fog precipitation on the Pacific Coast. There forests of redwood, tanbark oak and Douglas fir are bathed in fog that blows in from the ocean daily, condenses on the branches of the tall trees and drops to the ground. Experiments show that fog drip increases precipitation by two or three times. The height of the trees has much to do with this by increasing the collecting area.

121. What is the function of cypress knees? This is one of the mysteries of botany. The woody projections are thrust up from underwater roots of bald cypress, *Taxodium distichum,* growing to a height about equal to average high-water level. They are a familiar sight in the cypress swamps of our southern states, resembling stumps sticking out of the water, rounded on top and well described by the word "knees." The theory that they bring air into the living tissue of underwater roots has been widely accepted, but this has never been proved. Experiments made by the Department of Botany at Duke University conclude that knees play no important role as aerating organs, as little or no gas exchange occurs between them and the roots. Moreover, the most deeply submerged roots, which would most need oxygen, do not erect knees.

Fluted trunk and knees of bald cypress

122. What is an Indian trail tree? These are trees that as saplings were bent in certain directions to show the trail—the same purpose as tree blazing. The postures of some old trees around historical Indian meeting places cause them to be called Indian trees. Such trees have been found, among other places, at Pond Crossing in Lawrence, Long Island, New York.

123. What is a sausage tree? A tree from Brazil, related to the common catalpa, from which pods two feet long dangle like huge sausages at the end of long strings. Although these weird objects look as though they would make giant hot dogs, they are as tough as gourds and are not edible. The name: *Kigelia pinnata.*

124. What is the strangler tree? This starts as a fig vine climbing on any tree that will hold it up. As the fig matures, the stem flattens and encompasses the tree in a cylinder resembling concrete. Big leaves sprout from the top and cut off the light of the host tree which is strangled and dies. This leaves a big fig tree with a hollow trunk. Its name sounds innocent enough—*Ficus aurea,* the golden fig.

125. What is the dragon tree? A very ancient tree, native to the Canary Islands, with dark red resin called dragon's blood. It resembles a mushroom in shape. This tree is the same genus as *Draecena,* a common house plant and is a member of the lily family. The most famous dragon tree grew at Tenerife, Canary Islands. When blown down in 1868, it was 70 feet high and 45 feet in girth, and was supposed to be 6,000 years old, but this has never been proved.

126. Are there any tree lilies besides the dragon tree?　One other. The Joshua tree, *Yucca brevifolia,* is a tree of the lily family, averaging 25 feet high. Its heavy eccentric branches end in balls of sharp, slender leaves 10 inches long; white lilies bloom within these balls. It grows only in the southwestern desert of our country. The best display is in the Mohave Desert, due east of Los Angeles. Joshua tree looks like a purely imaginary tree, unreal in our world. It is slow growing and its age is unknown because the trunk is pithy and does not develop wood with annual rings. The Joshua tree's wood is so light and tough it is used for artificial limbs.

127. What is the maidenhair tree?　Its other name is ginkgo, often seen in big-city streets, as it has a constitution to survive the dangers there: polluted air, desert aridity of pavements, salt used to melt ice on sidewalks, and visits of male dogs. Fan-shaped leaves resemble the fronds of maidenhair fern. This is one of the two trees that have sur-

Ginkgo leaf

vived to our day from the Coal Age. (The other is cycad, which is halfway between a fern and a palm.) Pollen of the maidenhair tree is like the swimming spores of ferns. Instead of being carried by winds or insects, like the pollen of other trees, it must swim to the female flowers through rain or dew.

It is as though the maidenhair tree had been delivered to us by parcel post from the early Mesozoic Era, 120 million years ago. It had the narrowest escape from extinction, surviving only at a remote sanctuary in western China, where it had been tended by monks for generations as a temple decoration. Neither a fern, a pine tree, nor a hardwood—it is a combination of all three. (See Question 442.)

128. Does the grass family produce any trees? The nearest that grass has come to creating a tree is bamboo. The scientific name, *Dendrocalamus,* means "tree reed." It is a perennial evergreen native of the tropics, chiefly in the Orient. Like most grasses, bamboo grows in clumps, elongating so fast you can almost see it grow—as much as 18 inches a day, or an average of ¾ inch per hour. In the Far East tender young bamboo shoots are a table delicacy and bamboo that towers 50 to 100 feet is cultivated for construction and to make mats and window shades. In our most southern states bamboo is grown only for decoration. Harvard University's Atkins Garden and Research Laboratory at Cienfuegos, Cuba, is experimenting with commercial species to develop seed for horticulture and for reforestation with bamboo in tropical America.

129. What tree has no trunk? The banana tree has no trunk. The huge leaves are attached to the crown of the roots. However, the bases of the leaves are joined, making a structure that serves as a trunk.

130. Are any palm trees native to the United States? In southeastern United States, especially Florida, the cabbage palm, or palmetto, *Sabal palmetto,* is a familiar feature of the landscape. Its leaves are big fans radiating from the top of a heavy trunk forming a round pincushion. The trunk is enclosed in a coarse basket made by the crisscrossing of old leaf stems.

The Washington palm, *Washingtonia filifera,* is a superb native of our southwestern desert. It may reach 80 feet, crowned by a ball of fan leaves that seems too small for such a lofty tree. One of the best wild groves is in Palm Canyon near Palm Springs, California. It is planted extensively, giving a romantic look to streets, parks, and hotel grounds from Beverly Hills southward.

The third fine palm of our country is the royal palm, *Roystonea regia,* whose original home was on the hammocks of the Florida Everglades. The trunk, which looks like a huge cement column, is crowned by a spray of big leaves that are feather-shaped, instead of fan-shaped, as are the other two. The royal palm may be seen in a native setting at Royal Palm Hammock, a State Park of southern Florida.

There are also a number of small and often disorderly palms of the sand dunes and pinelands of the South and the Florida Keys—buccaneer palm, saw palmetto, thatch palm, silver palm, and needle palm.

131. Which palm is used by churches on Palm Sunday? This is usually from the cabbage palm, also called palmetto, and from low shrubby palmettos in Florida.

132. How do trees get their common names? There are seven chief sources for common names. 1. The place where a tree grows: beach plum, sandbar willow, mountain ash, river birch, swamp white oak, valley oak, old field pine. 2. Geographic area: Ohio buckeye, Kentucky coffee tree, Virginia pine, Canada balsam, Southern magnolia, Southern red oak, English elm, Pacific yew, Monterey cypress, cedars of Lebanon. 3. A distinctive feature: redbud, shagbark hickory, bigleaf maple, whitebark pine, weeping willow, red maple, quaking aspen, big tree, tulip tree, hawthorn (this name neatly combines two features—the haws or fruit, and the thorns). 4. A use: sugar maple, canoe birch, shingle oak, lodgepole pine. 5. Adoption or variation of its scientific name: elm, catalpa, sumac, magnolia, juniper, poplar, pine, sassafras, eucalyptus. 6. A native language, often Spanish or Indian: papaw, wahoo, mangrove, madrone, chinquapin, avocado. 7. To commemorate somebody: Douglas fir, Engelmann spruce, Jeffrey pine, Sequoia, Torrey pine, Joshua tree.

133. Does the rose family produce any trees? Some of the most important trees in the world. Among them are apple, pear, peach, cherry, plum. Shadblow and mountain ash are roses. So is hawthorn.

134. Does cactus ever make trees? The tallest cactus, which best qualifies as a tree, is Saguaro, *Carnegiea gigantea,* that lifts its heavy trunk and branches some 50 feet above the desert sand. This is most characteristic of Arizona, but it is a familiar symbol of the southwestern desert. The finest stand is in the Saguaro National Monument, 20 miles east of Tucson. Other cactuses achieving height, which could claim to be called trees, are the organ pipe cactus near the

Mexican border of southwestern Arizona, and heavy, waxy *Pachycereus* of Mexico, which raises spectacular angled columns to the sky.

135. What is a weeping tree? A tree whose twigs are soft and flexible so that instead of thrusting out stiffly from the branch, they dangle and are pendulous. Some of them may even sweep the ground. This characteristic has been bred into many horticultural varieties to give them a special decorative appeal. Weepingness in nature occurs occasionally, even in stiff-branched trees. A weeping spruce has been found high in the Siskiyou Mountains straddling the Oregon-California line. A weeping hemlock, found on the banks of the Hudson River, has become the source of a widespread horticultural item. Best known is the weeping willow whose "long, pliant branches droop disconsolately like the unbound tresses of a woman overwhelmed with grief." Willow takes root from twig cuttings and thus weeping willow has become naturalized all over the world in moist ground and beside streams and ponds. Fabre says that it was native to the banks of the Euphrates (scientific name is *Salix babylonica*), whence it was imported to England at the time of the Crusades. Another story is that a flexible, green twig was used to tie up a box of fruit sent from Smyrna. Alexander Pope, the English poet, stripped it off and planted it saying "Perhaps this will produce a tree that we do not have in England." The *Yearbook of Agriculture,* 1949, says that the weeping willow is a native of China. But Frank Lamb in "The Book of Broadleaf Trees" says that it may have been introduced into China from India. The origin of this interesting tree seems to be a subject of wide debate.

136. What is the bong-tree mentioned in the Edward Lear poem "The Owl and the Pussy-Cat"? The betel-nut palm, which produces seeds as big as plums that are sliced and rolled in betel pepper leaves. When chewed, the seed turns the saliva bright red and aids the digestion. Betel trees are grown in many tropical lands where natives like to chew the seeds.

137. What is a lime tree? In Europe this is the linden. The small-leafed lindens, or limes, played a great part in German and English history. Berlin's famous street was Unter der Linden. The American linden is a different species, has a bigger leaf, and very fragrant flowers, and is wrongly called lime. Its alternative name is properly basswood.

The citrus tree of the Florida Keys and southward, that produces lime fruit, is, of course, a "lime tree" but not the traditional one.

138. What is the difference between tamarack, tamarisk, and tamarix? Tamarack is another name for the larch tree, *Larix laricina*. Tamarisk is the family name of a genus *Tamarix,* and these two words are used interchangeably for the same tree. A species, *Tamarix aphylla,* is cultivated in every state of our Southwest as a hedge or street plant. It becomes a large tree around Indio and Yuma and on the school grounds at Florence, Arizona. Tamarix is native from Egypt to Afghanistan where *Tamarix mannifera* yields manna of Biblical days and is eaten by Bedouins today. An insect punctures the bark of young twigs and a white substance oozes out. This dries and flakes fall off, so that the ground is "white with manna from Heaven."

139. What are witness trees? These are trees referred to in old land deeds. They were blazed with a marking that corresponded to a nearby square corner post used in land survey. The tree was supposed to be more permanent than the post—and many witness trees were. Sometimes the marking was buried by later growth, but when this was cut away the original inscription appeared as a raised mirror image of the early marking. These sections have been admitted as evidence of ownership in court, where the original posts have long since disappeared.

140. What is the Tree of a Hundred Horsemen? This is an enormous chestnut on the slope of Mount Etna in Sicily. Fabre called it the largest tree in the world, a title that is not justified because it is formed by a group of five trees growing together. Thirty men holding hands could hardly circle its more than 160 feet of trunk. When Queen Joan of Aragon came to see the volcano, the party was caught by a sudden downpour. The Queen and her 100 horsemen took shelter under the mighty canopy, says the legend. It is reported to have fallen into ruin, perhaps because of abuse from a carriage road that went through it, and from pilgrims despoiling the big cavity inside.

141. Is the horsechestnut related to the chestnut? No, the horse-chestnut, *Aesculus,* is a member of the buckeye family, while the true chestnut, *Castanea,* belongs to the great beech family, along with oak.

Horsechestnut leaf

142. How did horsechestnut get its name? The shape of the leaf scar left on the twig where a leaf stem has fallen off resembles a horse's hoof.

143. Are the nuts of horsechestnut edible? Although they look like big chestnuts, so good when roasted, horsechestnuts are bitter and narcotic, as are also those of the tree's relative, the buckeye.

144. What tree is most often featured in legends? The oak has its roots deep in the legends of European races. It was pre-eminently the sacred tree of the Aryans, and the worship of the oak was shared by all branches of the Aryan stock. In ancient Greece, Zeus was the god of the oak, and of thunder and lightning. In ancient Italy every oak was sacred to Jupiter, the Roman counterpart of Zeus. The Celts took the myth of the druids to ancient Gaul, Ireland, and Britain. The name druid means "oak men." Some of the evidence against Joan of Arc accused her of hanging garlands on a fairy oak, and dancing and skipping about it, reviving the worship of the oak's spirit and thus receiving her charmed sword and banner. James Frazer's vast work on the myths and legends of humanity takes its title from Turner's painting of the Golden Bough, which was mistletoe growing on an oak. Frazer points out that the reverence which ancient Europeans paid to the oak can be traced to the connection between the tree and the sky god—the oak is struck by lightning much more often than any other tree of the forest. (See Question 113.)

145. What is the importance of the olive tree in legends? The olive was very important in ancient Greece and in Biblical days, but it is a tree of the warmer Mediterranean climate and did not get the widespread recognition of the oak which carried throughout Europe, including Scandinavia. The olive is Minerva's tree. She bade it rise from the earth when Neptune caused a salt spring to open on the Acropolis. On the Mount of Olives the word "gethsemane" means "olive oil press." The Greek epic poet Homer tells how Odysseus wrought some beautiful carpentry with olive in his home: "Within our court had sprung a stem of olive, bushy, long in leaf, vigorous; the bole of its column thick. Round it I plotted my bed chamber walled entire with fine-jointed ashlar (hewn stone) and roundly roofed. After adding joinery doors, fitting very close, I then polled the olive's spreading top and trimmed its stump from the root up, dressing it so smooth with my tools and so knowingly that I got it plumb, to serve for bed post just as it stood. With this olive for main member (boring it with my auger whenever required) I went on to frame up the bed, complete, inlaying it with gold, silver, and ivory and lacing it across with oxhide thongs, dyed blood purple."

146. Who are the Men of the Trees? The first Men of the Trees were young African warriors in Kenya who banded together in 1922 with a sacred pledge to plant trees and protect the forest. The organization grew under the inspiration of Richard St. Barbe Baker, who labored patiently for years with a knowledge of the natives and speaking their language, to turn them away from tree destroying. It had been the custom (and still is) of many nomadic African farmers to clear a patch of the forest by fire and machete and after a short period of cropping to move on and repeat the process. They were finally reached through ceremonial dances. Each member swears to plant at least ten trees per year and never to cut down a tree unless he plants another. Men of the Trees come together from many tribes to compete with dancing and costume aimed at celebrating trees. Today the movement has spread to England where Men of the Trees publish an illustrated quarterly called *Trees and Life* from their office at West End, Southampton.

147. What is the cascara tree?   A 30 to 40 foot tree of our Northwest and British Columbia, especially in rich bottomland of the Puget Sound area. It is the top-ranking, and one of the few, medicinal plants native in the United States. The interior surface of the bark is bright yellow, turning to brown, and contains a laxative substance that is the source of the official drugstore product, Cascara Sagrada. A handsome tree with bigleaf maple and alder on the fringes of the dark Douglas fir forests. Bigger cascaras have been killed by stripping its valuable bark, so trees over 6 inches in diameter are seldom seen today. Fortunately stumps sucker freely so trees and medicine keep coming.

148. What is the banyan tree?   One of the wonders of the plant world. A species of fig native to eastern India whose seed may germinate on another plant which it uses for support. It grows for a time by getting its sustenance from the air. Roots grow down from high branches and after penetrating the ground they increase in thickness, forming great pillars supporting the branches. Thus a single plant which began without ground roots can turn into a kind of forest a thousand feet across.

The banyan tree is sacred to Indians, and young roots may be provided with bamboo tubes to protect them on their way down, while the ground is prepared for their arrival. The Botanical Garden in Calcutta has a banyan trees which began on top of a date palm a hundred years ago. Today the palm is gone and the banyan tree has taken its place with a trunk 12 feet in diameter and some two hundred smaller ones. A tradition persists that a huge banyan tree once sheltered seven thousand men of Alexander the Great's army.

149. What is the traveler's tree?   A close relative of the banana tree in Madagascar which collects good drinking water in a pocket at the base of each leaf stem. Travelers puncture the leaf stem close to the trunk and out spurts the water.

150. Do any other trees store drinking water?   The barrel cactus of southwestern Arizona contains pith loaded with water that can be squeezed out to relieve thirst.   In other cactuses water is bitter and not potable. The most interesting tree water reservoir is the baobab tree of Africa. This low tree has a hollow trunk that bulges out 30 feet in diameter and holds water for long spells after a rain. African game hunter John Taylor says "These weird vegetable monstrosities are plentiful . . . elephants rear up against them, keeping their hind legs on the ground, and reach as far as they can with their trunks, down into the 'tank' as the level of the water drops. These reservoirs keep hunters going since men can draw water from them long after elephants are unable to get down far enough. But toward the end of the dry season the water evaporates from all but the biggest of the trees."

151. Are there any trees in the Sahara Desert?   South of the Mediterranean floral zone the mobile sands of central Sahara bear no plant life. This is the most typical and absolute of all deserts on earth. However, it is not continuous but broken by oases from which have been recorded 300 species of flowering plants. Of these, two are trees: date palm, *Phoenix dactylifera,* and acacia. In former geologic ages the Sahara was green with many trees. There are remains of Roman cities in regions that are arid today, and the Kharga Oasis on the eastern edge of the Sahara was a lake which later became a swamp, and since then has waxed and waned and trees and humans with it.

152. Where are the world's most varied and luxurious forests?
In the Malayan Archipelago. New Guinea has the most interesting and peculiar forest in the world. The Himalaya area of northeast India was a crossroads of the travels of the forests through the ages so that here are intermingled trees of Tibet, China, Burma, and India. In this remarkable forest, near Darjeeling, at about 7,000 feet altitude, grow walnut, hickory, sycamore, sassafras and many others of the same kind of trees that compose the hardwood forests of northeast United States.

153. Where is the most lush and varied forest in the U.S.?   In the southern Appalachians, centering near Chattanooga, Tennessee.

154. Would not the great Northwest and Pacific Coast forests have a better claim to the title?   Those are the deepest, darkest and have the biggest trees, but they are not at all so lush and varied as the eastern hardwood forests. Often the western forests are dominated by one kind of tree—an entire stand may consist of Douglas fir, Engelmann spruce, lodgepole pine, etc. Also, the ground under the trees is almost bare. The eastern hardwood forest is a symphony of many species of trees, and has a lush ground cover of shrubs, flowers, ferns, and clubmosses.

155. What is a rain forest? Where rainfall of over 100 inches is distributed through the year, and the temperature is warm enough to permit year-round growing, and the forest is undisturbed by fire and man, a rain forest develops with these characteristics: (1) Many different kinds of plants growing together with jungle density. (2) Strata with certain kinds of plants and animal life at each level. (3) The appearance of lianas (woody climbers) and epiphytes (air plants living on the branches and trunks of trees).

In the caldron of vegetable growth, trees and bushes are in violent competition for light, striving to overtop one another. While such a struggle takes place in the sapling stage, this is a false concept of an established rain forest—a beautifully balanced organization. The tree species fall into groups with certain height and illumination limits. The members of the different tiers are not trying to overtop each other but are quite precisely adapted to each particular stratum.

The real struggle is for root room. Because of rapid decay, combined with intense leaching from heavy rain, the vegetable mould in which roots feed is shallow and roots cannot settle for different levels as they do in a temperate forest. Thus the trees of rain forests are not anchored deeply. Moreover, because the ground round about is packed with roots they cannot run out widely. Thus the congested taller trees do not have much holding power, while their compact foliage is pressed against strongly by the wind, and the trees cannot flex. The wonderful logic of nature provides mighty buttresses at the bases of tall tree trunks in a hot rain forest. This stabilizes the tree in the face of wind-shaking that might tear and loosen the roots. Wing outgrowths may extend 25 feet up the trunk and from them drop heavy roots standing above ground level. Sometimes stilt roots are separated from the main trunk by a gap, forming a flying buttress. Lianas are also important in the composition of the rain forest. They act as stays in the upper part of the canopy. Instead of strangling the trees as some people think (strangling fig is an exception) they are a great assistance. Many of the giant lianas extend from tree to tree like cables, reducing the wind-shake before the strain is put on the roots.

156. Are there any rain forests in our country? Although most rain forests are tropical, there is a superb rain forest on the westward coast of the Olympic Peninsula, Washington, and near the coast in northwest Oregon. Westerly winds pick up a big load of moisture from the warm waters of the Pacific, and when this hits the Olympic Mountains it is suddenly cooled and dumped. This delivers 140 inches of rain a year on a lush area near the coast, not much touched by winter freezing. The result is a beautiful rain forest where shafts of sunlight slant down through a lofty canopy, and ferns and lianas and giant tree boles are like ghosts in the misty twilight.

157. What is the most extensive virgin forest in the world today? The Amazon valley forest extending from the Atlantic Coast into the foothills of the Andes, and from Bolivia through Colombia, Venezuela and the Guianas is the largest unbroken forest belt in the world. Over a billion acres contain about 5,000 species of trees. It is not a solid mass of vegetation from end to end. It is interrupted here and there by treeless plains and meadows, some of them hundreds of square miles in extent. Only part is true jungle with "the steaming stillness of an orchid scented glade," where there is neither thicket nor tangle but tall trees with tiers of birds, animals and epiphytes at different levels, and with long lianas swaying in the dusk. Other parts of this immense virgin region are open woods through which a traveler may wander with as much freedom and ease as in the beech-oak openings of Wisconsin—if he does not encounter hostile Indians. Other parts, near the streams and along the main channel of the Amazon River, are flooded much of the year.

158. What is the world's greatest reserve of timber? The tropical hardwood forests of the Amazon valley and central Africa. Those of Africa are the most luxurious known, with tall hardwoods into which thousands of years of undisturbed growing have invested superb, colorful graining combined with great strength. African timbers are 50 to 150 percent stronger than the structural timbers of Europe and America. Less extensive, but equally beautiful, are the deep tropical hardwood forests of Malaya and the larger islands of the Far East.

The African forests have been shrinking due to burning by the natives, decreased rainfall, and by expanding exploitation centering in the Belgian Congo. They are only about one-third of their former size. Future generations will doubtless be thankful to find some of the great trees of the past still standing in these tropical forests when the day comes that they are faced with their final assault—as are the marvelous Douglas fir forests of our Northwest and British Columbia today. The tropical hardwoods are so slow growing that it is not practical to plant and grow them for use in the same generation. But with the Douglas fir it is possible to grow marketable sizes in 50 years, and the mass assault on the ancient giants with their irreplaceable forest glades of lakes and streams and wildlife is brazen and unnecessary opportunism.

159. What is the proportion of softwood (coniferous) to hardwood trees in the world? About two to one more hardwood, due to the vast tropical hardwood forests. But the amount of temperate hardwoods in usable forests is less than softwoods. In the United States about 62 percent of commercial forest land is softwood, and 80 percent of our commercial wood needs are filled by softwoods.

Vegetation maps of both the hardwood and softwood belts are deceptive. Man's felling of trees which started merely as personal use and clearing for living space has become a tidal wave of large-scale mechanical destruction in our day, and much of the forest of "forest areas" has ceased to exist.

160. What are evergreen hardwoods? These are hardwood trees with broad leaves which clothe the branches throughout the year. Examples are cork oak, pistacia and olive of the Mediterranean region; and live oak, sweet bay, southern magnolia and holly of the southern United States.

161. What forests are there in the United States? There are six principal forest belts:

1. *West Coast,* dominated in the north (coasts of Washington and Oregon) by Sitka spruce, lodgepole pine (also known as beach pine), western red cedar, Port Orford cedar, Douglas fir, Pacific dogwood, Oregon myrtle, red alder, bigleaf maple and cascara; in the center (north and mid-California coast) by redwood, golden chinquapin,

tanbark oak; and in the south by three famous old trees that are native nowhere else in the world—Monterey cypress, Monterey pine and Torrey pine.

2. *Western Forest.* This embraces the vast inland mountain forests of the Cascade, Sierra Nevada, and Rocky Mountains. It is dominated by Douglas fir and ponderosa pine in the north, and by pinion pine and western juniper in the south. Lodgepole pine is the commonest tree in the Yellowstone Park sector. Other great members of this forest belt are noble, red, grand, silver and white fir; western white, Jeffrey, knobcone, bristlecone, sugar pine; and western larch. In the valleys, blue oak, interior live oak, white alder, willow and black cottonwood.

3. *Northern Forest.* This belt stretches across northern Minnesota, Wisconsin, Michigan, New York and New England, with arms down the Appalachians into North Carolina. It is dominated by white, red and jack pine, larch, spruce, hemlock, balsam fir and arbor vitae. Along with these conifers are poplar, paper birch, beech and maple.

4. *Central Forest.* This is the great hardwood belt from Iowa eastward across the Middle West to the Atlantic Coast. It is dominated by oak, elm, maple, hickory, walnut, tulip tree, basswood, sweet birch, ash and black cherry. It fronts the Atlantic with a strip of pitch pine, which also climbs to the tops of hills. Hemlock and yellow birch mingle with the hardwoods in the hilly, rocky places. Poplar, sycamore and willow are widespread in the valleys. This is the remnant of the primeval forest that stretched unbroken from the Atlantic to the prairies when the white men first came. It gave shelter and supplies to the Indians.

5. *Southern Forest.* A broad belt from Maryland to east Texas dominated by longleaf, shortleaf, loblolly and slash pine. In moist places and swamps bald cypress, black gum and water tupelo take over. In the richer valleys are pecan, black walnut, elm, holly, magnolia, sweet gum, persimmon, and the famous evergreen live oak.

6. *Subtropical Belt.* This is a curiosity at the southern part of our country which picks up trees from Mexico and the Caribbean area. It is dominated by introduced trees such as citrus fruits, date palms, Australian beefwood, but it is termed one of six forest belts of our country because of the smattering of mahogany, strangler fig, mastic, gumbo limbo and Jamaica dogwood. Most conspicuous are the pond

cypress of the Everglades, and slash pine and palmetto of the dry, sandy places.

162. What is meant by the balance of the forest? When new growth balances decay within a forest, it is in balance. A continual shower of leaves, seeds, seed cases, bud scales, flower parts, pollen, pieces of bark, twigs and branches blown off by the wind, pine cones cut off by squirrels, fallen tree trunks, descends in the forest. This vegetable waste combines in the ground with by-products of animal life and dead animals, insects, birds. Then, through decay, a marvelous stew is mixed which nourishes more trees, bushes, flowers and animals. The phenomenon of growth which locks up elements, followed by decay which releases the elements, and then their reassemblage in the ground in such a way as to promote the forest like a well-balanced organism, is one of the greatest miracles of life. The balance of the forest is a beautiful achievement of uninterrupted natural processes.

163. What kind of trees grow in Siberia? Northwestern Siberia: silver fir, Siberian cedar, spruce, stone pine, and larch. Southwestern Siberia: fir and Siberian cedar (*Pinus cembra*) dominate, with a good deal of white birch and aspen mixed in, and alder, willow and mountain ash in thickets. Eastern Siberia: Scotch pine is by far the predominant tree, with localities of spruce, larch, fir and white birch. The forests of Siberia constitute some of the world's greatest tree resources, but they are not primeval forests and they contain much swamp forest with stunted trees (taiga), and vast areas have been ravaged by fire. The trees are hardly more than half a century old. One of the coldest places on earth lies within the Siberian forest, proving that certain trees can survive prolonged winter temperatures of 50° below zero and colder.

164. What is the easternmost tree in the United States? A red spruce beside the lighthouse at Lubec Point, Maine.

165. What is the westernmost tree in the United States? A redwood close to the coast, about 40 miles south of Eureka, California.

166. What is the southernmost tree in the United States? A sea grape facing the beach at Key West, Florida. It has big round leaves

about 8 inches across with bright red veins. Big clusters of purple
fruits hang from crooked branches.

167. What are the southernmost trees of the world? Rigorous
Tierra del Fuego, south of the Straits of Magellan, has pure stands of
a tall dynamic tree called Lenga (*Nothofagus pumila*). It has smooth
silver gray bark, resembling our beech, to which it is related. *Nothofagus* is one of the two most important genera of timber trees of the
Southern Hemisphere, the other being the *Eucalyptus* of Australia.
Also a remarkable magnolia (*Drimys winteri*) grows on the Tierra
del Fuego. The nearest relatives of these trees are in New Zealand,
thousands of miles away across the Pacific, a curious fact that points
to land connection between New Zealand and South America in geologic time. Forests at corresponding latitudes in the Northern Hemisphere are mostly evergreen (coniferous), but on tree-bearing land
closest to Antarctica, trees of Tierra del Fuego are summer green.
The forest is spotty but dense and dark, with rotting trunks lying in all
directions and luxuriant moss with the odor and feel of the rain forest
of our Olympic Peninsula.

168. What kind of trees grow in New Zealand? New Zealand has
so long been isolated from other land masses that 80 percent of its
flowering plants are peculiar—the species native nowhere else in the
world. The forest has a dual nature. New Zealand's most famous tree
is a member of the subtropical forest: the Kauri pine (*Agathis aus-
tralis*). This raises a massive canopy 150 feet high, far above other
trees, on a pillar 20 feet thick that rises 80 feet without a branch.
The Kauri is one of the stateliest and most useful timber trees in the
world, but this distinction has almost spelled its doom. Today only
large blocks of Kauri forest remain in Trounson Park, the Waipoua
Kauri Reserve, Puketi Forest, and a few forest remnants in the
Coromandel Ranges and Waitakere Hills. The Kauri is a marvelous
living relic of the *Araucarias,* the same kind of trees that created the
Petrified Forest of Arizona. (See Question 86.)

Separated by twenty miles from the southern tip of New Zealand's
mainland lies Stewart Island which is second only to Tierra del Fuego
as tree-bearing land closest to Antarctica. Here, on 650 square miles
is a marvelous forest paradox. Instead of sparse and stunted vegetation so close to Antarctic conditions, the mountains and valleys of

Stewart Island (Rakiura in Maori, meaning 'Isle of Glowing Skies'')
are clad with a beautiful rain forest. Fern Gully has luxurious tree
ferns that are a vision from the Coal Age, 200 million years ago.
Grass trees (*Dracophyllum* sp.) stand in open spaces draped with
leaves like light green grass. Rimu, relative of our yew, is the feature of this forest. The marble leaf tree (*Carpodetus*) named after its
polished mottled leaves, is unique on the face of the earth—a single
species in its genus. It is loaded with little white flowers that cover
the ground after a heavy rain. The tree's local name is puta-puta-
weta. "Weta" is a large beetle of New Zealand that likes to bore
holes in this tree. The Maori name means "full of beetle holes."

169. What is Australia's tree heritage?   Eucalyptus is Australia's
gift to the world. This fast-growing tree has deep plunging roots that
can tap water in near-desert conditions. Eucalypti from Australia
are widely used for windbreaks and street decoration in California,
Florida and in the dry countries around the Mediterranean and South

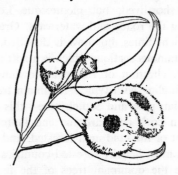

Eucalyptus globulus

Africa. Australia has 230 species with various names such as blue
gum, iron-bark, stringy-bark, blood-wood, and mallee. Some species
reach enormous heights. One (*Eucalyptus regnans*), on Mount Baw
Baw near Melbourne, is 326 feet high, and 25½ feet in girth at six
feet above the ground. The most common is "gum" eucalyptus, char-
acterized by smooth bark, often beautifully mottled blue and white.
The blood-wood group has scaly bark that showers off in chips. The
stringy-barks are felted in longitudinal strips that peel off and dangle. The iron-barks have hard, furrowed black bark. Many yield
valuable lumber. This is one of the world's most exciting and valuable
plants.

Another native of Australia is beefwood, also called Australian pine, although not a member of the pine family. Beefwood grows rapidly in sand and is a feature planting around the Gulf Coast; and is used as windbreaks for orange groves in southern California. Long pendulous branches wave in the wind. The tree is tall and feathery and sways gracefully. The pattern of the twigs resembles the ancient horsetail plant.

Compared to New Zealand and the Malay Archipelago with which it is associated botanically, Australia is sparsely forested. For a huge continental island, it is astonishing that less than 6 percent is forest land, this confined to coastal strips, especially eastern. Eucalyptus and acacia are dominant.

170. What is the tree pattern of Europe?   About 30 percent forested, of which three quarters is coniferous in the mountains and in northern Europe. Central lowland forest is hardwood, mostly beech, oak, and linden with a smattering of maple, ash, elm; and, of course, in France the tall, weedy, shortlived, but picturesque Lombardy poplar has been planted along the roads and waterways. Greece was magnificently forested in ancient times, but now is denuded. Spain's forests are restricted to mountainous sections which is a sort of crossroads of trees with oak, ash, chestnut of European lowland entering Spain in the Pyrenees, mingling with typical mountain trees such as white and silver fir, Austrian pine and Scotch pine—this blended with Mediterranean evergreen cork oak, arbutus and laurel southward. Finland with 60 percent of the land area forested, and Sweden with 55 percent are Europe's most heavily forested countries. Scotch pine and Norway spruce are the dominant trees of the fine Scandinavian forests.

171. How do the trees of the British Isles compare with the rest of Europe?   Up to 400 years ago, England was well forested. Now barely 4 percent is covered with forest, this mostly in the highlands of Scotland. Today the "green that is England" is largely grass green, and the green of thorn hedges, hedge row timber, and orchards. The hedges are unique with England. They consist of quickthorn, hawthorn and blackthorn mixed with walnut, beech and other hardwoods. They make excellent substitutes for barbwire to keep stock from straying and, at the same time, are useful for shade in summer and as windbreaks in winter. These famous hedges take about 10 years to mature, and may last 100 years. The hedgers are careful to leave sapling oak, beech, ash, chestnut, willow and, especially, elm, to grow in the hedges. Thus are lined up the descendents of the former forests of Britain which were once lush and widespread. Big estates also contributed to the preservation of some of the old forest land where they preserved parks, copses, and cover for game in the hunting days of the 18th and 19th centuries.

Much of Ireland and Scotland is bare moorland and bogs. Western Ireland has good rainfall, and many broadleafed evergreens and trees imported from Australia, Chile and California have been planted to make woodland.

172. What kind of trees grow in Hawaii? The showy trees commonly seen by tourists are imported, such as the African tuliptree, monkey pod tree, orchid tree. The native plants of Hawaii, including the trees, are famous because 73 percent of their species are found nowhere else in the world. Outstanding among these are ohia (*Metrosideros collina*); koa (*Acacia koa*); members of the coffee family (*Bobea, Gouldia,* and *Straussia*); also cocoa palms. A botanical curiosity found elsewhere only in East Africa is a tree form of *Lobelia,* the genus of some of our prettiest summer wildflowers. Mysteriously, the Hawaiian Islands have no conifers, no oaks, no maples, and only one distant and rare relative of the elm (*Trema ambonensis*). For further information see the checklist of plants of Hawaii compiled by Gunnar Fagerlund, and Mitchell, in *Hawaii National Park, Natural History Bulletin No. 9;* the pamphlet guides to nature trails: *Halemaumau Trail and Kipuka Trail* by George C. Ruhle, and *Trailside Plants*. These are all published in Washington, D.C., by The National Park Service. (See Question 246.)

173. What are the trees of the Philippines? Some of the finest forests in the world occupy about 40 thousand square miles of forest area in these islands. They are part of the Polynesian tropical hardwood forests. A wealth of unique species includes 24 different kinds of magnolias, and there are a thousand species of orchids in the forests. One of the best-known valuable trees of the Philippines is called lauan (*Dipterocarpus*)—a fine timber tree of great size that also produces a superb resin used in varnish.

The Philippine forests are better known and managed than any other important tropical hardwood forests in the world, due to the special interest by Gifford Pinchot and other pioneer American foresters between 1905 and 1913, when they were mapped, island by island. Under Arthur Fischer, the last American Chief of the Philippine Forest Service, the hardwood forests were put on a sustained-yield basis. Here is one spot on earth where wisdom and vision have frustrated exploitation of a great tree heritage.

174. How can a tree travel?   Seeds are the footsteps of the forest. When they step out they seem to be the haphazard playthings of wind and gravity, but the law of averages, which nature loves to use —when she produces far more seeds than are needed—causes more seeds to sprout on the warmer side if driven by cold, or on the moister side if driven by increasing aridity, or on the drier side if swampland is expanding. Thus trees move. They travel as a woodland with its various trees and small plants keeping together. So, in the case of the typical woods of northeastern United States, oak, hickory, elm, ash, maple, beech, poplar and birch keep together in their worldwide travels, and the woodland flowers and bushes go along with them.

175. What is meant by migrations of trees?   During geologic time trees have traveled far and wide around the globe. They are ever driven by changes of moisture and temperature to hold on to the situation suitable to their particular natures. They are doing this today, but it is an almost imperceptible movement in the brief observation of our time.

176. How do we know about these travels through the ages? The fossil record contains imprints of seeds, cones, leaves, twigs, bark, in rock, coal and peat. These can be identified as the ancestors of trees we see living on earth today. Geologists know the ages of these various vaults in which the picture story of plant life is preserved, and so the marvelous drama of certain kinds of trees growing in entirely different parts of the world in time past emerges.

177. What are examples of long-distance tree travels?   Half way up the west coast of Greenland, at Disko Island, 75 million years ago grew sycamore, magnolia, laurel and other familiar members of our eastern woodland, plus some tropical trees such as cinnamon, moonseed and breadfruit. That remarkable mixture of temperate and tropical trees was growing where today the land is in the grip of the Arctic cold, and the continental ice cap of Greenland rises to two miles depth of solid ice. The temperate woods have come to our northeastern United States and Europe. The tropical trees have retreated farther south. In those ages sequoia, now confined to one small area in California, was spread across four continents. They ranged from Spitsbergen to Japan, they grew in France, Greece, Italy and America. Ginkgo spread all over the world in the Age of Reptiles, 120 million years ago. A ginkgo grew in New Jersey, at Woodbridge, as recently as 60 million years ago—and today the only spot where ginkgo grows as a native tree is in central China. Bald cypress also wandered across Europe, Asia and North America from Alaska to Mexico, and today its retreat is a coastal area in our South and in coves of the Mississippi River, and a spot in Mexico.

178. How can trees cross seas to travel from continent to continent? Only coconut and mangrove trees, which have buoyant seeds impervious to harm from salt water, use sea lanes. Birds eat only the berries of trees and their transport over water is only a few miles at the most. The forests have not crossed the seas. They have used paths of migration along mountain ranges; one of the longest is the Rocky Mountain system, which extends through Central America to become continuous with the Andes. The Appalachian Mountains offered a route for northern trees retreating before the advance of the glaciers of the Ice Age. Today northerly trees such as spruce, fir, and white birch are carried deep into the South along the Great Smokies. For paths of migration east and west between continents, trees used land routes which are nonexistent today. Millions of years ago land masses were very different. Then the ocean currents were also different, as when warm currents from the tropics flowed northward along the coast of Greenland, accounting for the difference in climate in the Far North. Bering Strait was a land bridge between Asia and North America when trees from northeast Asia marched across.

It is a well known fact that the elevation of land in relation to the sea is constantly changing. Point Barrow, Alaska, is today retreating

at the rate of about 7 feet per year. The coast of New Jersey is said
to be sinking at the rate of about 3 feet per century. Cape Cod is
building up visibly. Its curved tip is elongating and land and water
have changed before the eyes of a single generation. In the Polar
North where masses of rock and talus slopes have been undisturbed
by man for hundreds of years, there are raised beaches vividly to be
seen 400 feet above sea level. Today land masses appear to be about
600 feet lower (or seas 600 feet higher) than in a former age. If we
look at this 600-foot submarine contour as representing the outlines
of the continents, an astonishing revelation occurs. Great Britain is
joined to Europe; the Straits of Gibraltar disappear so that Europe is
joined to Africa; North America and Asia are joined at Bering
Straits; the Arctic Archipelago disappears. Newfoundland is joined
to Canada; the north Atlantic is all but bridged; Cuba, the Bahamas, Florida and Yucatan become connected; Japan is joined to the
mainland; New Guinea and Australia are joined: the Philippines,
Borneo, Java and Sumatra are tied into Asia with the Malay Peninsula.

Finally, the drifting-continent theory, which was so eloquently supported by botanists to account for the locations of the same kinds
of trees in far separated continents (but so disputed by geologists),
was announced as a proven fact in 1956 at the annual meeting of
twenty-two Nobel Prize winners from eight countries. On the basis
of many measurements the assumption was made that England has
drifted north from a place much nearer the Equator and has re-
volved clockwise more than 30° in the last 150 million years. That
America and Europe have drifted apart, was said to be a "certain
probability." "Without doubt" India was situated south of the Equator 70 million years ago. Measurements point to the fact that Africa
has drifted directly over the South Pole in the last 300 million years.
During the world's history land masses have drifted large distances,
and "it is nearly certain" that migrations of land toward the poles
have taken place, with remarkable drifting.

**179. Where did trees start from on their journeys around the
world?**   This question is involved with the miracle of evolution, and
plumbs the occult depths of time. "Start" is a relative word. Because
the oldest fossils of our familiar hardwoods are Arctic, it has been
said that the hardwood temperate forests of the northeastern United

States had their origin in a circumpolar forest that surrounded the Arctic Ocean some 75 million years ago. Many of their wildflowers and much of their wealth of species must have evolved in coping with the vivid changes of climates of the Far North, and in travels southward into Europe, Asia and America, but the tree genera must have been derived from much more ancient ancestors. There is increasing evidence that more remote types had their origin in the tropics or possibly in the Southern Hemisphere—or land that was in the Southern Hemisphere before it drifted north. The actual origin is thus a mysterious sort of fairy tale like that origin of all life.

Based on a study of the present-day distribution of trees (without using fossils) the places where there are the most species is supposed to be the original center from which a genus radiated into the rest of the world. This does not mean the places where the most individuals grow. This would put the center of origin of most of our familiar hardwoods in northeast Asia. Our Appalachian woods have their match in China. For example, the center of maple is in west China (the Yunnan and Hupeh Provinces). It is startling to think that the ancestors of Vermont's sugar maple trees emigrated over the Aleutian landbridge and arrived in Vermont via Alaska, Greenland and Tennessee when the rise of the big glaciers of the Ice Age blotted out the circumpolar forest and drove the northern hardwoods southward. In this country they found refuge near Chattanooga, Tennessee, and traveled northward again behind the retreat of the Big Ice. In the western part of China also are locust, hackberry, persimmon, black gum and sweet gum. Most remarkable confirmation of China as the center of origin of trees of our landscape is the discovery in recent years of two living trees in western China which were known only as fossils in other parts of the world. These are ginkgo and metasequoia, the first a combination of a fern and a seed tree, the latter an ancestor of our sequoia and bald cypress. Their presence indicates that the area where they grow must have been stable in climate and free of volcanic disturbances and mountain upheavals through long ages—back into the Age of Reptiles and beyond. The world of that day was very strange. The continents were not the same shape as today. The seas had other shorelines. Animal life was just beginning to evolve mammals to replace reptiles. Yet here are two trees that survived for us—whose creation was far in the future—to see in leaf and seed. They have been passing along their chromosomes as though endowed with eternal life. The queer little mammal with an axe should stand in awe before a great tree.

180. Will tree types on the verge of disappearing from the earth take on fresh vigor if planted elsewhere?   Yes, and taking advantage of this wonderful fact can help save mankind from his folly. Eucalyptus, native only in Australia and Tasmania, with a few in New Guinea, is a landmark in California and subtropical countries. A vast zone from Spain to India has been made arid by deforestation and mismanagement from the days of Solomon through two world wars. This includes North Africa, the Mediterranean islands, Libya, Greece, Turkey, the Near East, Iran, Pakistan and China. Out of 300 species of eucalyptus a few have proved marvelous for reforestation in those countries. They quickly reach a size that eliminates danger from grazing animals which have destroyed so much potential forest where native trees are very slow growers. They throw out new shoots easily and resist fires.

There are many cases of old, stable trees waking up and growing with remarkable vigor when planted in far-away soils, albeit climate must approximate that of their native land. For example, the Monterey pine, which survived on a tiny strip about 10 miles long near the coast in southern California, has become one of the chief timber trees in New Zealand and Australia. Sequoias and Sitka spruce grow readily in England where they are well-known features of parks and estates. Gingko, rescued from extinction from temple grounds in central China, is rapidly becoming the most reliable tree of our cities. Poplars and acacias are almost universal trees throughout the temperate zones of the earth. The metasequoia, recently brought from China, is taking hold with great vigor in the eastern region of the United States. The ancient *Nothofagus,* a remarkable tree of New Zealand, and the farthest-south forest in Tierra del Fuego, is becoming a part of the tree population of the English landscape. Although this is a slow growing old hardwood in its native land, it makes between 3 and 4 feet of growth per year in England, and it seeds freely.

181. What trees have been featured by foreign countries on their stamps?   The *palm tree* has been featured by Cuba, Belgian Congo, Turkey, Vatican City, Paraguay, Iraq, New Zealand, New Guinea, North Borneo, El Salvador, Samoa, Seychelles, Senegal, Sudan,

Rarotonga, Tripolitania, Guadeloupe, Mauritania, Penrhyn, French Guinea, Liberia, Fiji, Gibraltar, Gilbert and Ellice Islands, Labuan, Dahomey, Ivory Coast, Granada, Jamaica, Panama, Cook Islands, Cayman Islands, Canal Zone, Solomon Islands, Colombia, Bolivia, British Guiana, Brazil, Aitutaki, Batum, Algeria.

Among other interesting trees featured on their countries' stamps are: *Apple:* Liechtenstein. *Bamboo:* Belgian Congo, Jamaica. *Breadfruit:* Tonga. *Cacao:* Togo, Nigeria, Ecuador. *Cedar:* Lebanon, Russia, Spanish Morocco, Israel, French Morocco, Japan. *Cherry:* Japan. *Chicle:* British Honduras. *Citrus lime:* Dominica. *Cypress:* Cyprus. *Ebony:* Cameroons, Nigeria. *Eucalyptus:* Ecuador. *Fig:* Turkey, Eritrea. *Grapefruit:* Jamaica, British Honduras. *Juniper:* Bermuda. *Kapok:* Cuba. *Kauri:* New Zealand. *Laurel:* Cuba. *Mahogany:* Ivory Coast, British Honduras, Cayman Islands. *Mango:* Cuba. *Mangrove:* Kenya, New Caledonia, Mozambique. *Maple:* Canada. *Maquilishuat:* El Salvador. *Monkey puzzle:* Monaco. *Oak:* Costa Rica, Lithuania, Italy, Sierra Laone, French Morocco. *Olive:* Turkey, Spanish Morocco. *Orange:* Pitcairn, Zomambique, Union of South Africa, Orange River Colony. *Pandanus:* Gilbert and Ellice. *Papaya:* Tripolitania. *Pine:* Japan, Chile, Russia, Liechtenstein, Bahamas. *Plum:* Japan. *Pomegranate:* Tripolitania. *Poplar:* Liberia, Canada. *Rubber:* Cameroons, Ceylon, Mozambique. *Spruce:* Finland, Newfoundland. *Sycamore:* Switzerland. *Teak:* Burma. *Traveler's tree:* Madagascar, Liberia. *Willow:* Switzerland.

(For trees featured on stamps of the United States see Question 91.)

182. What is the Maquilishuat tree? A hardwood of tropical America related to the catalpa of the eastern United States. Its genus name is *Tabebuia*.

183. Does the economy of any country depend entirely on trees? That of Finland comes the closest.

184. In the distribution of trees, which is more important—temperature or rainfall? Temperature dictates the zones—that only the tropics and the temperate zones of the earth shall have trees. Rainfall is more important in determining what kind of trees grow in any given region.

185. How can I recognize the trees I see? This can be the most important question in the book. The answer opens doors on discoveries that will make the outdoors more exciting. One tree leads to another, and there is always something else just around the corner. Study the details of a tree for the purpose of identification, such as lobes, sinuses and margins of leaves; winter buds, bud scales and the rhythm of their opening to pour forth their contents; color and styles of pith; color of hairs; texture of bark; breathing pore of twigs; flower of trees; varieties of fruit and seed; amazing mechanical devices for seed distribution; the angles of twigs, and their patterns; the art and design in every item; the engineering genius in the way every part is fitted together to make the whole tree—all this is both an inspiration and a highly refreshing activity that can be enjoyed with children and friends.

There are two ways to know trees. One is to find a person well versed in trees who will take you out for a walk and tell you about them. This approach is fine for a beginning, especially if your guide will go slowly, and patiently point out the details for recognition while you take notes. Too often this approach is just a memory test for names, and it does not indicate the relationships of trees and how they are organized into hardwoods and softwoods (or flowering trees and cone-bearing, or deciduous and evergreen) and how each of these broad categories is organized into families, genera and species. Nor is a personal guide always available. You must be on your own in order to serve the mood and opportunity.

In the long run the second way is the best way—use a guide book (see Question 187), and go out by yourself. A magnifying glass can be a great help. (See Question 189.)

Begin with a tree you know, say an oak, apple, elm or maple; note its details, such as the vein pattern of the leaf, lobes, margins; whether the margins have teeth and lobes; whether the teeth are double or single, point forward or straight out. Is the leaf hairy? Shiny? Compare the bark with that of other trees—its tones, whether deeply sculptured or smooth, perhaps flaky. Note the nature of the twigs. Are they fuzzy or shiny, heavy and stiff, slender and flexible; what is the color of the youngest part of the twig? Slice a twig with a sharp knife and note the color and character of the pith. Taste the twig. Does it have a spicy, bitter or aromatic flavor? If this tree is an oak, note the form of its acorns. Is the cup shallow or deep? Is the nut part slender or fat and does it extend out from the cup or form a low dome? When the tree you know the name of has been explored in detail and you have seen the marvelous details and realize that every kind of tree is endowed with its own peculiar and remarkable details, you will have the inspiration for tree recognition. This is much more than just calling trees by name.

Take the *twelve* most important kinds of trees in your vicinity and after that you can go on and on. It is likely that twelve kinds of trees will give you a large majority of the trees commonly seen in your part of the woods.

There are three broad considerations before you can pinpoint the trees you see. What part of the country are they growing in? What type is the locality (rocky, dry, sandy, marshy, streamside, upland pasture, woodland)? What time of year is it? This indicates what to stress—flowers, fruits, leaves, winter buds, fall colors, branch patterns.

186. What are the Seven Regions of Tree Discovery? 1. *The Great American Woods*. These are the trees of eastern United States, one of the most varied tree areas in the world. 2. *The Middle West*. This is contained within the first region, but has *some* of its own characteristic trees. 3. *The South*. This is also contained within the first region, but has *many* of its own characteristic trees. 4. *Southern Florida and Gulf Coast*. A unique region with subtropical trees. 5. *The Northwest*. Greatest forest region of our country and the biggest trees in the world. 6. *California*. Trees native nowhere else in the world, with many unique and beautiful trees introduced from all over the world. 7. *The Southwest*. Peculiar, arresting desert and dry mountain trees.

187. What is a good tree guide book? It is important to distinguish between a small guide to carry in the car or on a walk, and reference books. A good beginners' guide book covering all parts of the country, to take into the field, is *American Trees: a Book of Discovery,* by Rutherford Platt (New York: Dodd, Mead & Company), with color illustrations. There are also pocket guides to the trees of the National Parks, and some regional guides in which, however, trees are often included as part of the whole flora. A good regional guide book with lots of photographs is *Trees of the Eastern United*

States and Canada by William H. Harlow (New York: McGraw-Hill Publishing Company).

188. What are some good tree reference books? *Trees,* Year Book, Department of Agriculture, 1949 (Washington, D.C.: Govt. Printing Office). *Knowing Your Trees,* by G. H. Collingwood (Washington, D.C.: American Forestry Association), has photographs of leaf, flower, fruit and bark as well as of full trees, of more than a hundred native trees. *Handbook of Trees,* by Romeyn B. Hough (Boston: Houghton Mifflin), is an old classic with photographs of details of bark, leaf and fruit that have never been surpassed in scope. It contains all the trees of the eastern United States. *Manual of the Trees of North America,* by Charles S. Sargent (Boston: Houghton Mifflin), is a great reference book for the advanced student who wants a comprehensive volume. Line drawings (783 of them) shows leaves and fruits of every species with accuracy.

189. What kind of magnifying glass is best for field study? Any low-power magnifying glass will help. Remember they are easy to lose. The best equipment is a small lens, an inch across, that swings into a protective cover. Magnification around 10X is best. Hold the material with one hand, and the lens between thumb and first finger of the other hand, then bring hands together and put your eye close to the lens. This gives the firmest set up and a much better view than if your eye is at a distance from the lens. Be sure to secure the lens by a cord or strong black ribbon so that it can dangle from around your neck, out of the way, yet ready for quick looks.

190. What are points of identification? These are points to consider: leaf, bud, bark, relative thickness of trunk and twigs, color of twigs, taste of twigs, color of under bark, pith color and whether divided with cross partitions, flowers, fruit, seeds, style of branching—whether trunk separates into limbs or whether it goes from ground to top with branches coming off at wide angles. Hairiness, smoothness, roughness, shininess of parts are also considerations. As you approach a tree, its general outline is often eloquent. For example, the fountain of the American elm, the long oval of sugar maple, the broken, wide-reaching outline of the black willow. The intertwining pattern of branches against the sky. Accessory growths such as thorns and corky ridges of bark. The breathing pores of

barks are prominent in birches and cherry trees. The clearest identification in winter will be the details of the buds and here is where
the magnifying glass helps.

191. What is a "key" to trees? A key puts the characteristics of a
tree into a series of choices which lead to the name of the tree. It is
like the "true and false" quiz and an excellent way to find out what
a tree is. Botanical manuals use keys with scientific nomenclature, but
there are some good keys for people who are not botanists. A key
in ring-book form for the serious beginner is *How to Know the Trees,*
by H. E. Jaques (Dubuque, Iowa: William C. Brown Company).
Another, in book form, with excellent identification drawings is *Illustrated Guide to Trees and Shrubs,* by A. H. Graves (New York:
Harper & Brothers).

192. Is there a simplified key to some of the commonest trees?
Here is a key * to the naming of common trees from small clues:

IN WINTER

Directions:

First, look for the buds. Note their arrangement, shape, size, and
scales. Pay special attention to buds at end of twig.

Second, look for the leaf scar. Note its shape and the dots in it.

Third, look for other clues. These may or may not be present;
bright colors, thorns, catkins, peculiarities of pith, sap, twig, or bark.

Answer questions below as though "true or false." If the first A
does not fit, go on to the next A. When A fits, then take B under the
A that fits. So on, until you reach the answer.

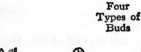

Four
Types of
Buds

Overlapping   Two Scales   Single Scale   Naked
Scales   like a valve   covering Bud   (No Scales)

* This key is from the author's book, *This Green World,* published by Dodd,
Mead & Company.

Explanation of Certain Words:

Leaf scar: Mark on twig where last season's leaf fell from stem. Usually found just below bud.

Bud scales: The hard outer covering of buds.

Pith partitions: The pith is the core of a twig. When sliced lengthwise you sometimes see partitions like the rounds of a ladder.

Catkins: These are little tassels (often 1 or 2 inches long) that hang on some trees. Frequently found on the birches.

Witches' brooms: A dark bunch or tangle of twigs, often seen on hackberry.

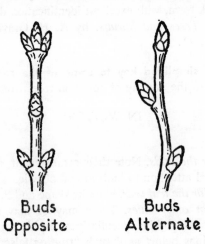

Buds
Opposite

Buds
Alternate

A. *Buds opposite*
  B. *Buds large* (½ to 1 inch or longer) blunt, oval . . . .
                                                     HORSE CHESTNUT
  B. *Buds small* (½ inch or less)
      C. *Scales meeting at edges,* but on end of twig like a silver-gray shoe-button with 4 scales . . . . FLOWERING DOGWOOD
      C. *Scales overlapping*
          D. Bud oval, those at end of twig in threes with middle one much longer. Leaf scars narrow, triangular with 3 dots
                                                                MAPLE
          D. Buds fatter, dark brown. Buds at end of twig close together making fancy design. Leaf scars shield shape, or almost circular, with many dots forming a horseshoe . ASH

A. *Buds in whorls of three*
Tiny fat buds. Leaf scars round, standing out on platforms; two large scars and one small scar in each whorl . . . . .CATALPA

A. *Buds alternate*
  B. *Sap milky*
    1. Buds triangular with 2 or 3 red brown scales . . . .MULBERRY
    2. Tiny brown buds and powerful thorns . . . . . .OSAGE ORANGE
    3. Pith orange, small tree or shrub . . . . .SUMAC
  B. *Sap not milky*
    C. *Twigs with thorns*
      1. Buds sunken out of sight in bark, thorns long, *branched*
                                   HONEY LOCUST
      2. Buds sunken out of sight in bark, thorns short, unbranched, *in pairs* at leaf scars . . . . .BLACK LOCUST
      3. Single thorns, from side of twig; buds minute . .HAWTHORN
      4. Single heavy thorn at end of short twig . . . . .PEAR
    C. *Twigs without thorns*
      D. *Pith with partitions*
        1. Spaces between partitions empty. No scale on buds . . .
                                    WALNUT
        2. Pith white, buds light brown with 2 scales like a duck's bill . . . . .TULIP TREE
        3. Pith partitions unequally spaced. Buds dark red-brown with about 4 scales . . . . .TUPELO
        4. Pith partitions unequally spaced. Buds dark, triangular. Bark in square chunks . . . . .PERSIMMON
        5. Partitions close together. Bark warty. "Witches' brooms" often visible . . . . .HACKBERRY
      D. *Pith without partitions*
        E. *With catkins*
          1. Bark smooth, or papery and curly . . . . .BIRCH
          2. Bark in narrow, ragged vertical strips . . . .
                                HOP HORNBEAM
        E. *Without catkins*
          F. *Buds usually clustered toward tip of twig* . . . . . .OAK
          F. *Buds not usually clustered toward tip of twig*
            G. *With distinctive twigs*
              1. Twigs green with spicy taste . . . . . .SASSAFRAS
              2. Older twigs with corky ridges. Buds mahogany brown, shiny . . . . .SWEET GUM

3. Young twigs red above, green beneath . . . PEACH
4. Twigs with bitter taste like cherry pits. (Young bark smooth like birch) . . . . CHERRY

G. *Without distinctive twigs*

H. *No scale on buds.* Tiny folded leaves of buds sulphur yellow . . . . BITTERNUT HICKORY

H. *One scale showing on buds.*

1. End bud big, sometimes an inch long, oval, hairy . . . . MAGNOLIA
2. Buds like light brown conical hats. Leaf scar makes narrow circle around base of bud . . . .
                                                                          SYCAMORE
3. Buds red, pressed against twig . . . . . WILLOW

H. *Two scales showing on bud*

1. Little round buds set into the top of a big oval leaf scar. About 9 dots just inside edge of leaf scar . . . . AILANTHUS
2. Green or red scales, one of which bulges, making bud lopsided . . . . LINDEN
3. End bud fat, wide oval. Scales soft, light gray, or tan. (Note: the tough outside scales fall off early) . . . .
        MOCKERNUT HICKORY or PIGNUT HICKORY

H. *Three scales showing on bud*—Buds smooth, oval, brown. Pith star shaped in cross-section.
                                                                          CHESTNUT

H. *More than 3 scales showing on bud*

1. Inner scales soft gray. Outer scales with long points . . . . SHAGBARK HICKORY
2. Light brown. Longest, sharpest of all buds. (Often ¾-in. long) . . . . BEECH
3. About 6 scales arranged in two vertical rows. Bud usually tipped and on one side of leaf scar
                                                                          ELM
4. Long sharp buds often shiny as though varnished and pressed close to twig. Pith star shaped in cross-section . . . . POPLAR
5. Blunt, woolly, so that scales may not show clearly. Squatty tree. Trunk often leaning . . .
                                                                          APPLE

BEECH

ELM

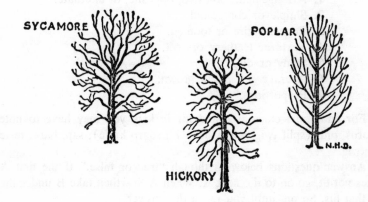

SYCAMORE

POPLAR

HICKORY

WHITE OAK

BLACK-WILLOW

APPLE

IN SUMMER

Directions:

Note points about leaves in this order:

1. Arrangement: whorled, opposite, or alternate.
2. Simple or compound.
3. Edges: entire or toothed.
4. Texture: leathery or soft.
5. Shiny or dull.
6. Average size if full grown.
7. Proportions.

For additional clues as called for in key, you may have to note thorns, pith (split twig lengthwise with sharp knife), sap, bark, taste of twig.

Answer questions below as though "true or false." If the first A does not fit, go on to the next A. When A fits, then take B under the A that fits. So on, until you reach the answer.

A. *Leaves in whorls of 3*
Leaves large, 6 to 12 inches .... CATALPA
A. *Leaves opposite*
  B. *Leaves compound*
    C. *Palmately compounds* (like the fingers on your hand) ......
                    HORSECHESTNUT and BUCKEYE
    C. *Pinnately compound* (like a feather)
      3 or 5 leaflets .... BOX ELDER
      5 to 11 leaflets .... ASH
  B. *Leaves simple*
    1. Large, heart-shaped, edge entire, 5 to 15 inches . PAULOWNIA
    2. Three major lobes (smaller lobes also) .... MAPLE
    3. Smooth ovals, edges entire .... DOGWOOD

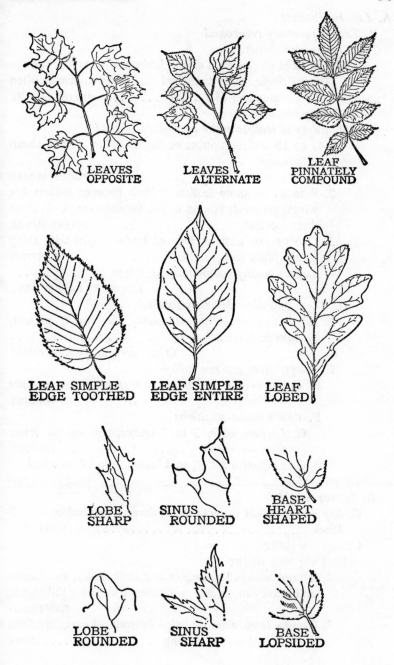

LEAVES
OPPOSITE

LEAVES
ALTERNATE

LEAF
PINNATELY
COMPOUND

LEAF SIMPLE
EDGE TOOTHED

LEAF SIMPLE
EDGE ENTIRE

LEAF
LOBED

LOBE
SHARP

SINUS
ROUNDED

BASE
HEART
SHAPED

LOBE
ROUNDED

SINUS
SHARP

BASE
LOPSIDED

A. *Leaves alternate*
   B. *Leaves pinnately compound*
      C. *Twigs with thorns*
         1. Thorns in pair on each side of leaf stem ...BLACK LOCUST
         2. Thorns single, often branched like daggers, leaves often doubly compound like a fern ....HONEY LOCUST
      C. *Twigs without thorns*
         D. *Edges of leaflets entire or slightly toothed*
            1. 7 to 13 leaflets, flowers or berries white, tree or shrub of swamps
               (DON'T TOUCH THIS) ....POISON SUMAC
            2. 9 to 21 or more leaflets, midrib between leaflets has wings, yellowish flowers or red berries, tree or shrub of drier locations ....DWARF SUMAC
            3. One or two teeth at base of leaflet tipped with shiny gland, often seen in cities ....AILANTHUS
            4. Leaves doubly compound like a fern ....
               KENTUCKY COFFEE TREE
         D. *Edges of leaflets definitely toothed*
            E. *Small tree or shrub, sap milky; flowers, if present, yellowish; berries deep red* ....
               STAGHORN and SMOOTH SUMAC
            E. *Larger tree, sap not milky*
               F. *Pith of twigs has partitions with spaces between empty*
                  WALNUT
               F. *Pith without partitions*
                  G. *Leaflets large,* 3 to 7 inches, and usually fewer than on walnut ....HICKORY
                  G. *Leaflets small,* ¾ to 4 inches, 9 to 17 on a leaf ..
                     MOUNTAIN ASH
   B. *Leaves simple*
      C. *Sap milky,* leaves variable, heart-shaped, unlobed or 2 or 3 lobes ....MULBERRY
      C. *Sap not milky*
         D. *Twig with thorns*
            1. Thorns attached at base of leaf stalk, leaves small, oval and heavily toothed or with lobes, fruit like a little apple
               HAWTHORN
            2. Thorns from ends of twigs or spurs. Leaves medium ovals, 2 to 4 inches, shining ....PEAR

D. *Twigs without thorns*
  E. *Leaf as broad or nearly as broad as it is long*
    1. Leaf heart-shaped, 3 to 5 inches, edge entire . REDBUD
    2. Leaf lobed like a maple, bark with white patches ...
        SYCAMORE
    3. Leaf triangular, edge with fine teeth or scalloped ...
        POPLAR
    4. Base lopsided, heart-shaped, fine teeth ..... LINDEN
    5. Leaves squared off at top. Trunk a tall straight
      cylinder .... TULIP TREE
  E. *Leaf oval, longer than broad*
    F. *Edges entire or almost*
      1. Small leaves, 2 to 3 inches, leathery, shining dark
        green on top, whitish below .... LIVE OAK
      2. Large leaves, 6 to 20 inches, leathery, highly pol-
        ished, very dark green .... MAGNOLIA
      3. Leaves 4 to 6 inches, not leathery. Bark in square
        chunks. Occasional teeth .... PERSIMMON
    F. *Edges of leaves scalloped or wavy*
      1. With prickles, dark, leathery, polished .... HOLLY
      2. Leaves 3 to 6 inches, long, oval, bark smooth,
        silver-gray .... BEECH
      3. Leaves with wavy edges, bark dark and deeply
        sculptured .... CHESTNUT OAK
        (*Note:* Do not confuse chestnut oak with Ameri-
        can chestnut. The latter has been killed by a blight.
        You often see shrubby forms or suckers of the true
        chestnut. They have handsome slender oval leaves,
        6 to 10 inches, with scalloped edges and sharp
        teeth.)
    F. *Edges of leaves with teeth*
      1. Teeth sharp and double, leaf leathery, base lop-
        sided .... ELM
      2. Leaf tapering, curved, soft texture, base lopsided
        HACKBERRY
      3. Fine teeth, broad oval 2½ to 4 inches, twigs
        slightly hairy, small, stocky tree, often a shrub ...
        SHADBLOW
      4. Leaf broad oval, dull, woolly beneath, 3 to 5 inches
        APPLE

5. Symmetrical oval leaf, shiny green, 2 to 5 inches,
   upper bark and twigs smooth deep red with prominent raised dots . . . . CHERRY
6. Teeth small and crowded, leaf soft, slightly hairy
   on both sides, bark shredded in vertical strips . . . .
   HOP-HORNBEAM
7. Leaf smooth and soft similar to preceding, bark
   dark gray, smooth, muscular ridges . . BLUE BEECH
8. Leaf similar to preceding but smooth bark, sometimes peeling off in horizontal strips, white, yellow,
   or dark red . . . . BIRCH

F. *Leaves lobed* . . . . OAK
   (Southern oaks without lobes are not included.)

E. *Tree with broken twigs and suckers, leaf very long and*
   narrow.
   Heavy tree in wet places, leaves 3 to 6 inches long . . . .
   BLACK WILLOW

PICTORIAL KEY TO NATIVE EVERGREENS

Evergreen names are often confused although the different kinds
can be easily identified.

The trees commonly known as evergreens are members of the Pine
Family. Their leaves are needles, and they produce cones. A few
trees in other families with broad leaves are also evergreen. This is
true of the live oak, magnolia, and rhododendron. On the other hand,
two members of the Pine Family are not evergreens: the larch and the
bald cypress shed their needles in winter.

The six shown here cover most of the common evergreens, except

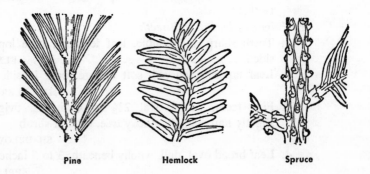

Pine   Hemlock   Spruce

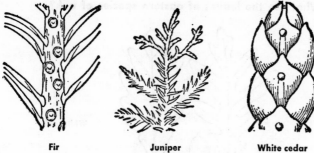

Fir   Juniper   White cedar

cultivated kinds and some that are restricted in their distribution.

PINE: Long needles held together at the base by a sheath of papery bark. The number of needles in each cluster tells you the kind of pine. For example: white pine, 5 needles; red pine, 2 needles; pitch pine, 3 needles.

FIR: The only native fir east of the Rockies is the balsam. Needles in two ranks make a flat design. Pluck off needle and you see on the twig a little round scar with a dot in the center.

HEMLOCK: Needles in two ranks like the fir, but shorter, flatter, and blunt. Dark green and shiny above, pale below with 2 parallel dotted lines. Along top of twig you see little upside-down needles.

JUNIPER: Common tree form called red cedar whose red heartwood scares off moths. Two kinds of needles often grow on same shoot: sharp awl-shaped projecting at angles; and flat overlapping scales that hug the twig.

SPRUCE: Needles are short, four-sided (awl-shaped), arranged in spirals on the twig. Pluck off needles and you see their stems left on the twig like little hooks or projections.

WHITE CEDAR: Common form called arbor-vitae. Needles in four ranks, flat, shiny and overlapping closely, forming geometric design. Center needles with dots. (Drawing magnified about 6 diameters.)

193. What is the best way to know the different kinds of oak?
The differences are in the leaves, acorns, winter buds, bark, and in the tree's outline and place of growth. Of these, the leaves offer the best way as they are always interesting and conspicuous, and they are apt to cling throughout winter or can be found on the ground under the tree.

194. What are the leaves of eastern species of oak?

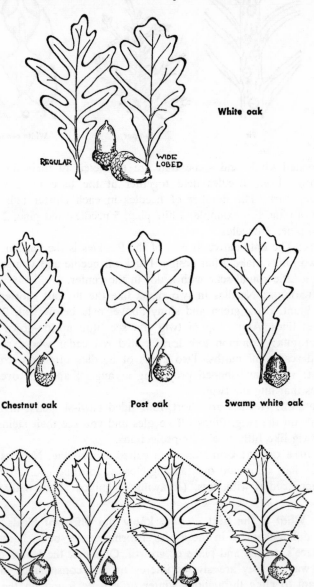

White oak

REGULAR   WIDE LOBED

Chestnut oak   Post oak   Swamp white oak

Red oak   Black oak   Pin oak   Scarlet oak

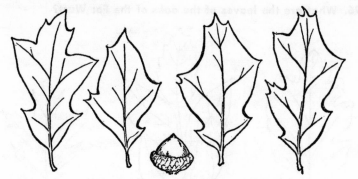

Scrub oak bears many whimsical patterns

195. What are the leaves of the oaks of our southern states? The first five are evergreen.

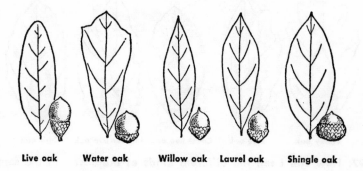

Live oak   Water oak   Willow oak   Laurel oak   Shingle oak

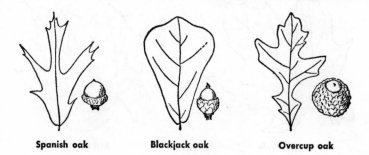

Spanish oak   Blackjack oak   Overcup oak

196. What are the leaves of the oaks of the Far West?

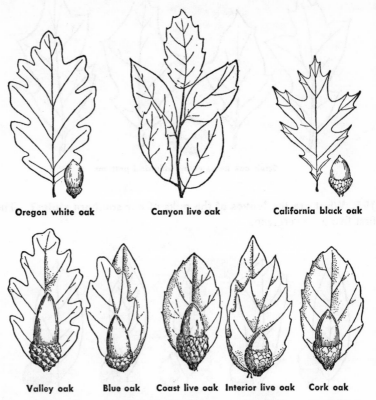

Oregon white oak   Canyon live oak   California black oak

Valley oak   Blue oak   Coast live oak   Interior live oak   Cork oak

197. How can I tell the different kinds of maples? In the same way as the oaks, except that maples all have winged seeds instead of

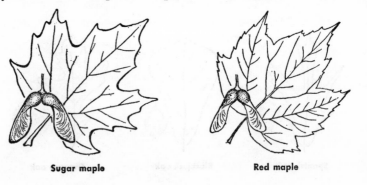

Sugar maple   Red maple

acorns. Here are the leaves of ten species of maple. The bigleaf maple
and the vine maple are of the Far West.

Silver maple

Black maple

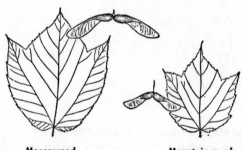

Moosewood

Mountain maple

Sycamore maple

Japanese maple

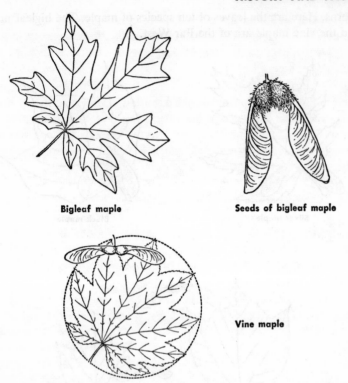

Bigleaf maple

Seeds of bigleaf maple

Vine maple

198. On what kind of trees does mistletoe grow? It prefers members of the pine family, but occasionally grows on oak, sycamore, and mesquite.

199. What American tree has the longest thorns? Honey locust, with wicked spikes, in clusters, may be several inches long.

200. What tree has the crookedest branches? Normally scrub oak and hawthorn have picturesquely crooked branches. But any tree in rocky ground and exposed to winds may develop tortured twists and turns in its branches.

201. What tree has the straightest branches? Ginkgo branches tend to grow in straight lines, although they may shoot out at eccentric angles and make sharp turns.

202. What tree has the most fanciful bark? Ponderosa pine has cinnamon red plates which flake off in the shapes of fanciful animals—little dogs, owls, long-necked horses, skunks with huge tails, wild geese, etc.

203. What tree has the roughest bark? Old sequoia has mighty bark with deep fissures and big ridges, but these are in keeping with the proportions of the tree and may not be called conspicuously "rough." Mature chestnut oak and sassafras have deeply sculptured bark that is a vivid point of recognition for these trees.

204. What tree has the smoothest bark? Birches have bark that is elastic so that it expands with the growth of the trees and does not break into rough texture. Beech is silvery smooth and the bark of aspen is polished green. Holly has no true outer bark and its smooth gray surface is very sensitive to injury and sunburn.

205. What makes birch bark white? It is made of very thin laminated layers. Inner layers are corky and tinged with tannin that makes them a beautiful orange-red when first exposed. Tannin is an acid compound very common in most barks, which gives them dark hues. In some oaks with blackish bark, tannic acids are 40 percent of their dry weight. The outer layers of white birch bark have no tannin; their cells are empty and reflect light because of the myriad microscopic air spaces which deflect the light in all directions. This is the same phenomenon that makes snow white.

206. What tree has the biggest buds? The twig tips of magnolia bear fat flower buds that may be an inch or more long. Horsechestnut has large handsome buds. Those of beech are ¾ of an inch or so long, very sharp and slender.

207. What tree has the smallest buds? Hawthorn has tiny buds best seen with a magnifying lens.

208. Is there any tree with no buds? All trees have buds, but the buds of black locust are invisible, buried in the bark of the twig. The buds of sycamore do not show when leaves are on the tree because they are covered by the stem of the leaf which fits over them like a candle snuffer.

209. What trees have brightly colored buds?   Red maple buds are carmine; willow, yellow. Shadblow buds are mottled red and yellow.

210. What tree has bud scales that look like flowers?   Flowering dogwood has little gray "shoe buttons." When they open the bud scales expand enormously and become the big white "petals" of the famous dogwood flowers.

211. On which trees do dead leaves cling all winter?   Mostly oak. In late fall and winter, when other trees have shed their leaves, oak trees can be identified by the tan and red leaves that rattle in the wind, crisp and dry. They cling especially to young trees and the younger branches near the tops of older trees. Dead leaves also cling to beech trees all winter.

212. What makes leaves drop off in the autumn?   Trees drop their leaves at the same time that they turn color in the fall because a disk of cells called the abscission layer forms at the base of the leaf stem. These are loose dry cells that cause the leaf to break off of its own weight. A peculiarity of oak and beech is that this abscission layer often does not form until their wood is older.

213. Is it true that oak trees should be shunned in a thunder storm?   Yes. Another peculiarity of the oak is that it is struck by lightning much more frequently than any other tree. The bigger and taller oaks are first struck, and especially if they have any rotten wood. It appears that electricity has easier passage through oak wood than through other kinds and possibly an area of damp, decayed wood acts as a sort of storage battery in which negative potential builds up.

This attraction of oaks to lightning is credited with promoting the reverence with which ancient people regarded the oak. They traced a connection between the tree and their sky god. They heard his voice in the roll of thunder and saw him descend in a flash of lightning. Often oaks riven and blackened were enclosed and treated as particularly sacred. (See Question 144.)

214. Do oak trees have flowers? Yes, all hardwood trees have flowers, although many are inconspicuous. Oak has two kinds of flowers. The female (pistillate) is the size of a little bud and will turn into an acorn. The male (staminate) is in the form of a slender tassel about two inches long. Bunches of these pale green tassels dangle from the ends of twigs for a few days in late spring.

215. When do the various hardwood trees bloom? While days and nights are still chilly and, before the leaves come out in very early spring, the flowers of willow, elm, poplar, ash, maple and birch bloom profusely. A little later the flowers of sassafras, walnut, sweet gum, sycamore, beech and oak unfold. This happens at the same time that the leaves come out so the flowers are often hidden. These are wind-pollinated trees that do not need conspicuous flowers to attract insects. Later in the spring, when warmer days have brought the insects, linden produces fragrant flowers with sticky pollen to get the help of the insects. Linden flowers are pale green and easily overlooked, but fragrant and interesting and easy to see if you take a second look. At insect time, also, the trees with showy flowers bloom —apple, cherry, peach, magnolia, sorrel, dogwood, redbud, hawthorn, horsechestnut, catalpa, locust.

216. How can I see elm flowers? In late winter when the snow may still be on the ground, after a clear day, look high up near the tops of the tall elms. You will see a dark purplish gauze against the sky. This is a mass of elm flowers called forth suddenly by the radiant warmth of the sun.

217. How can I see maple flowers? They appear first like a rich red tint near the tops of the red maples growing in low, wet places. This is the same time that the pussywillows are shooting out their white silvery brushes. Sugar-maple flowers appear a week or two later. Just before the leaves come out the sugar maple takes on a bright chartreuse-green gauze. This may be mistaken for new leaves, but it is a mass of maple flowers all over the tree.

218. Surely pine trees do not have flowers? Botanically, organs that produce seeds are flowers, and thus the flowers of pine trees are their cones. The pollen cones are comparatively small. In early spring they appear like knobs near the tips of twigs and top branches, gush great quantities of pollen, shrivel and disappear. The seed cone is green and tightly closed at first. These are scattered all over the tree and harden into the familiar pine cones. The length of time they stay on the tree depends on the species. Some are cast off the first year, others stay on their trees many years.

Cone of white pine

219. Do any native trees grow in our southwest deserts? Desert vegetation is predominantly shrubby. The Joshua tree and saguaro cactus are true trees of the desert floor. Other remarkable trees of low stature are:

Mesquite, in a sense the most important tree from Texas to southern California, has thorny branches, feathery gray leaves, masses of yellow flowers, and honey-sweet pods. Wide branches cast thin shade across fifty feet where the sand is covered by pods avidly eaten by animals. This tree is an indicator of ground water in the desert, though it may be hard to dig as deeply as the roots go.

Palo verde has interlocking spiny branches. A bluish tree of the desert expanses from California across southern Arizona. In late March masses of yellow flowers are visible for miles. This remarkable tree has plenty of leaves after a shower, but they fall off promptly so water is not lost during hot dry months and the green trunk, meanwhile, serves for leaves.

Crucifixion thorn grows on mesas and in canyons of southern Utah and in washes of Arizona desert. This tree has no leaves. Trunk is green like palo verde and its chlorophyll for foodmaking is increased by long, green, elastic thorns. Thorns and woody fruit give no satisfaction to browsing animals, but tree helps control erosion and rouses curiosity on the desert landscape.

Desert ironwood is an unusual tree of the deep desert. It has lavender sweet-pea type flowers and blue-green foliage. When flowers are not showing, gray stringy bark distinguishes it from the palo verde with its tight green bark. It is well named—the wood is iron heavy, dulls tools, and can hardly be cut with a saw.

Smoke tree (Dalea spinosa) is a small tree with a compact mass of leafless branches, ashy gray, looking like a puff of smoke in the distance. It grows in gravelly washes and is profuse with bright purple flowers in early summer.

Elephant tree is a weird little tree of very dry places that gets its name from the swollen paper-bark trunk. Contrasted with white bark of trunk, that of twigs is a rich red-brown. Fat trunk stores sap moisture and contains abundant aromatic oil that resists drying.

In canyons and washes, and along the few streams, there are other more familiar trees. These are sycamore, ash, walnut and cotton-wood, and in places watered by springs are the tall Washington palms of southern California.

220. What are "tree faces"? Droll faces are sketched by the thousands just below buds. These are scars left when last year's leaves fell off. They are easy to see in winter when a tree is bare of

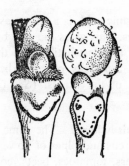

Butternut (left) and mockernut faces (enlarged)

leaves. Most can be seen with the naked eye; others must be discovered with a magnifying glass. Hickory has some of the largest and most whimsical faces. Butternut suggests a horse with a long chin and forelock. Elm has a sleepy expression and a hat tipped to one side. Poplars are pompous and scholarly. Looking for tree faces offers an amusing winter pastime among trees.

221. What makes the fall colors of leaves?   Pigments produced in the leaf's chemical laboratory. In summer there are three kinds of pigments floating around in the sap as separate tiny nuggets, not dissolved. The predominant one is chlorophyll which masks the others with its intense green. When fresh sap is cut off from the leaf by the formation of the corky (abscission) cells at the base of the stem, chlorophyll is the most unstable and disappears first. After that the other two, xanthophyll, a yellow pigment, and carotene, an orange or red pigment, color the leaf. The abundance of each pigment, and hence the color, vary with each species. (*See Question 42.*)

222. What is anthocyanin?   This is another kind of pigment usually not present in tree leaves in summer, but it appears dissolved in the sap when trapped in the leaf in the fall. This chemical, made by the sap "aging," is versatile. It may turn the leaf colors from scarlet to purple. It is this that gives the purplish tone to the ash tree's fall colors. It tends to the blues when the sap is more alkaline—acting like litmus paper. In a few trees anthocyanin is present in spring and summer. This gives the purple color to the leaves of Schwedler's maple, and to copper beech and plum, and the red of the Japanese cutleaf maple.

223. What is tannin?   Tannin, or tannic acid, is a strong astringent in tree bark, bud scales and pine cones. This gives the rich brown to oak and beech leaves. Since tannin is not destructible like the other pigments, it remains in fallen leaves, especially oak and beech, all winter. This colors the brown carpet of the woods. (*See Question 618.*)

224. Are tree leaf pigments found elsewhere?   The same kind of chemicals produce the bright yellows, reds and blues of flowers. They also give the colors to oranges, peppers, tomatoes, beets, corn, rose hips, carrots, etc.

225. Does a tree benefit in any special way by its fall colors? Only by being admired. Fall colors are considered to be an incidental chemical reaction of no importance in the life of the tree.

226. Is it possible to preserve leaves with their colors? There is no completely satisfactory way. The *Scientific American* (October 1950) offers these suggestions:

One method involves drying the branches in warm sand. Clean, dry sand (screened, builder's sand is best) is heated in a metal can until it is very warm, but not painful to touch. While this sand is heating, another portion of sand, which need not be hot, is poured into a large box and smoothed out. The branches are then laid on this sand-bed in a natural position, and their outer ends carefully nailed to the sides of the box and supported by a few wires or sticks. The warm sand should then be sifted into the box, rather quickly and very evenly. The warm sand not only promotes evaporation of water from the leaf cells, but also presses the leaves evenly in a natural position. The excellence of the colors preserved by this method is surprising. Even the deep reds, among the most difficult to keep, lose very little of their natural beauty.

Single leaves can be preserved by coating them individually with paraffin. This may be done either by dipping the leaf into a pan of melted paraffin or by pressing it on each side with a warm flatiron upon which a little paraffin has been melted (a steam iron should not be used). The coating of paraffin should be thin, for a thick layer will dull the color of the leaf. This method preserves the color indefinitely.

227. What are the native cedars of eastern United States? In the eastern United States a native cedar is red cedar, *Juniperus virginiana;* that is, a species of juniper. Another is the northern white cedar, *Thuya occidentalis,* whose name is arbor vitae. And a third cedar is the southern white cedar, *Chamaecyparis thyoides,* a Latin name that signifies "false cypress."

228. What are the native cedars of western United States? The Pacific Northwest has four towering cedars, all different but each remarkable. Western red cedar is a giant version of arbor vitae. Alaska cedar has a dusty look; it is sharp and compact, suggesting a collapsed tent. Port Orford cedar is, in size of trunk, fragrance of wood and a peculiar waving form of foliage, one of the great trees of the world. And incense cedar is the giant of cedars whose wood makes lead pencils smell good.

229. What is the true cedar? The true cedar is the genus *Cedrus.* This is the Atlantic cedar of Algeria, the Cedar of Lebanon of ancient Palestine, and the Deodar cedar of India, made famous by Kipling. The well-known Bermuda cedar is a juniper like the eastern red cedar.

The above are all members of the pine family. But to make cedar utterly confusing, there are some important "cedars" of the genus *Cedrela,* which are tropical hardwoods akin to mahogany. These are the toona cedar of Australia, also called Australian red cedar; West Indian cedar whose wood is used for fragrant cigar boxes; and bastard cedar, a valuable timber tree of India and Ceylon. Locally, bastard cedar is variously called white cedar, Indian red wood, Chittagong. Its Latin name is *Chickrassia.* Yellow cedar is a tropical hardwood of still another genus, *Tecoma.* South America has an important white cedar of another genus of tropical hardwood, *Tabebuia.*

Thus, there is no such thing as *the* cedar tree. What you call a cedar depends entirely on the part of the world you are in.

230. Is there any other name as confused as cedar?   Although cedar is the outstanding example in botanical manuals, there are many ambiguities among local colloquial names, and also among trade names of commercially important trees. America's most valuable tree, Douglas fir (not a true fir) is known as Oregon pine in the timber trade. The tulip tree, *Liriodendron,* one of the superb trees of eastern United States, is called yellow poplar by lumbermen in the South. Oak is truly *Quercus* throughout the world but oak is a trade name for holly in Dominica, for hickory in Ceylon; and the Australian pine, *Casuarina,* is called "she oak."

231. What is ironwood?   Ironwood is another name which designates no certain kind of tree. It is applied to a different tree in every country. This is no surprise since the name is so vivid for describing a quality of wood. Eastern United States has two small but arresting ironwoods—one is *Carpinus,* the blue beech; the other is *Ostrya,* hop hornbeam. Our southern states also claim two ironwoods—*Bumelia,* a stray from the great sapodilla forests of Yucatan; the other, *Cyrilla,* otherwise known as leatherwood on the coastal pine plain. South America, striving to give wonderful hardwoods a good name in commerce, turns up with fourteen ironwoods, of which the most important is *Guaiacum,* the famous lignum-vitae.

As an example of the way local colloquial names are confusing, the *Bumelia* ironwood (see above) is also called antswood, black haw, buckthorn, chittimwood, downward plum, gum elastic, saffron plum, sloewood, boxwood, breakbill, zapotilla bravo, huicicialtemetl, bebelama, and forty-nine other names on record. This indicates that everybody who would know trees accurately should learn their Latin names.

232. What trees of special interest can a tourist find in each state? The best way to find this answer is to look up the National Parks, National Forests, and National Monuments in the state. Then check on state parks and arboretums. In addition, here are a few suggestions:

Alabama: February–April, parks and gardens in Brewton and Greenville; pink and white dogwood between Red and Shade Mountains; redbuds in spring in Tennessee Valley; fine old trees on University of Alabama campus at Tuscaloosa; longleaf pines in Baldwin County. Bellengrath Garden near Mobile contains beautiful plantings of southern trees with camelias and azaleas.

Alaska: (See Question 256.)

Arizona: Plantations of University of Arizona east of Phoenix; Boyce Thompson Institute at Superior; saguaro and organ pipe cactus of southern Arizona; superb virgin ponderosa pine, piñon, spruce and aspen in mountains, especially around Flagstaff.

Arkansas: April, redbud throughout state, apple orchards in Washington and Benton Counties. Holly in woodlands of southern Arkansas. Fine trees in state parks and in Hot Springs National Park. Wahoo, the burning bush, becomes a tree in Arkansas.

California: Redwood Highway north from San Francisco for tall redwood sight found nowhere else in the world. In northern California, visit Stout Grove near Crescent City, and Brewer spruce (remarkable weeping spruce) around Sanger Lake in Siskiyou Mountains. Big tree sequoias are mostly in National Parks in Sierras, eastern California. Vast orchards of English walnut, prune and almond in Sacramento Valley. Orange, avocado, olive and date palm in southern areas. Twisted art of Torrey pines few miles north of Santa Barbara. Weird Joshua trees in Mojave Desert, east of Los Angeles. Lovely Santa Barbara Botanical Garden has plantings of native California trees and shrubs.

Colorado: Eastern trees have their frontier where mountains rise just west of Denver. Above 7,500 feet, ponderosa and Douglas fir. Aspens are a striking sight in the fall when they turn yellow among evergreens. Blue spruce grows in its native place in lower mountain meadows. Alpine fir and Engelmann spruce are higher up near tree line.

Connecticut: Typical eastern hardwood forest dominated by white oak, elm, ash, sycamore, sugar maple, red maple, hickory, white pine, hemlock—especially in hilly northwestern Litchfield County. Woodland around Bear Mountain, state's highest, has chestnut oak and striped maple. Superb old trees in Connecticut River Valley from Old Lyme northward. In southwestern Connecticut, Audubon Society Center near Greenwich. Southeastern area, arboretum at Connecticut College near New London. Trees in grounds of Aetna Life Insurance Company, Hartford, are labeled for identification.

Delaware: Route 52, west of Wilmington, twelve miles to Kennett Square, Longwood Gardens. Southeastern area in Sussex County near the coast, holly and loblolly pine. This is most northern reach of bald cypress.

Florida: Slash pine across sandy prairie is sculptured into infinite variety of forms against sky. Hammocks of Everglades have bunches of palmetto. Open forests of pond cypress along Tamiami Trail. Cypress Gardens has famous bald cypress with big knees. Miniature scrub forests on old sand dunes from Fort Pierce to Fort Lauderdale, and at southern tip of central ridge of state.

Georgia: Superb live oaks with giant spread on old plantations near Savannah. In middle Georgia typical unique trees of the South— silverbell, cherry laurel, sweet bay, cucumber tree, yaupon, southern magnolia. Bald cypress in swamps. Bamboo and other imported plants at United States Import Station, 12 miles south of Savannah. Founders Memorial Garden on campus of University of Georgia. In spring, flowers of tung oil trees along coastal highway, and of peach trees inland.

Idaho: Wilderness areas in northwestern part of state deep with ponderosa pine and virgin forest inaccessible until recent years. Hawthorns in valleys and canyons beautiful in early summer. Apple orchards around Boise.

Illinois: Chicago Zoological Park, Brookfield, Route 66, fine native trees, some over 200 years old—bur oak, swamp white oak, black walnut, ash, hackberry, slippery elm, many flowering crabs and hawthorns. Tree alders, honey locust with clusters of giant thorns, many other fine specimens at Morton Arboretum, Lisle, 25 miles west of Chicago. The Abraham Lincoln Memorial Garden, Springfield, displays countryside of Lincoln's time including oaks, wild plum, silverbell, dogwood, redbud, hawthorn. Northern part of state, White Pines Forest near Oregon, Illinois, has virgin beech, red maple, shortleaf pine, tulip tree. Bald cypress crept up the Mississippi and established coves of this unique tree along rivers of southern part of state.

Indiana: Combines typical midwest trees such as bur oak, box elder, pawpaw, persimmon, osage orange, sorrel with some southern types—the golden rain tree at New Harmony in the southwestern part of the state, and bald cypress at Hovey Lake. Excellent state parks and arboretums.

Iowa: Much of state is contour planted for corn and pasture. Famous crab apple collection in Water Works Park, Des Moines. Native forest areas at Amana Colonies, 20 miles southwest of Cedar Rapids. Fine stand of white pine at Luxemburg, near Dubuque. Largest rock elm in the United States on the Mississippi at Le Clair, 11 miles northeast of Davenport. Peru has the original Delicious apple tree.

Kansas: Among vistas of corn and wheat eastern part of state has glimpses of redbud, dogwood, sassafras, wild plum. Willows and cottonwood along streams. Trees much as they always have been in this purely prairie state.

Kentucky: Lush and beautiful woods of native oak, maple, ash, tulip tree and black locust preserved in twenty-two state parks, including My Old Kentucky Home and Natural Bridge. Kentucky coffee tree has enormous double multiple leaves three feet long; tree is bare until late spring and leaves drop off before all others in fall. At Mammouth Cave beautiful native woodland.

Louisiana: Trees of the deep South in all their glory—bald cypress with knees in swamps, and avenues of live oak draped with Florida moss (actually a member of the pineapple family) around old plantations. Acres of hawthorn form haw flats that hold red haws all winter. Spectacular glimpses of cucumber tree and the southern magnolia. Only virgin forest of slash pine in existence at Fontainebleau State Park, north shore of Lake Pontchartrain. Groves of tung trees in Washington and Tangipahoa Parishes. Avery Island, south of New Iberia, off Route 90, has jungle garden.

Maine: The Pine Tree State is best known for its spruces—mostly red spruce in the lake country and along the coast. The taller white spruce inland in lumbering country. Black spruce, the tortured drawing-board spruce of cold bogs. The Maine woods also take pride in balsam fir, and hemlock. The northern white cedar (arbor vitae) and larch are also natives of the cold swamps. On the rocky shore, especially from Bar Harbor eastward to Lubec Point where red spruce is bathed in cold mist and spray, the trees are veritable gardens of lichens. Fine displays of white birch from Bethel to New Hampshire.

Maryland: Flowering dogwoods are a pride of the state. Good display, late May, at Sherwood Gardens, Baltimore. Rhododendron in Green Ridge State Forest, east of Cumberland, off Route 40, are in prime last half of June. Fine stand of virgin hemlock in Swallows Falls State Park, off Route 219, near Oakland. 400-year-old white oak at Wye Mills, Route 50, near Easton. October–November, fall foliage, in mountain forests, of maple, hickory, scarlet oak, black gum, sweet gum, dogwood. This is a unique combination for the most play of colors.

Massachusetts: Elm-arched streets of New England towns are beautiful across this state. The trees of Boston Common and Public Garden are labeled for identification; among these are purple beech, golden rain tree, saucer magnolia, Belgian elm, weeping American elm, golden leaf elm, sycamore maple and some fine old English elms. Consult Massachusetts Audubon Society (155 Newbury Street, Boston) for list of their sanctuaries from Berkshire Mountains to Atlantic coast. Also, Trustees of Public Reservations (Boston) has list of historical and wildlife places under their care.

Michigan: Lake Michigan dune lands have interesting scrub and sand cherry. Niles, redbud trail beside St. Joseph River is in this region with outstanding variety, including dogwood, coffee tree, tulip tree. Traverse City is famous for cherries. Remnant of virgin forest of white pine at Hartwick State Park and Wilderness Park, west of Mackinac City. Upper Peninsula offers beautiful sample of Canadian forest with white and jack pine, white birch, striped maple, mountain ash.

Minnesota: Great is the scope of Minnesota's trees. A superb coniferous forest occupies the northeast part, prairie the western part, and a healthy strip of deciduous forest between. Among the conifers are stretches of aspens which are gradually surrendering to sugar maple and linden. This in turn changes to fir-spruce-birch forest—with balsam fir predominant. This can be seen in the Itaska Park area. The fir-spruce-birch is a climax type of forest and will continue indefinitely if not disturbed. Another interesting place is Wilderness Research Center, 15 miles northeast of Ely. Superior National Forest is the heart of the famous canoe country with forests of spruce, balsam, northern white cedar, aspen and birch. Nerstrand Woods State Park has noble remnant of virgin oak, maple, elm, linden, ash.

Mississippi: The famous Mississippi cypress has been largely cut but a few survivors of these trees of the geologic past can be seen near ponds, bayous, and lakes. Greenville Garden Club is interested in preserving some virgin bald cypress for all to see. Near Picayune, plantings of tung oil trees are beautiful in spring. National Forests have fine southern pines—longleaf, loblolly, slash. Beautiful plantings around ante-bellum homes in Natchez.

Missouri: This state has excellent climate and soil for tree growing and many nurseries for brand apple trees; in southern sections, peach trees. A ginkgo, four feet in diameter, grows near Herman. Chestnut trees planted in 1902 were doing well at last report, near Rosatti, about 100 miles south of St. Louis on Route 66. State Park in southeast, near Charleston, has 80 acres of virgin forest, including cypress and big, old persimmon trees.

Montana: This is the state for snow-festooned evergreens at ski resorts and other mountain areas. Eastern two-thirds is vast expanse of upland prairie range, but western part is superb Rocky Mountain country with giant evergreen forests in twelve National Forests, including ten primitive areas.

Nebraska: This state has corn in the east and wheat in the west— trees are mostly plantations of redbud, hawthorn and apple. National Forests are development areas, more arresting for their flowers than their trees. A natural woodland area is in northeast corner, Route 20, near Chadron.

Nevada: In addition to its desert drama, Nevada has spectacular trees on snow-clad mountains in the Sierra Nevada along the southwest line. Here are Jeffrey pine, white fir, sugar pine (which has the biggest cones in the world), incense cedar, ponderosa, red fir, lodgepole pine, mountain hemlock, whitebark pine (a remarkable tree-line tree with flexible branches), and western white pine.

New Hampshire: Along Route 31, between Wilton Center and Lindeboro, is state's largest stand of native dogwood. New England fall foliage at its height among the oaks, beeches, poplars, birches, and sumac of this state. White Mountains in northern part show wild, original forest types with white pine, hemlock, red spruce; northerly white spruce, arbor vitae, balsam fir; southerly red cedar, pitch pine.

New Mexico: Glaring, flat, white desert suddenly gives way to southern Rocky Mountains with forest trees on the higher slopes. Starting on the lower levels and going up, are mountain mahogany, piñon pine (the one needle pine famous for its delicious seeds), ponderosa, western white pine.

New York: No state of the eastern United States has a greater range of trees. North, the Adirondack Mountains wear a beautiful quilt of red and white spruce, balsam fir and larch. Central New York is famous for its sugar maples. Cherry Valley Road west from Albany and the Finger Lakes region, lovely rolling dairy country, are famed for superb old hardwoods that echo the original virgin forest of this lush region. Farthest south on Fire Island, deep within the unmolested dunes of the middle Atlantic coast, is hidden The Sunken Forest. Preserved in 72 acres is a gem of coast forest as it was in another day when climates were warmer. Here are large holly trees, tupelo, sassafras bedecked with Virginia creeper and sweet briar, and birds abound in banquets of berries. Brooklyn Botanic Garden has spectacular display of pink Japanese cherries and copper-leafed Schwedler maples, also a Japanese garden with torii amid sculptured Japanese trees. New York Botanical Garden preserves remnant of native hemlock forest of this area. Parkways through Westchester County have fine dogwood and redbud with many beautiful native trees.

North Carolina: Around Fort Bragg Military Reservation a good example of longleaf pine and turkey oak on coarse sand uplands. Swamp forests of bald cypress in interesting corners. Westward, highest point in eastern United States in Great Smoky Mountains with deep rhododendron forest. Spruce and balsam fir on higher ridges demonstrate vertical magic by which every 100 feet of height is about 30 miles north for plant life.

North Dakota: In a state whose landscape is a vast perspective of dark green spring wheat, and alfalfa showing deep green and purple, finding trees across seemingly treeless horizons becomes a treasure hunt. Peace Garden on the Canadian border has rolling timbered land with lakes and fall colors. Creeping red cedar and western red cedar in clay formations along Little Missouri River. Elm, green ash along streams.

Ohio: North, rich glacial plain on Lake Erie shore at Painesville and Mentor contains famous nurseries. Cleveland, interesting experiments in city tree planting, and Route 282, Nelson Ledges Park, giant sugar maples (called hard maples in midwest). Wooster Agricultural Experiment Station, hardwood and evergreen forest plantation. Southeast, Hocking County, unspoiled rough hilly region, crossroads of northerly and southerly forests with sorrel trees. Cincinnati, Rowe Arboretum with evergreens labeled; Dawes Arboretum, 50 acres of virgin forest. Spring Grove, fine old plantings of holly, dogwood, larch, tree peony.

Oklahoma: Vivid contrasts from treeless Black Mesa in northwest panhandle to pockets of the eastern bald cypress in southeast, some of oldest trees near Mountain Fork River at Broken Bow. Ouachita National Forest in mountains of eastern border has healthy pine and hardwood forest. Westward two-thirds of state is historical grazing country where cottonwood is welcome landmark.

Oregon: Wind-contoured Sitka spruce on northwest coast. Odd form of lodgepole pine in coastal sand dunes. Some wild tree adventures at Oregon Caves National Monument in southwest. Northeast, Route 82 through Wallowa Mountains, spectacular mountain tree country. Cherry, walnut, filbert and apple orchards great sight in Willamette River Valley. Port Orford cedar and Oregon myrtle rare old trees to seek out on coast highway. Rogue River Valley pear orchards. Western juniper fills air with balsam-like fragrance at Peter Skene Ogden Park, near Bend, Route 97. Rangers at Mount Hood and Crater Lake point out marvelous tree sights such as whitebark pine, incredible mountain hemlock, and sharp firs in Annie's Creek section.

Pennsylvania: Astonishing depths of wild Appalachian forest for a great industrial state. Look up list of state forests for some key points. Cook Forest at Tionesta, virgin white pine. Scott Foundation at Swarthmore, fine collection of flowering cherries and crab apples. McKeesport Arboretum has every kind of tree native to state. Hemlock arboretum at Charles Jenkins is on Germantown Avenue, near Philadelphia; also botanical garden on campus of University of Pennsylvania. Longwood Gardens near Kennett Square have cedar of Lebanon and young big tree sequoia.

Rhode Island: Fine gardens around famous old estates at Newport reward tree explorer—among these, fern-leaved beech, magnolias, Japanese cherries, weeping beech. Providence, Roger Williams Park has unusual trees. Fine ginkgos on Blackstone Boulevard. On Rhode Island State College campus—splendid lindens, elms, Carpathian walnut, katsura tree, sorrel. For cross section of trees of state try Route 102, Victory Highway.

South Carolina: Famous for its southern gardens preserved from old plantations where widespreading live oaks are draped with Florida moss. Back of sand dunes along coast, yaupon (a species of holly) is covered with red berries in winter. With the yaupon are exciting contorted versions of live oak and mockernut, which are usually among the giants of eastern trees. Central and western areas flash acres of peach blossoms in spring. State rises into Great Smoky Mountains through silverbell, cucumber tree, white pine, hemlock.

South Dakota: Meeting place of eastern and western trees. Both eastern red cedar (*Juniperus virginiana*) and western red cedar (*Thuja plicata*), the giant arbor vitae, on the respective borders of the state. Here also is sagebrush country with western cottonwoods, so welcome to the ranger who rests himself and his horse in its shade. Interesting tree exploring to be found in Black Hills, foothills of the Rockies, named for dark needled ponderosa which makes the hills look black from a distance. Here also the Black Hills spruce (*Picea canadensis,* variety: *albertiana*).

Tennessee: Lush with trees statewide. Eastern side, Great Smoky Mountains has most variety in one forest area anywhere in the world, with possible exception of Himalayas near Darjeeling, India. Chattanooga area was refuge for northeastern hardwoods surviving the Ice Age; they radiated from here northward to repopulate New England and northeast United States when glacier melted back. Elise Chapin Wildlife Sanctuary has marked trails through beautiful area. Revelation of reforestation of 12,000 acres with loblolly and shortleaf pine at Natchez Trace State Forest, west of Tennessee River. Near Memphis, off Highway 51, Shelby Forest Park has dense cypress, cottonwood, beech, hackberry, black locust.

Texas: Texan claims to the finest trees in the world are worth checking: holly, live oak, magnolia, maple, birch, pine, yaupon, in parks and gardens around Orange, Houston and Beaumont. Palms at Bougainvillaea Trails in southeastern Texas. The "only *Sabal texana* in the world" at Rabb Palm Grove. Virgin forest area of southeastern Texas with hawthorn, magnolia, dogwood, fringe tree and cypress. "World's best citrus fruit orchards" of Rio Grande Valley.

Utah: In mountains along U.S. Route 89, glimpses of stream-gathered willow, red birch, box elder, dogwood, maple. On higher, more fertile slopes, native Utah cedar, black locust, piñon pine, poplar, ash, elm, red mulberry. Around a mile high, Utah has risen from its white alkaline flats around Great Salt Lake to forested mountains with lodgepole pine, ponderosa, Engelmann spruce, Colorado blue spruce (the Utah State Tree) and mountain ash.

Vermont: This state considers its trees a feature of its landscape, in contrast to timber resources. Thus, trees which are the cream of New England play a major part in attracting tourists for outdoor life —skiing among the spruce-covered slopes of Mount Mansfield and other well known spots, and for foliage of Green Mountain valleys where sugar and red maple startle the imagination with their red, yellow, and orange pageant early in October. Twenty state forests and forest parks offer goals.

Virginia: Visitors at Williamsburg find also a tree heritage from Colonial times. Winchester, famous for its Apple Festival at flowering time in the spring. Skyline Drive in Shenandoah National Park leads through hemlock and rhododendron country and otherwise fine forest. See paper mulberry contorted with burls at Jamestown, also old sycamore growing out of grave of original settler. Arbor vitae over 1,000 years old grows at Natural Bridge. Dismal Swamp, Routes 58 and 460, has impressive water oaks and cypress despite its gloomy name.

Washington: Dramatic tree state with a rain forest of tropical grandeur on Olympic Peninsula, west side of Cascade Mountains, and dry range land east of Cascades extending to the Rockies at Spokane. In south center of state, near Ellensburg and Yakima, sights of great fruit orchards—apples, peaches, pears, prunes, cherries, apricots. Ginkgo State Park, near Ellensburg, has petrified trees ten million years old. Mammoth hemlocks, western cedars and firs on Pacific side of state. Vine maples and madrone trees worth looking for among these.

But the pressure for timber is on the vast Douglas fir resources of the state. Timber companies are getting results with long-range forest management that grows wood annually to offset and surpass timber cut. Excellent as this policy is for insuring future supplies, it ignores the aesthetic value of the primeval heritage of a thousand-year-old forest with its wildlife of fern, and elk, bear and cougar. The old forest can never be replaced with new wood. Why not put every primeval tree over a certain size of trunk or height on the public-treasure list? It is true that museum specimens of the great forest will be preserved on a fine scale in National Parks, but is this enough? Our generation has just this last part of the extensive forest where the animals can lead their own lives without being stared at and fed on peanuts. We are responsible to the next generation. We do not need to take the lives of these monarchs for our survival. Every tree that has lived quietly on earth for 500 to thousands of years deserves to be protected and admired just for itself.

West Virginia: With deep, rich veins of coal beneath, showing that 250 million years ago horsetail and clubmoss trees grew in a steaming swamp in this area, today—high on the Appalachian ridges —are red spruce and balsam fir. On the western slopes, hemlock, rhododendron, white pine. In the Kanawha Valley, fringe tree, silver-bell and red bay. Oglebay Park, Wheeling, has plantations of choice horticultural varieties. Monongahela and George Washington National Forests preserve the wonderful inheritance of hardwoods and evergreens native to this fine tree region.

Wisconsin: A beauty-conscious state which saved enough of its superb white pine heritage to reestablish much of the forest before it was all gone. The northern part has wild, lake-canoe country with typical red spruce, balsam fir and birch wilderness. Ridges Sanctuary at Bailey's Harbor on the Door Peninsula is a beautiful example of woodland floor on sand ridges with bog between. Here an exciting variety of wildflowers, many rare elsewhere, grows with the assistance of native spruce and fir. Door Peninsula has outstanding cherry orchards which attract visitors from afar when they bloom in late spring.

Unique is the driftless area of Wisconsin, an hour's ride north of Madison, extending westward into Minnesota and the northeast corner of Iowa. This was not covered by a glacier in the last Ice Age. The soil is shallow; steep-sided nubbles stick up from level ground like stone ships. Across this iceless island, where mineral rock lies near the surface, are the most primitive trees of the northeastern United States (found elsewhere on mountains and farther north), larch, hazel, alder, birch, northern red oak, jack pine, Norway pine. Most of this "northern New England" company of trees is hidden in the ravines and on the shelves of the rocky nubbles.

Wyoming: Wyoming provides the tree explorer with Yellowstone Park. While there, see Amethyst Mountain with its vivid exhibit of the ability of trees to survive through the ages. A forest of conifers, related to our pines, was growing on level ground, fifty-five million years ago, when it was buried by volcanic eruption. That was when Amethyst was starting to rise. After a few thousand years a second forest of the same kind of trees grew on higher ground, above the buried stumps of the first forest. Then the volcano erupted again and the second forest was buried. As epochs rolled by, this happened sixteen times. Today you see the seventeenth forest of fine Engelmann spruce growing on Amethyst Mountain where, judging by past history, it is less triumphant than it looks.

Best tree adventures in the state lie along state highways that vanish into western mountains, rather than along the transcontinental highways that cross treeless miles of dry plains.

For frequent references to tree goals in many states, I am indebted to *A Traveler's Guide to Roadside Wildflowers, Shrubs and Trees of the U.S.,* edited by Kathryn S. Taylor, prepared under the auspices of The Garden Club of America and the National Council of State Garden Clubs, Inc.

II. FORESTRY

233. What is silviculture?   Silviculture is the science of developing and taking care of forests.

234. How does silviculture differ from horticulture?   Horticulture is the science of producing special plant types, for flower and vegetable gardens, and ornamental and orchard trees. Silviculture is concerned with the growth and health of forests.

235. Is silviculture the same as forestry?   No. Forestry puts the emphasis on the management and protection and use of forests, while silviculture puts the emphasis on forest growth, improvement and health. They are complementary sciences.

236. What is the United States Forest Service?   A division of the Department of Agriculture, the Forest Service has its headquarters in Washington, D.C., but most of the organization is in field service throughout the forty-nine states and Puerto Rico. There are five divisions: Administrative and Information; National Forest Administration; Land Acquisition and Forest Land Planning; State and Private Forestry; Forest Research.

237. What are the responsibilities of the Forest Service?   To administer the National Forests; to do research to determine the best kinds of trees for reforestation in the various National Forest regions; and to cooperate with state and private forest projects in promoting forest protection and good cutting practices.

238. How big are our National Forests?   Their total area is 230 million acres. Within these are enclaves of private holdings, so the nation holds, in this respect, title to 180 million acres, or 9½ percent of our country's land.

239. Where are the National Forests?   Scattered through thirty-nine states, and in Puerto Rico. The largest percentage is in our new state, Alaska. There, 20,840,000 acres are designated as National Forest. These lie entirely in the well timbered south-coast region. (See also Questions 255–259.)

240. How can the Forest Service administer such far-flung forests?
By decentralization, and delegation of authority to those on the spot. Less than 2 percent of Forest Service personnel is in the small coordinating office in Washington. This wise policy was established by the first Chief of the Forest Service, Gifford Pinchot, in 1908, under the leadership of Theodore Roosevelt. His instructions: "Each locality to be dealt with on its own merits."

241. Who is the man on the spot with authority to manage the forests? The ranger is the local manager who lives on the National Forest assigned to him, where he is in direct contact with the public and meets timberman, stockman, and camper, face to face. He supervises sales of timber, issues permits, measures products sold, establishes protection against fire, insects, erosion, and carries on planting programs.

242. Is cutting of trees forbidden in National Forests? The cutting of trees is encouraged, but under regulations that will promote the health and continuation of the National Forest and its resources, including watershed, camping, fishing, hunting, and even grazing. The Forest Service was born in 1905 with instructions issued by the Secretary of Agriculture which included: "All the resources of the forest reserves are for use, under such restrictions only as will insure the permanence of these resources."

243. Is the Forest Service on its own in carrying out these vast responsibilities? Other government bureaus cooperate in special problems such as the control of insect and tree diseases, and the forecasting of fire weather.

244. What forest lands other than National Forests are administered by the Federal Government? Eight other types of forest are under government control:

1. *Revested lands.* 2,500,000 acres in western Oregon, the Oregon and California Railroad Grant Lands, recovered from early grants of land through violations. Superb forest, nearly 70 percent domi-

nated by Douglas fir but also containing the giant western true firs, western red cedar and Port Orford cedar (one of the most beautifully grained woods in the world). Half the area supports virgin timber. The fine old timber is being sold according to a policy of controlling annual cut so as not to exceed annual new growth of wood. But those who look upon trees hundreds of years old as a national inheritance feel the destruction of the old giants is an irreplaceable loss.

2. *The Tennessee Valley Authority* owns 340,000 acres of forest around its series of reservoirs. Much has been cut, grazed and burned in the past. Without hurting the watershed and under the rules of good forest management, the Authority sells timber, cordwood and poles.

3. *Land utilization projects* contain hundreds of thousands of acres of forest land in nineteen states. Much has been misused and most of the trees are second growth. Under the direction of the Land Management of the United States Forest Service and some state agencies forests are being revitalized. Considerable saw timber, pulpwood, fuel wood, posts and poles are being sold from these forests.

4. *Military reservations* are so extensive today that they embrace considerable forest land, particularly in the South where southern pines are predominant. The Air Force has 495,000 acres of forest land.

5. *Federal wildlife refuges* have 797,000 acres of forest administered by the Fish and Wildlife Service of the Department of the Interior. Much of the farmland has been abused in the past, but the opening up of the forest is often to the advantage of wild fowl and other kinds of wildlife. Today the forested areas are administered for

the restoration and conservation of wildlife or to test practical methods of game management. Trained foresters supervise the work, keeping in mind the needs of wildlife such as den trees for the bear and food for browsing animals.

6. *American Indian lands* contain 16 million acres of forest and woodland of which 6 million acres are in commercial forests. It is distributed through twenty-six states. The Bureau of Indian Affairs, Department of the Interior, recognizes that these forests are an important asset of the Indians and has set them aside for their use. Considerable timber and other wood products are taken from the lands annually, but through sound forestry practices the productivity of the land is maintained.

7. *The unreserved public domain* consists of remnants left from large grants and the establishment of National Forests and other federal reservations. This is administered by the Bureau of Land Management, Department of the Interior. Much is grass, semidesert and desert, but there are still about 28 million acres classed as timber or woodland. In addition, the largest block of unreserved public domain is in Alaska, with 265 million acres, much of which is forest. About 103 million acres of this land will be granted to the new State during the next twenty-five years. Timber and other forest products are sold from these lands in accord with good forest management, but big forest fires in inaccessible areas destroy much of this forest reserve annually.

8. *The National Parks and Monuments* contain 7 million acres of superlative forest which is about one third of the total National Parks area. In addition, there is a type of tropical rain forest in Hawaii National Park, and a northern mixed hardwood and conifer forest in Mount McKinley National Park in Alaska. Forestry of the National Parks aims to preserve the forests in their primeval or natural conditions and as the home of their original wildlife. Lumbering is prohibited and cutting of trees is allowed only to fight diseases and for fire protection. The National Parks and Monuments have their own forestry organization headed by the Chief Forester in the office of the Director of the National Park Service.

245. Are any National Parks established primarily to preserve trees? Yes, Sequoia National Park in California is the last citadel on earth of the big tree sequoia. The Olympic National Park in the

State of Washington is centered on Mount Olympus whose rare and wonderful beauty is enhanced by the rain forest in the lower valleys of its western slopes. Yosemite National Park, in the Sierra Nevada Mountains of California, is dominated by virgin forests of sugar pine, ponderosa, incense cedar and white fir. The Great Smoky Mountains National Park has about 200,000 acres with a remnant of the original virgin forest of the eastern United States. Higher slopes bear dense spruce, balsam fir and hemlock. Lower slopes are typical hardwoods of the Appalachian forest. This park has 130 native tree species.

246. What kind of forests are in the Hawaii National Park?   In the Kilauea-Mauna Loa volcano section of the park there is astonishing contrast because on the windward side of the 13,680-foot peak of Mauna Loa the trade winds bring about 100 inches of rain a year, and on the leeward side the rainfall is only 15 inches a year, while on the heights of the mountain colder temperatures influence the forest. On the dry lowland there is only barren lava with some brush and grass, while on the wet lowland there is a small rainforest with a candlenut tree (*Parmentiera obovato*), whose inflammable wood is used for fireworks by the natives, and screw pines, and Olapa. A half mile high on the rainy side are ohia trees (the most abundant and important tree in the park) and tree ferns. Still higher, around the mile elevation, are more ohia and koa and mamani. All these have tropical relatives in Central America. Above 7,000 feet the forest turns into cold-weather shrubs, but there are no cone-bearing trees anywhere in the park. The cattle and goats were eating the young koa and mamani trees so that these rare and wonderful trees had almost disappeared when the National Park prohibited grazing. Now the koa, at least, is making vigorous recovery. (See Question 172.)

247. What are wilderness areas? Reservations of the National Forests set aside to remain in a primitive state. No roads or provision for motorized vehicles; no timber cutting except for protection from fire; no permits for motels, stores, resorts, summer homes, organization camps, hunting or fishing lodges; no airplane landings on land or water and no motorboats (except for policing and emergencies); no modification except by order of the Secretary of Agriculture when it is clearly in the public interest to sacrifice wilderness values. "Public interest" in terms of water power development is today the greatest threat to the sanctity of wilderness areas.

248. How is a wilderness area designated? By the Secretary of Agriculture, based on recommendation of the Chief Forester.

249. How many wilderness areas are there in the United States? To be preserved as wilderness, 77 areas have been designated in 73 National Forests in 11 states. Of these, 28 areas, each over 100,000 acres in size, are true wilderness areas. Smaller tracts of not less than 5,000 acres are called wild areas.

250. Who uses the wilderness areas? They are open to the public without restriction, except for fire regulations. Hunting and fishing are permitted in accordance with state laws.

251. How do people travel in wilderness areas? By walking the trails with a back pack, by horseback, burro or canoe. A popular way is to walk the trails leading a burro with a camp pack on its back. Horses, pack animals and guides, if desired, are available near most wilderness areas.

252. What and where are the twenty-eight wilderness areas? In order of size:

1. Selway-Bitterroot W.A., 1,581,210 acres. Idaho mostly, partly in Montana. Big mountain and forest country with abundant wild-

life. Headquarters: Orofino and Grangeville, Idaho; and Missoula and Hamilton, Montana.

2. Idaho W.A., 1,232,744 acres. Idaho. Big rough mountain country. Good fishing. Headquarters: Challis, Salmon and McCall, Idaho.

3. Bob Marshall W.A., 950,000 acres. Montana. Remote high mountain area. Hunting and fishing. Headquarters: Kalispell and Great Falls, Montana.

4. North Cascade W.A., 801,000 acres. Washington. Very wild and rough, easy to get lost. Headquarters: Okanogan and Bellingham, Washington.

5. South Absaroka W.A., 614,216 acres. Wyoming. Glacier and deep canyon country. Even pack horses have problems. Headquarters: Cody, Wyoming.

6. Gila W.A., 567,054 acres. New Mexico. Rough with deep box canyons. Scattered tree land. Headquarters: Silver City, New Mexico.

7. Teton W.A., 565,291 acres. Wyoming. High slopes, forested valleys, big game. Headquarters: Jackson, Wyoming.

8. Bridger W.A., 383,000 acres. Wyoming. Barren land, mountain meadows interspersed with heavy timber, rushing water, and the highest mountain in the state. Headquarters: Kemmerer, Wyoming.

9. North Absaroka W.A., 379,460 acres. Wyoming. Glaciers and standing pertified forest. Fine hunting and fishing. Headquarters: Cody, Wyoming.

10. Salmon Trinity Alps W.A., 285,432 acres. California. Granite peaks above spire forests and lakes alive with salmon. Headquarters: Yreka, Mt. Shasta and Weaverville, California.

11. Three Sisters W.A., 246,728 acres. Oregon. The sharp Three Sisters Mountains overlook forest slopes and fine big glaciers. Headquarters: Bend and Eugene, Oregon.

12. High Uintas W.A., 240,717 acres. Utah. Only big east-west range of mountains in the United States with plenty of scenic excitement. Headquarters: Vernal and Salt Lake City, Utah.

13. San Juan W.A., 240,000 acres. Colorado. Virgin forests, rugged mountains, timberline wildlife. Headquarters: Durango, Colorado.

14. Marble Mountain W.A., 237,527 acres. California. The unique

forests of the Siskiyous with rare native weeping spruce, interesting knobcone forest with built-in fire insurance. Headquarters: Yreka, California.

15. Beartooth W.A., 230,000 acres. Montana. Glacier country and highest mountain in state. Headquarters: Billings, Montana.

16. Eagle Cap W.A., 220,280 acres. Oregon. Wildest part of eastern Oregon with great fishing. Headquarters: Enterprise and Baker, Oregon.

17. Blue Range W.A., 218,164 acres. Arizona. Last and largest wilderness in Arizona. High-mountain forest, with ponderosa below and big game. Headquarters: Springerville and Safford, Arizona.

18. Mazatsal W.A., 205,346 acres. Arizona. Rocky cliffs and forest clinging to precipitous ledges. Almost impassable for the average person. Headquarters: Phoenix, Arizona.

19. Sawtooth W.A., 200,942 acres. Idaho. Mountainous and rough ravine country, good fishing, much small game. Headquarters: Boise, Challis and Hailey, Idaho.

20. Glacier W.A., 177,000 acres. Wyoming. Some of the roughest and wildest country, with biggest living glaciers, in the United States. High mountain peaks and forest. Headquarters: Cody, Wyoming.

21. Black Range W.A., 169,984 acres. New Mexico. Rough forest with deer, bear, trout. Headquarters: Silver City, New Mexico.

22. Stratified W.A., 147,000 acres. Wyoming. Narrow valleys cut through flat-top lava mountains with open forests of pine and spruce. Interesting remains of petrified forest and glimpses of wild animals. Headquarters: Cody, Wyoming.

23. Anaconda-Pintlar W.A., 145,000 acres. Montana. Barren mountain peaks with long, sloping spruce forests below. Wild, rather dry, terrain. Headquarters: Dillon, Hamilton and Butte, Montana.

24. Middle Eel-Yolla Bolly W.A., 143,426 acres. California. Diversity of wilderness with plenty of wild animals lurking in the forest and ravines. Headquarters: Willows and Weaverville, California.

25. Pecos Division W.A., 137,820 acres. New Mexico. High back country. A lost land. Headquarters: Santa Fe National Forest, Santa Fe, New Mexico.

26. Superstition W.A., 131,820 acres. Arizona. Desert and mountain brush and piñon pine. Easiest to see and traverse of all wilder-

ness areas. Enchanting. Headquarters: Safford and Phoenix, Arizona.

27. Flat tops W.A., 117,880 acres. Colorado. A unique sort of virgin land with animals and fish. Headquarters: Glenwood Springs, Colorado.

28. Superior Roadless Area, 889,975 acres. Minnesota. Not designated as wilderness area, but known as a wild area. In the canoe country of the deep woods. A canoeist can spend weeks and might get lost traversing lakes by network of connecting streams. Bird and other wildlife. Headquarters: Duluth, Minnesota.

253. Are there any wilderness areas east of the Rockies? They are all in the West where the country is on a larger scale and some of its virgin land and great forests are untouched by man because of the great mountain ridges and deserts. There are a number of wilderness tracts, known as natural areas, in the eastern states.

254. Where are important National Forest areas in eastern states? Osceola, Florida; Rock Creek, Kentucky; Black Mountain, North Carolina; The Bowl, New Hampshire; Tioesta, Pennsylvania; Little Laurel Run, Virginia; and Ramsey's Draft, Virginia.

Moquah, Wisconsin, is an experiment involving 640 acres, to see what will take place in the passing years if the area is given fire protection only. It formerly supported a heavy forest of Norway and white pine, but fires and man converted it to grass and brush. Moquah is classed as a natural area.

255. Where is the biggest virgin forest of the United States today? Alaska. With 44 million acres of standing timber and an additional 89 million acres of open woodland and scrub, making a total of 133 million acres classed as forest land.

256. What kinds of trees are in the Alaskan virgin forests? There are two divisions, the Coastal Forest and the Interior Forest, separated by the Coast Mountains in southeast Alaska, the St. Eleas Mountains in the Gulf of Alaska area, and the Chugach Mountains north of Prince William Sound. The southern Coastal Forest has western hemlock (*Tsuga heterophylla*), Sitka spruce (*Picea sitchensis*), western red cedar (*Thuya plicata*), Alaska yellow cedar (*Chamaecyparis nootkatensis*), mountain hemlock (*Tsuga merten-*

siana). The Interior Forest, inland beyond the mountains, covers a tremendous area northward to the treeless Arctic tundra. This includes an empire of aspen (*Populus tremuloides*), and Alaska paper birch (*Betula papyrifera* var. *humilis*) in areas where there have been extensive forest fires, and in unburned areas white spruce (*Picea glauca*) and black spruce (*Picea mariana*). About a million acres of Alaskan forest burn every year.

257. Are the Alaskan virgin forests being cut for commercial use?
Yes, although as late as 1956 some 36 million acres of the Interior Forest were called inaccessible. Most of the cut timber is coming out of the Tongass National Forest, under the control of forestry practices designed to replace the forest with new stands when the virgin timber is exhausted. The Tongass National Forest and the Chugach National Forest contain almost all the usuable timber along the coast. The Tongass stretches for 400 miles over the islands of Alaska's lower coast with over 16 million acres of one of the world's finest forests. The Chugach is farther north along Prince William Sound with 5 million acres. These Coastal Forests are 74 percent hemlock and 20 percent spruce.

258. What steps have been taken to protect some of the great Alaskan forests and their wildlife? Strict protection is accorded only to Mt. McKinley National Park and Katmai National Monument. The latter is one of the last haunts of the huge Alaska brown bear (which "walks like a man"), but even this sanctuary is threatened by leases for oil drilling on the Katmai Peninsula.

259. Are there no wilderness areas in Alaska? There is so much wilderness in the interior that nobody has yet got around to the protection of a designated wilderness area in the official sense. But the declaration of wilderness areas, if it can come soon enough, is the best hope of saving the ancestral haunts of the big brown bear. With the discovery of petroleum and the mounting demand for more paper and wood, things are moving fast in the new state.

260. What are some events that have stimulated forestry in our country? 1. The organizing of The American Forestry Association in 1875 created a conservation movement where none existed before.

For more than eighty years the Association has provided public education and forest conservation guidance.

2. The establishment of the Division of Forestry in 1886 with foresters but no forests. For fifteen years this service was devoted to gathering information which brought about an awakening to the need for a federal forestry policy. This led to the establishing of the U.S. Forest Service in 1905.

3. In 1891 as part of the amendment of land laws, Congress authorized the President to reserve forest lands of the public domain in any state or territory. The first reservation was created on March 30, 1891, by President Harrison as Yellowstone Park Timberland Reserve.

4. In 1898 Cornell University established the first professional forestry curriculum of collegiate rank in the Western Hemisphere.

5. The Weeks Law of 1911 set a new governmental policy for creating national forests by purchase, and initiated a program of federal-state cooperation in the protection of forests from fire.

6. The Clarke-McNary Act of 1924 authorized the Secretary of Agriculture to enter into agreements with the states for the protection of state and private forests from fire. This momentous law provided also for federal-state cooperation in the production and distribution of trees for reforestation, for cooperative work in farm forestry extension, and for studies in forest taxation. (*See Question 382.*)

7. In 1933 the Civilian Conservation Corps was authorized by Congress to help relieve unemployment. They made the whole nation aware of the need for forest, range, watershed, and soil conservation.

261. What is the most southerly National Forest in the United States? The Ocala National Forest, also known as the "Big Scrub," in north-central Florida.

262. What is the principal tree of the Ocala National Forest? Sand pine. In fact, this is the only large, concentrated stand of sand pine (*Pinus clausa*) in the world. It covers more than 200,000 acres of the half-million-acre forest.

263. Were there any tree cutting laws in colonial days? The first one of record was issued in the Plymouth Colony on March 29,

1626, and forbade the export of timber from the Colony without the consent of the Governor and Council. In 1632 the General Court at Boston forbade the cutting of timber from public ground without a permit. Similar regulations about the use of timber from common, that is public, lands were published in other English colonies.

264. What was the first federal step toward forest management and the planting of trees? In 1828 the depleted supply of live oak timber along the coasts of Georgia, Florida, and North Carolina prompted President John Quincy Adams to launch a project for growing live oak trees to protect the future needs of the U.S. Navy.

265. Does a hardwood forest have more wildlife than an evergreen forest? Yes. The evergreen forest is not so rich with wildlife because the needles that drop off the trees are resinous and do not decay as fast as ordinary leaves. The slower decay cuts down on the growth of berry-bearing shrubs and insect life on which birds, burrowing and fur-bearing animals thrive.

266. What is the difference between "commercial" and "noncommercial" forest land? Commercial forest land can produce, now or in the future, timber of a quality and quantity available for purchasers in the paper, lumber and other timber markets. Noncommercial forest lands are timberlands set aside for parks, wilderness areas, and game reserves; forests inaccessible in high, ravine-split country; and lands that are too arid, too marshy, too rocky and poor for timber. Such forest land may have value as watershed protection, recreation, or livestock grazing.

267. What percentages of the total forest areas of the United States are commercial and noncommercial? Of the 622,000 acres of forest land in the United States, about three quarters or 460,000 acres, are commercial.

268. How much more wood is being removed from U.S. forests than new wood growth every year? The greatest annual deficit is in the felling of big old trees and these diameters cannot be replaced for hundreds of years. The over-all picture, disregarding size of timber, but including all cutting versus all new growth of wood, shows that the gap has been closed. *Timber Resources for America's Future,* U.S. Forest Service Report No. 14, January 1958, says that in growing stock, six inches or larger, growth exceeded all cut by 32 percent. The government and industry drive for forestry practices to protect future timber needs is definitely getting results.

269. How much wood per acre can be cut without exceeding the annual increment? Loblolly pine and shortleaf pine in the mid-South, if reasonably well stocked, will produce 450 board feet of new timber or 1.0–1.5 cords of pulpwood per acre per year without exceeding annual increment. On very good soils growth may be even faster (*Farmers' Bulletin,* No. 2102, USDA). Studies in the Northwest indicate Douglas fir plantations over extensive areas are growing at a similar rate.

270. What is the total output of the world's forests? The latest survey made in 1955 by the Food and Agriculture Organization of the United Nations reported a total of 1,598,300,000 cubic meters (one cubic meter equals about 10.8 board feet). This is an increase of 20 percent in the period from 1946 to 1955.

More than three-fourths of the global supply of industrial wood comes from coniferous species with the broad-leaved types predominating in South America, Africa, Asia and the Pacific area.

Since many of these areas have no planned reforestation program and since the increase of output means an increase in cutting it also means that destruction of world forests is on the rise.

271. What is a sound conservationist viewpoint about cutting down trees in a flourishing forest? A conservationist can share the modern viewpoint of raising trees for crops. He should encourage the educational campaigns of paper and lumber companies which are teaching conservation for use, trying to show the folly (especially in the South) of burning to clear land on the mistaken old pioneering theory that burning helps raise better crops. He should try to awaken farmers to the opportunity they have to profit by rebuilding their abused forests, and arouse public consciousness of the waste and loss to everybody from forest fires, making people more careful with matches, cigarettes, and camp fires.

But true conservationists will discriminate between a forest managed for crops, and the plundering of the last strongholds of the primeval forests and their wildlife. Governments and states are still permitting the destruction of irreplaceable trees. The people are told that forest management is growing these forests faster than the wood is being taken out. This can be a fact but it misses the point. What has a young "annual increment" of wood replaced? If anyone wants to wait three hundred to six hundred years for such a forest to be replaced, will they then also find deer, bear, cougar, antelope, beaver and wolverine? Will they see ferns in the glades, mosses and lichens, lakes, streams, and trout? Will bighorn be surveying the dark spires from a rocky shoulder, and will the bugling of the wapiti be heard?

It is argued that the great timber trees—Douglas fir, redwood, western red cedar, western white pine, the true firs, ponderosa, are part of the wealth of the people and we must use them to make ourselves richer and provide more comfortable homes. But the conservationist who knows the spell of the forest which took hundreds of years to grow should remind government and private company foresters that the *whole* forest, the created world of the big old trees, is a great and irreplaceable heritage. This is a form of wealth that cannot be replaced once the bulldozer and the power saw scream through it. Millions of seedlings will not replace it. Every tree over a certain diameter should be a sacred public trust. *The resources and skill of modern forestry can grow all the wood needed*. Let great bald cypress stand in its swamp. Let the remaining old white pines of the eastern and lake states be admired—serene where they stand. Let all the giants of the eternal forests of the Northwest be preserved for future generations.

It will be argued that the public heritage is protected by National Parks, Monuments, and Wilderness Areas. Only in part. Why not extend the same protection to all the old forests? People talk about overriding public benefits in order to take great bites out of a wilderness area—perhaps next it will be out of a National Park in order to have a big dam to "increase wealth."

Thus, let the conservationist understand the distinction in cutting down trees, and be on his guard lest words like "annual increment" and "waterpower project" obscure the distinction between destroying the last of big forests, and growing a forest for crops and managing it to get good lumber and pulpwood.

272. How many community forests are there in the United States?
More than 3 thousand community forests cover some 4½ million
acres with trees. Over a thousand are municipal forests, mostly for
beautification of the community and love of trees, and about one
third, the most extensive, are for watershed protection. A few municipal forests are used to raise commercial timber and reduce the taxes
of the residents. Some 1,300 school forests are for educational purposes and outdoor exercise for the children planting and caring for
the forest. About 600 county forests are among the largest: some are
for recreation, some for the growing of timber. About a hundred organizations, such as the Boy Scouts of America, maintain local forests.

273. When did the planting of town forests start in this country?
In 1913 the Massachusetts Forest and Park Association, after a
study of community forests in Europe, persuaded the city fathers of
Fitchburg to start a forest for timber. Up to that time many towns
had planted trees to protect their water supply, but this was the first
community forest to grow timber to sell as a substitute for taxes.
Today there are 127 town forests in Massachusetts, on which more
than eight million trees have been planted, with an average area of
three hundred acres each.

274. What are some inspiring examples of community forests?
Champaign County, Illinois, has a 260-acre woodland, with a lake
for swimming, boating, skating, fishing, plus camp and picnic grounds
in the woods, and nature trails. The school children use it as a real-
life classroom for nature study and biology sciences. Allegany County,
New York, has designated a 2,500-acre county forest system—including parcels of idle land not paying taxes, and erosion problem
land—to be planted, restored and turned into assets for beauty,
recreation, water protection, and timber value. The city of Springfield, Illinois, has a municipal forest of 4,300 acres which is the basis
for water and electric power, and also produces some $50,000 a year
revenue through public use. The large watershed forest owned by
Manchester, New Hampshire, is managed so as to bring in about
$20,000 from timber sales. And there are many others.

275. Are there many school forests in the United States? There
are numerous small school forests created where a school board or

a public spirited citizen is aroused by the inspiration and value of a school forest in the education of children (and parents!), and for enriching the life of the community. School forests are showing that children who participate in their management are getting healthy recreation and an understanding of the relation of forests to our way of life; the music teacher, who has her class listen to the rustle of leaves and the whisper or roar of winds in the branches, teaches a lesson in musical appreciation never forgotten when the class catches the mood and tempo on an instrument; pupils who survey the forest can have a practical lesson in algebra and drafting; and those who, as a result of the survey, find a site for a shelter in their forest and build that shelter, have a practical lesson in carpentry.

276. How big should a school forest be? Not less than twenty acres. The ideal is an acre per pupil.

277. Who holds title to a school forest? It should be held by the school. This is better than by a trustee, a donor, or the community, because the pupils know that the forest is their own.

278. What is an outstanding example of a school forest? Wisconsin leads the nation with 368 school forests. Famous is the Nels P. Evjue Memorial Forest with 765 acres managed by the high school of Merrill, Wisconsin, but used intensively by all the schools of the community. After a day in the forest one child said: "We went to the forest in a bumpy bus. We saw a tree that was sick. A worm laid an egg in the top of it. The babies bit the top off the tree. They got sick and died. Now the tree will grow crooked. We saw a big stump, black, from being burned. A seed blew into it, and now an evergreen is growing in it. Rotten wood turns into soil and the little tree can grow. We saw a rabbit. There is a hole under a stump where he could make his home. Fire burns animals and their homes. We used a planting bar to plant trees." (The kindergarten planted thirty trees that day.)

279. How can one start a community forest? First get public title to the land by persuading the county board, or the mayor and his aldermen, or the school superintendent and school board to fight for the idea. Get the support of public service organizations to help with the financing or to consult with the authorities of the community about the best way to finance the plan—whether through forest bonds or some other form of financing. This depends on the purpose and nature of the forest. Find the right people who will serve actively—not just lend their names—on a forest board to plan and manage the project. Get the help of the local forester, if any, or the county forester; write to the U.S. Forest Service, Department of Agriculture, for advice.

280. How many private small forests are there in the United States? The four and one half million farmers and city dwellers who own small forests control 60 percent of all the commercial forest land of our country. These small private forests comprise about 75 percent of all privately owned forests, despite the huge forest tracts of a few large lumber and paper companies. Small private forests total 265 million acres; about half of this is unused farmland.

281. What is the best location for a small forest? Location does not matter so much for the wildlife forest, which can stand high on hills, or cling to stony sides of ravines and be a constant source of beauty. But for cash timber, your forest must be where the climate and soil can grow pay trees, and land must be fairly level so that those who harvest the crop can get to the trees and haul them out without too much expense.

282. How does a person manage his forest for timber? He consults somebody who has been to forestry school. This may be a local forester who is familiar with tree management problems in the neighborhood, or it may be a consulting forester, or the county agent of the state agricultural extension service. Also inquire of the Superintendent of Documents, U.S. Government Printing Office, Washington 25, D.C., about Farmers' Bulletin, No. 989 (*Managing the Small Forest*), U.S. Department of Agriculture.

283. What are the criteria of a well managed forest? 1. Its floor is covered with leaves, needles, twigs and small branches. Beneath the litter, a layer of humus holds plenty of water which growing trees need. A mixed-stand forest has trees of all sizes from seed-producing mature trees with good volume of wood to seedlings.

Grazing animals are kept out. The forest is posted against the making of fires and careless smoking. Fire equipment is handy and fire trails reach vulnerable parts of the forest.

2. An acre of well-stocked hardwoods grows about a cord of new wood per year, an acre of pine perhaps two cords. Cutting more than this per acre decreases the capital asset of that acre.

3. Weed trees, such as chokecherry, gray birch, scrub oak are thinned to encourage faster growth of more valuable trees. Thinning reduces crowding and the shading of seedlings which need sunlight to grow, and also involves the art of selective cutting of trees to be sold for timber so that other mature trees will have room to spread their crowns wider. Thinnings yield firewood, pulpwood, bean poles.

4. Trees for selective cutting are marked in advance. Do not choose and cut at the same time, as that leads to too many mistakes. The pattern of selective cutting is vital to getting the most cash timber the fastest. Mark trees with a paint brush or squirt spots of paint with a hand-spray gun. Blazing with a hatchet may injure the wood and let in insects. Put a patch of bright paint breast high and, if somebody else is to do the felling, another mark below the stump height for checking.

284. Which trees should be marked for selective cutting in managing a timber forest? Catch the feel of your forest, and know how the different trees respond. Fast growing trees like loblolly pine, poplar, sweet gum, can be opened up more at each thinning than slow growers like white oak, ash, linden, walnut, hickory. Harvest trees must be felled at the height of their value; at a certain age trees slow down new growth so much that it doesn't pay to let them get larger. These are the ideal trees to fell—making room for neighbors to grow faster, and keeping the forest as a whole productive with vigorous seedlings.

285. What is stumpage? Salable timber standing in a forest before the trees are felled. A stumpage price is based on the purchaser of the trees doing the felling and hauling.

286. What is roundwood? A section of tree trunk ready for market, after the tree is felled.

287. Who uses roundwood? Roundwood designates logs used in three kinds of markets: saw logs, pulp wood, and fuel wood.

288. What is the minimum size of a saw log? Generally five inches in diameter is the minimum. Smaller sizes are used for special purposes.

289. Is thin veneer sawed or sliced from the log? The modern veneer manufacturer mounts the log on a huge lathe and presses a knife against it while the log revolves. The wood is peeled off like paper being unrolled. (See Question 844.)

290. What is a cord of wood? A pile of wood eight feet long, four feet wide, four feet high—a total of 128 cubic feet.

291. Does every cord have the same amount of solid volume? No. Fuel wood may run 75 cubic feet to the cord, and pulp-wood logs may run 90 cubic feet. This is due to the smaller average size of pulp-wood logs, and hence smaller air space when a stack of logs is measured.

292. Will suckers from stumps become good trees for restoring a logged forest? Many trees in an untouched natural forest are from suckers sprouting from the old stumps instead of from seeds. A managed forest can be made to replace trees this way under certain circumstances. They must be the right kind of trees—hardwoods sprout from stumps. So do shortleaf and pitch pine, while other conifers do not. Stumps should not be over sixty years old. As trees get older they lose their ability to sprout, probably because mature trees channel energy into seed making in the top branches so that dormant buds down near the ground do not open and thrust out vigorously. The exception is basswood which sprouts from old stumps.

293. How is a small forest managed to perpetuate itself from stump sprouts? This is called the coppice method and the result is a coppice forest. Trees should be cut in fall or winter, when dormant; then the stumps will sprout strongly in spring. If felled in spring or summer, the sprouts may appear the same season, but they will be feeble and liable to death from frost in the fall. For sprout reproduction the stump should be cut low. This brings the sprouts close to the root collar where they can form their own root systems quickly, and have the protection of litter and snow during the winter when the buds are dynamic. Indeed, for good sprouting, cut level with the ground. The cut must be smooth— made with an axe instead of a saw, which tears fibers, roughens the surface. The slant sheds water, keeps the stump sound longer.

294. Does decay in an old stump hurt the sprout? This does not seem to affect the vigor of the sprout in the early years, but the sprout root system is so entwined with that of the old stump that it is apt to be infected and decay early before the new tree has become marketable.

295. Since sprout potency decreases with age, how can timber-producing forest be grown by this method? Sizable saw wood cannot be raised in this way. For fully vigorous sprout reproduction the cycle of cutting must be less than ten years. This produces only poles and brushwood with a dubious market value. With forty-year cycles the coppice forest produces cord wood and some narrow board timber, but by that time sprouting is falling short of full reproduction and must be supplemented by seeding. For mature timber trees natural seeding or other methods of planting must be used to keep up the forest. However, sprouting will help some, for example, with basswood. Even good old white oak sprouts a bit after it is sixty.

296. Is it possible to afforest a harsh, treeless tract? There are different kinds of harsh, treeless tracts. It is not practical to try to raise a forest on rocky land without pockets of moisture holding soil; desert land without irrigation; and sandy grit without enough fine particles to draw up ground water by capillary attraction and hold rain water long enough to put decay to work in creating nourishing soil. But it is surprising what can be done even when the ground looks hopeless. The answer is found in the ability of the soil to retain water; this is proportional to the amount of fine material in the form of silt and clay. Soil with a small amount of fine material will support trees which can live on small amounts of moisture and nutrients (all nutrients used by a tree must be dissolved in water and picked up by the roots from the spaces between grains of soil).

297. What trees have low-moisture requirements? Pines have generally lower moisture requirements than hardwoods. A mixed list of trees which do best in sandy places (these are also trees which need sunlight to thrive) are pines, scrub oak, white birch, aspen.

298. For a try at foresting a "hopeless" sandy place, what trees are the best bet? Jack pine in the lake states and red cedar. A variety of lodgepole pine will grow in the pure sand dunes of the Northwest Coast.

299. What trees are best to grow on bog land? On a peat bog in northern country: black spruce, larch, Scotch pine, birch. In a woody bog: black and white spruce, balsam fir, eastern white cedar (arbor vitae), black ash, red maple, willow, possibly elm. No bog land trees grow very tall and forestry thereon is only a stunt, or to improve wildlife or property value.

300. What trees are best for fairly dry or loamy sand areas? Red, Scotch, and jack pines in the North. Southern pines growing in an area indicated best trees in the South.

301. What trees are best for building forests on worn-out fields or cut-over, burned-over tracts with shallow soil? Pines are better than hardwoods. If sandy loam is no deeper than ten inches with coarse sand or gravel underneath, red pine is best. With fifteen inches of sandy loam, use white pine. If the light loam is two feet deep, spruce is right.

302. Can hardwoods be used on dry, sandy land? Yes, if sandy loam is underlaid with wet clay about four feet down. Spruce should not be used as it takes too long for the roots to reach the water and minerals of the clay. In this case the poplars (aspen, cottonwood, balm of Gilead) are good.

303. What kind of trees are best for fine, deep, moist loam? Both hardwoods and conifers which need lots of moisture and have deep plunging roots. For example, white oak, black walnut, ash, linden, sugar maple, white spruce and, in northern areas, white cedar.

304. What are the best trees for forest building in various parts of the country? A good rule of thumb is to choose trees that have grown well as natives, or have proven themselves in the locality. Some additional suggestions:

Central Midwest. Sandy soil: jack pine. Medium dry and coarse soil: red oak, white ash, cottonwood, red and white pine. Good soil: black walnut, tulip tree, white pine, hickory.

Lake States and New England. Worst soil: jack and Scotch pine. Medium good soil: white and red pine. Good soil: white ash, red and white oak, tulip tree. For complete lists ask your local forester or a nurseryman who supplies transplants for forest planting.

305. Are elm and Norway spruce good for building a forest? Elm is a good wild woodland tree, but not so good for timber. Norway spruce is a fast-growing tree and a superb accent in a park, but it is short lived and gets ragged and broken after thirty years. Other trees would make a better choice.

306. How long does it take to grow marketable saw wood? Pines in the South grow the fastest, 30 to 40 years. Pine further north, 60 to 70 years. Hardwoods, 100 to 120. West Coast, 100 years for fir and hemlock. Rocky Mountains, 150 to 180 for ponderosa. This is one reason for the private forest owner to stress wildlife enjoyment and let his descendents sell the timber. Or else grow it for other purposes than saw wood such as pulpwood for paper, composition boards, turpentine, cord wood, shelter belts, Christmas trees.

307. Can I get free trees from the government for planting a forest? The federal government cooperates with states in producing and distributing trees to plant on private lands. It does not give them away directly. Trees grown in state nurseries are sold at cost of production, except in Maryland where they are given to the landowners without charge.

308. How should one get in touch with nurseries that supply forest stock? Apply to your state forester for available trees and price list. Because state nurseries do not grow more trees than they can sell (seedlings cannot be held over another season; they become too large), it is necessary to plan ahead and order perhaps a year and a half in advance. Small orders may be filled with a few months' notice. Some private nurseries, especially those operated by paper companies, are prepared to sell private planters at shorter notice than state nurseries.

309. What is the difference between a seedling and a transplant? Both are little trees sold by the thousands to make forest plantations. The seedling germinates from a seed and may be one or two years old. Seedlings are the lowest cost trees for planting because more can be raised per acre, and there is no cost of handling individual trees in the nursery. Seedlings become transplants when lifted and spaced in the nursery and allowed to grow for another year or two. Transplants are stronger, a few inches taller, and have deeper roots. Seedlings and transplants are designated in the nursery catalogues as 1-0, 2-0, 1-1, 2-1. The first digit indicates how long the treelet has been in the ground without transplanting. The second digit indicates how long it has been in the ground after transplanting. Thus, 1-0 is a one-year seedling. This is all right for Jack pine forestry, but is too small to handle with a fair rate of survival. 2-0 is a two-year seedling. Some transplants go as high as 2-3 or 3-2, but these are often too big to plant economically.

310. Why does not transplanting damage the root system instead of making it stronger? Lifting a plant from the ground, without an earth ball, no matter how carefully, breaks delicate root tips. This is called root pruning and it stimulates more fibrous roots to grow. This survival mechanism of woody roots is used by nurserymen to build up bunchy root systems for nursery stock. Spacing trees also gives each tree less competition, more light and nourishment. Root pruning of older stock can be damaging unless handled with experience. (See Question 548 et seq.)

311. Which should be used for planting a forest: seedlings or transplants? If there is much ground to cover and the soil is moist, seedlings offer the most economical way to do a big job. Most large-scale planting by government agencies and private companies with forest empires is with one- or two-year-old seedlings, depending on growing conditions. On the other hand, for small forest planting where initial investment is not too important and where faster results are desired, transplants offer a fine-looking forest more rapidly. Higher cost of trees may be offset by higher survival. The more difficult the conditions for survival, the larger and stronger must be the stock. For example, poor soils, exposed sites, and areas in strong competition from grasses and weeds, may be more economically planted with 2-1 or even 2-2 transplants. The depth of soil dryness is most important. Seedlings need moisture near the surface to tap with tiny rootlets. Transplants have longer roots to reach below the dry topsoil layers during the dry season.

312. What is the best time to plant forest stock? In the late fall or early spring when the trees are dormant; that is, without light green fresh sprouts. In northern locations where small trees might be heaved out of the ground by frost, spring is better.

313. How far apart should trees be spaced when planting a forest? Aim to have about 1,000 trees per acre when the plantation is well started. A space of 5 x 5 feet takes 1,742 trees per acre. When you space 6 x 6 feet, it takes 1,210 trees per acre. Vary the spacing around these dimensions according to the type of stock and condition of soil, allowing greater or less failure of trees for a percentage to carry through. For slash pine in Georgia and Florida, 8 x 8 is standard practice.

314. Are there 1,000 trees per acre in a mature forest of timber stumpage? No. If all goes well a mature forest should average close to 100 timber trees per acre. This will be reached by good management that thins the forest, or by nature stepping in and doing the thinning.

315. How many seedlings per acre sprout naturally in a forest? A young forest may sprout as many as fifty thousand seedlings per acre. Compare this to the hundred trees per acre of the mature forest and the difference shows that nature works on a survival basis of one to five hundred.

316. How should seedlings be handled?   If planted within a day or two, the package can be loosened, trees moistened, and kept in a cool shady place while planting goes on. If it will be three or more days before planting, bundles should be opened and roots placed in a shallow trench, covered with moist soil or sand firmly tamped down so as not to leave air spaces around the roots. This is called "heeling in" and gives a fresh supply of trees to work with over a period of time. The length of the period depends on time of year and weather conditions. In spring the time is short because heeled-in trees start to grow and get out of hand.

317. What is the best way to plant seedlings or transplants?   Old fields, pastures and cut-over areas may not need preparation. Scalp the heavy sod or dense weeds with a blow of a mattock to make a patch over a foot wide, set in the tree upright, scrape together loose soil, tamp it down and move on. If there are too many competing plants, it may be easier to drive a furrow, then use a crow bar, rotating it to widen the hole. Learn to do this with skill so that roots are not crowded and folded up, and so that there are no air pockets at the bottom of the hole. Plant trees at the same depth they were in the nursery. Where furrow is plowed or no scalping of surface sod is needed, the slit stroke of a mattock or heavy hoe is quicker than the hole method with the crow bar. Just drive in the mattock, lift the handle to widen the hole, drop handle, place in tree beyond mattock blade, push back dirt, and tamp firmly with your foot.

318. Are wild seedlings from the forest good stock to use?   Yes, but it is a great deal of work to dig them up without harming the roots. It is easier and cheaper in the long run to buy trees, and results are more dependable.

319. Should trees be set farther apart for a more open forest? No, because they will not come through with the same spacing. Allow for mortality and get the texture of the forest later by thinning. If seedlings are set too far apart, you will end up with a grove or orchard of short bushy trees, and one in which inferior trees have survived and are reproducing. It is the struggle for existence that makes a forest instead of an orchard. Fierce competition from closely planted trees makes a straighter, taller and healthier stand.

320. Is it better to plant all the same kind of trees, or a mixture of different kinds? For timber, particularly with pines, the standard practice is to plant all the same kind of tree. Large operators will plant in blocks so as to have a checkerboard of different ages. Lumber companies reforesting a wide area may plant in huge spirals so as to get around to blocks of trees in their prime for cutting every fifty years or so. A pure stand is cheaper and easier to establish and manage, and requires less technical knowledge than a mixed stand.

On the other hand, a small private forest is more exciting, attracts more birds and other wildlife if it is a mixed forest. Other advantages of the mixed stand are that it maintains the fertility of the soil better, and this speeds up the rate of production. In theory, a mixed stand is more secure from destruction by fire, insects, diseases, and wind. The best mixed forest has several shade-enduring species mixed with several light-demanding species. The latter will grow much faster.

321. What is the best way to plant a mixed forest? Plant blocks and groups of different kinds of trees. Do not try to mix by putting one kind of individual here and another next to it. As these groups grow, the forest will mix itself according to the law of succession, and develop a healthy and sensitively balanced mixture.

322. What is the law of succession? It tells which trees will be suppressed and fail, and which kind will flourish and ultimately dominate the forest. This is the result of an interplay between species which grow well in the shade as against those which need lots of sunlight. A knowledge of this principle is a keystone of forestry. Moreover, the homeowner can save time and money in his landscape planting if he knows which trees will grow in the shade and which in the sunlight.

323. What are the shade and sunlight requirements of some common forest trees? The word "tolerant" is used by tree men for trees which are tolerant of shade; in other words, those which when young and small grow well in the shadows and are apt to be destroyed with too much sunlight. The reverse is "intolerant" for trees whose requirement is full sunlight, and which will not survive in shade. For example:

Very tolerant: Hemlock, balsam fir, Norway spruce, white spruce, arbor vitae, sugar maple, beech, elm, basswood, white fir, sitka spruce, Engelmann spruce, western red cedar, redwood.

Moderately tolerant: White pine, pitch pine, red pine, loblolly pine, yellow birch, walnut, hickory, white ash, tulip tree, white oak, red oak, Douglas fir, silver fir, noble fir.

Intolerant (i.e., do best in full sunlight): Jack pine, longleaf pine, shortleaf pine, paper birch, cottonwood, alder, aspen, black locust, willow, ponderosa pine, lodgepole pine.

324. How does the law of succession operate with a forest? If an area is cut-over or burned-over, the first forest cover consists of trees different from those which dominated the area previously. They are the trees which are intolerant, liking lots of light, and are known as "pioneers." When these trees are twenty years or so old, they cast so much shade that their own seedlings have trouble growing. At the same time, the seedlings of tolerant trees are coming along, encouraged by the shadows. After a number of years the tolerant trees overtop the intolerant which now die off because they don't get enough sunlight. In this way the pioneer trees are replaced by the shade lovers, whose seedlings continue to flourish in the shade of their parents. The permanent stand is known as a "climax forest."

325. How can the law of succession operate in a managed forest? One way is to imitate nature by selective cutting which leaves mature seed trees standing here and there to furnish enough shade for their seedlings. In the case of clear cutting, pioneer trees can be planted among the seedlings and transplants of the tolerant permanent crop so as to cast shade on them and keep them growing.

326. Do seeds offer a good way to plant a forest? Using seeds to grow seedlings in a nursery and then moving these to the site of the forest a year or two later is the standard way to plant. This is far more reliable than sowing seeds where the trees are to grow. However, good forest management will let nature do the seeding; by cutting selectively so as to leave mature trees with seeds falling in the spaces where trees have been cut. Or else the cutting may be in strips or squares within a forest so that seeds may blow from seed trees standing in uncut sections near by.

Sowing seeds to build up a forest on open land has proved to be a good supplement to speed up reforestation by the standard seedling or transplant methods. Also direct seeding may be used under certain conditions.

327. What are the opportunities for direct seeding?   Direct seeding is best in stony ground where it is hard to dig holes for seedlings, and difficult to find enough loose soil to refill around roots. Seeds among stones have a way of washing or falling into places where moist soil lies protected from sun and wind. Their roots extend into cracks and other spaces and they often make excellent growth. But direct seeding should be restricted to more favorable sites, with moist loam among the stones and within northern or eastern exposures, or on bottom lands.

328. How should the ground be prepared for direct seeding?   Unless the ground cover is sparse, ground should be disced or furrows plowed, spaced about seven feet apart. Depth should be just enough to turn a sod with furrow slices turned down slope. Where plowing is impossible, spots to receive seeds should be scalped at intervals of six feet or so, with mattock or hoe.

329. Is any preparation needed for seeding on freshly burned areas?   Wait for soaking rain to dissolve ashes or ashes should be raked or brushed aside in furrows. Fresh ashes prevent root growth and cause seedlings to die after they have emerged from seeds.

330. What is the fastest and cheapest way of sowing forest seeds by hand?   Use a hand cyclone feeder to deliver three or four seeds per foot. Cover them with shoe attachment on seeder or drag some brush along. In bare-spot seeding, sow about ten seeds per spot. Inquire of forester about a tool with soil scraper, seed container, and device for delivering a certain number of seeds per spot.

331. What are the advantages of direct seeding?   There is no need to depend on a nursery operation to get started. It is flexible, seed can be sown almost anytime there is bare ground, according to available labor, money and spare time. Normal root development can proceed without the setback of a year for transplanting. Direct seeding may save one to four years.

332. Will birds, mice, squirrels, etc. eat seeds before they sprout?
This is one of the chief disadvantages of direct seeding. This loss can be cut by covering the seeds immediately after sowing them. In the case of nut seeds, it may be better to plant them in spring when they will not lie around inviting squirrels, as in fall. This makes it necessary to store the seeds in a cool moist place over the winter.

Other disadvantages of direct seeding are the greater risk of wasting time and money, and of ending up with failure. Seeds are susceptible to all sorts of trouble—sunburn, drying, high soil temperature, insects, infections, root competition, and frost heaving. They are much more fragile and vulnerable than seedlings and transplants.

333. Can a person collect his own seeds for planting his forest?
He can if he is willing to climb trees, take trouble and devote time to cleaning and preserving the seeds. It is a professional job that takes experience in handling seeds properly and finding the best ones. Species and time of germination, and dormancy of seeds must be understood.

334. What is the dormancy of seeds? Some seeds sprout promptly, some do not sprout even when given best conditions of temperature, moisture, air and light. These last are dormant. Dormancy may be due to the seed coat being impervious to moisture, or so tough that the embryo cannot break through. Or seeds may be dormant because of inherent internal nature of the embryo. Some may be dormant on both counts.

335. What can be done to wake up dormant seeds? If the dormancy is due to seed case, nurserymen may soak them in sulfuric acid, or use abrasives to scratch the coats, or soak in almost boiling water for about twelve hours while the water gradually cools. To stir seeds from internal dormancy (which is due to freezing winter weather) they are buried in moist sand or peat moss, and kept chilled between 32° to 41° F. for a few months. Chemical fumes and acids have also been used to wake them up. The easiest way is to sow the seeds soon after collecting in late summer and fall, and let nature wake them up in her time-honored way.

336. When is direct seeding most often used? On stony ground, and with certain kinds of trees in certain areas where seeding has proven successful, as, for example, with white pine on burned-over slopes in the northern Rocky Mountains; in Douglas fir areas; on sand plains around the Great Lakes; old cut-over or burned-over sites of the Atlantic piedmont; and the better cut-over areas of the Ozark Mountains in Missouri. Also seeding is used by many farmers who want to build up a few acres of woodlot, because it can be done at odd times when they and their hands are not busy with other planting. The experienced farmer is in a good position to collect his own seeds and doesn't have to spend money buying seedlings from a nursery.

337. Are seeds taken from the caches of squirrels good for planting? Yes, squirrels, mice, and other rodents store only ripe seeds, collecting them when they are clinging to the tree. The squirrels work over a long period of time collecting at just the most vital time. But some seeds cannot be found in these caches; for example, jack and lodgepole pine keep their cones tightly sealed for years.

338. How does a seed collector find the caches of squirrels? He watches where the squirrels go, and tries to spot runways and trails. In a pine forest the best way is to look for heaped up piles of old cone scales, because squirrels often use the same location year after year.

Another way is to catch the squirrels red-handed. They cut off the cones from the tree tops, assemble them on the ground and separate the seeds from the scales. While this is going on the seed collector interrupts and takes the seeds.

339. How many seeds does a squirrel cache contain? Usually a few quarts. In the giant forests of the Far West a cache may hold as much as eight bushels.

340. How many seeds are there per tree? This varies with every single tree every year. A general estimate for important trees in a good bearing year is: ponderosa pine, 60,000 seeds (four bushels); white pine, 30,000 seeds (one bushel); Douglas fir, 180,000 seeds (three and a half bushels). Nut trees, which have very satisfactory seeds for planting, have few seeds per tree because they are heavy compared to pine seeds.

341. How long can seeds be stored without losing their vitality? This varies with the kind of seed. Usually seeds are gathered in the fall and held over winter in sacks at air temperature in cool cellars or seed storage houses. Cold storage is needed only if they are to be kept more than a year. Pine seeds, cleaned and sealed in glass or metal containers, kept at 34° to 38° F., will be vital for several years, as much as seven years if the moisture content is reduced to 5 percent before packing. The idea is to maintain low temperature, even moisture, and cut the seeds off from air. Seeds of some hardwoods (oak, hickory, maple) should not be reduced below 35 percent moisture content. Magnolia should not be dried at all. With proper care, most seeds can be kept five or ten years; some will be vital for decades.

342. Can a forest be seeded successfully from an airplane? Tests all show that seeding by airplane may cost less than by other methods. But success is highly uncertain. A man can seed only one to three acres per day by hand, while a plane can deposit seeds on a hundred acres in a matter of minutes. This is called broadcast seeding, like the old-fashioned, and obsolete, method of throwing seed on the ground haphazardly. Foresters say, "There is no more certain way to waste large quantities of seed and accomplish nothing than to broadcast it on unprepared ground." But there has been some successful airplane seeding, and experiments are proving more successful as the method improves.

343. What is the best way to handle airplane seeding? One way that has been used in Maine is to lay out narrow strips, about 50 feet wide and scoot along these strips with the plane only 50 to 75 feet above the treetops. Ground crews must first put up flags to keep the pilot exactly on the strip, and windsocks to give him the exact direction of the wind. Seeding must be done on a calm day. In one case the seed was mixed with sawdust (pine seed is so light that its flow cannot be controlled when pure seed is used) and carried in a 17-bushel hopper. The seeds flowed out at the bottom to a pan where it was picked up by the slip stream under the fuselage which was channeled to blow it in four directions. In setting up this method, use 12 to 1 proportions of sawdust and seeds to plant 4,000 seeds per acre; 6 to 1 for 8,000 seeds per acre of white pine. One of the chief problems is getting the seeds sufficiently covered to germinate before they dry out in the sun and wind. You can't go over the ground on foot and cover them because that would be too expensive and, further, you can't see many seeds. They vanish in the kaleidoscope of lights and shadows. The best way to get them covered is to sow on snow, preferably soft, wet snow. The melting-down action, frost, and spring rains may then bury them. Ground that has been recently bared by hot fire or flood is the best type for airplane seeding. This gives conifer seeds the mineral soil that helps them sprout, and rodent life is reduced, although some squirrels, rabbits, or mice, will probably be quick to find the fresh, ripe seeds.

344. Is it good business to raise trees for the Christmas tree market? This is a steadily growing business. Hundreds of new plantations are started every year. Some growers make extra money from bad pastures, stony hillsides, or otherwise idle land. Others are in the business in a big way with thousands of acres and machinery for planting, cutting, and bundling. Others enjoy it as a profitable hobby.

345. What is the size of the Christmas tree market in the United States? Forty million trees each year, averaging, perhaps, $2 each wholesale.

346. Where do Christmas trees come from? Cutting in wild forest land, 94 percent. Christmas tree plantations, 6 percent. About one fourth of the total comes from Canada and the rest mostly from the northern states, because the favorite types of trees, such as spruce and fir, are northern trees. The percentage from forests planted for the purpose is increasing, as trees from plantations started five and ten years ago appear on the markets. Cutting wild trees is not destructive if it is part of a forestry thinning program.

347. Are plantation trees better than those gathered from wild forests? Among points in their favor is that they are grown to have better form and to be fuller and greener. They can be cut later (after Thanksgiving) than trees which are in remote forests and have a long haul, and they arrive in the home fresher. The buyer can visit the nursery before cutting and see just what he is ordering. This reduces waste and expense.

348. How much land is needed for a Christmas tree forest? For a paying hobby that takes only spare-time work, two or three acres. For earning a living, a hundred acres or more.

349. What is the largest plantation of Christmas trees that can be managed by one person? Up to twenty acres. Even with this, extra help will be needed for the original planting, and especially during the week each year when the trees are cut.

350. What kind of land is the best for a Christmas-tree forest?
A large operation, using machinery for planting and cutting, must
have fairly level and rolling land so that it can be worked with a
tractor and trucks. For hand planting, more difficult land can be
used. Old fields and worn-out farmland are good. Christmas trees
do not need fertile soil—they have better form if they don't grow
too fast. Dry, gravelly soil is not good, and low, wet land must be
avoided. However, Christmas tree crops can use cheap land not
good for pasture and other crops.

351. Where should land for a Christmas tree plantation be located?
Within a hundred miles of the market where you will sell the trees.
Hauling cost is an important factor in competition.

352. What kind of trees are best for Christmas trade?   This depends on the demand of the market in your location. In the Northeast, spruce and balsam fir are preferred. In the Northwest, and today
finding a widening market, Douglas fir. The long-needle pines are
in demand in some markets. Before planting, inquire of the trade.
(See Question 586.)

353. What is the channel of trade for Christmas trees?   Every
market has Christmas tree wholesalers. In some places the big chain
stores act as wholesalers. If it is planned to sell all the stock to one
wholesaler, that is a matter of contract for which he should visit
the plantation, and take over the entire lot of that year's standing.
The owner may get a lower price but is relieved of cutting and hauling
and selling. Some growers with trucks sell direct to retailers and include delivery. If the owner gets a good location for a display and
stand, where there is traffic, he may want to sell direct to retail
customers. This involves energetic promotion with signs, perhaps
radio and newspaper advertising, but he gets retail prices to cover
the expenses.

Wholesalers and retailers may offer to take trees on consignment
—that is, they will only pay for what they sell. This is risky. It may
leave the owner with unsold trees. Sell the trees before cutting. A
cut Christmas tree after Christmas is worthless. An uncut tree may
be worth even more the next year. Don't just load up the truck and

drive to market to peddle the trees. Everybody who sees a load knows it must be sold, and the bidding may be ruinous.

354. How should Christmas trees be planted? Use transplants for a high rate of survival. Set out in rows spaced five or six feet apart for the normal Christmas tree that will be six or seven feet tall. (Spacing is very important; small differences make a big difference in the number of trees per acre. Adjust this to the kind of trees you are growing. Pines are wider and take more room. Spruce and fir and red cedar are more compact and slender and can be spaced closer.)

355. How many Christmas trees fit into an acre?

Planting space (in feet)	Number of trees per acre
3 x 3 (for small table trees)	4,840
4 x 4	2,722
5 x 5	1,740
6 x 6	1,210
7 x 7	890
8 x 8	680

356. Should machinery be used for planting Christmas trees? Less than forty acres can be planted by hand. More than that requires a planting machine.

357. What is a planting bar? This is a blade ten inches long and three inches wide, sharp and wedge-shaped with a T-shaped handle. It is driven like a spade vertically into the ground and by a simple sequence of pushing and pulling, it makes the hole and pushes over loose dirt quickly and easily.

358. Where are Christmas tree transplants available? Probably at a private nursery. Most state nurseries have sold all their stock to reforestation projects months, perhaps years, ahead of time. This is particularly true as long as the soil bank policy of the Department of Agriculture remains in force. Some state nurseries are prohibited by law from selling to Christmas tree growers.

359. How much do Christmas tree seedlings and transplants cost?
Prices varying according to locality, which reflects growing and labor conditions. The range of private nursery list prices is:

Type	Age	Price per 1,000 trees
Seedlings	2–0	$15–$35
Seedlings	3–0	$25–$60
Transplants	2–1	$30–$85
Transplants	2–2	$35–$125

360. If plans are made a year ahead, can Christmas tree stock be obtained from a state nursery at cost? Yes, in 29 states where tree plantations are rated as regular forestry. The states which sell stock to Christmas tree growers are: Alabama, Arkansas, California, Colorado, Connecticut, Delaware (free stock available), Florida, Georgia, Illinois, Indiana, Kentucky, Massachusetts, Michigan, Minnesota, Mississippi, Missouri, Montana, New Hampshire, New Jersey, New York, North Carolina, North Dakota, Oklahoma, Oregon, South Carolina, South Dakota, Tennessee, Texas, Vermont, Washington.

361. When is the best time to plant a Christmas tree forest? Spring is the usual time. The exact week depends on latitude: the latter part of May up north; as early as February in the south. Fall planting may be done with the understanding that loss may be high from winter killing. Growers are not so ready to supply transplants in the fall.

362. What are the most popular Christmas trees? Of all the Christmas trees sold in this country, 40 percent is balsam fir and black spruce; 27 percent, Douglas fir; 10 percent, eastern red cedar. The rest, 23 percent, consists of white spruce, Scotch pine, red pine, southern pines, red spruce, Norway spruce.

363. What tree can be used for Christmas tree plantations in the dry Southwest? Arizona cypress is excellent with its dense blue-green foliage.

364. Does a Christmas tree plantation have to be fertilized for best results? Generally, no. It hurts the shape to speed up growth. Some experienced Christmas tree growers are experimenting with fertilizing to improve the color of foliage.

365. Do the Christmas trees have to be pruned? Not necessarily, but it shapes the trees and brings higher prices.

366. What are the criteria of a good Christmas tree and which kinds meet these? White spruce has dense blue-green foliage, slender branches, and is graceful, but it tends to lose its needles quickly in a warm room. Balsam fir is popular for its marvelous fragrance, and it holds its needles well. Douglas fir has just the right length needles, holds them well in a warm room and responds to shaping in the nursery—but takes ten years or more to reach marketable size. The pines are the fastest growers, reaching a good size in five years.

367. What are the most marketable sizes? Standard floor Christmas trees are six to seven feet tall. Other sizes are table sizes and community sizes.

368. Is it practical to sell "living" Christmas trees? Trees sold in pots with root systems may be a profitable specialty, provided they are not sold as house plants but for planting outdoors as soon as possible. Steam heat is fatal to these needle trees in a few days.

369. What is a good book about growing Christmas trees? *Christmas Trees for Pleasure and Profit,* by A. G. Chapman and R. D. Wray (New Brunswick, N.J.: Rutgers University Press).

370. Is fire the most destructive agent of trees? Diseases and insects destroy twice as much timber as fire.

371. Does man cause more forest fire damage than lightning? From the viewpoint of an individual fire, that set by man is more destructive because it runs along roads, trails, streams, or starts lower down and runs up-hill. Lightning fires usually start on tops of ridges where they spread more slowly, and lightning is often accompanied by rain.

372. What is the safest way to make a camp fire? Scrape off inflammable litter down to the damp mineral soil on a circle about six feet across. Keep the fire small, and in the center. Do not build fires against trees or logs, under low branches, or in windy spots. Be sure it is dead, with no smoking coals, when you leave.

373. What are the different types of forest fires? *The crown fire* burns through the tops of trees, consuming foliage and branches. It is terrible to fight because it is explosive, high in the air, leaps over fire lines and travels with the speed of the wind. However, if the forest below and the ground are moist, it is possible for a forest to recover from a strictly crown fire.

The surface fire burns surface litter, fallen branches and ground-cover bushes. Trees with heavy bark may resist damage and, if foliage is unhurt, the surface fire may be the least destructive of all. Its greatest threat is destruction of young trees that are the next generation of the forest.

The ground fire burns beneath the surface of the forest floor where it may smolder for months and destroy nourishing humus. Its greatest danger is that it may break loose and turn into a surface fire and from that become a crown fire. Lack of moisture in the ground betokens a long drought, so every part of the forest is apt to be a tinder box when a ground fire is burning.

374. What is a smoke jumper? A parachute fire fighter trained to drop to the vicinity of a fire in inaccessible areas. His mission is to put the fire out while it is still small.

375. What is a back fire? A fire set on purpose on a control line near a fierce fire. The back fire is drawn by its heat into the main fire, which is slowed down by being deprived of material for burning. This is a small sacrifice to bring a raging fire under control.

376. What are the principal causes of forest fires? In the Rocky Mountain forests 70 percent are caused by lightning; 30 percent by careless smokers. In the big forests of the Northwest, 50 percent are lightning and 50 percent are careless smokers and campers who abandon live coals. In the Lake States and New England, almost all forest fires are caused by careless smokers, camp-fire abandoners, and ignorant brush burners. In the South, field burners and fire-setters clearing land are responsible for most forest fires.

377. Is it possible to get forest fire insurance?   Yes, in New England and the South. One such policy has a base rate of 56¢ per $100 insurance, subject to credits or extra charges. The credits are 5 percent to 10 percent for fire breaks in the forests, and organized fire protection; 5 percent for trees over one foot in diameter and for long leaf pine trees as they are more fire resistant than others; 2 percent for heavy density as this keeps the air moister and cuts down wind speed. The extra charges are 2 percent for lightning; and extra charges of various percentages for trees exposed to tapping for pitch to make turpentine and resin (naval stores), trees near railroads, recreation areas, paved highways, trees on steep terrain, or with heavy underbrush, and other obvious hazards. Annual rate is calculated on a premium 80 percent higher during the dry season, con idered to be February through October.

A few trees have built-in fire insurance. When aspen is killed by fire, its roots send up suckers, some of which develop into new trees. Certain pine trees (notably jack, lodgepole, and knobcone) hold their seeds for years inside unopened cones. These pop open in intense heat and the seeds are released. Big forests of jack pine in the Lake Superior area have been planted by forest fires.

378. What were the worst forest fires in the history of the United States?   The worst fire started near Green Bay, Wisconsin, in October 1871, on the same night that Mrs. O'Leary's cow kicked over a stable lantern starting the great Chicago fire. This tore through 1,280,000 acres of the finest Great Lakes white pine country, destroyed the lumber center of Peshtigo and other towns, killing about 1,500 people.

The Moose Lake region of Minnesota had a fire in 1918 that destroyed over 250,000 acres, wiped out the city of Cloquet, killing 453 people.

The biggest, in point of timber destruction, was in the Idaho panhandle in the spring of 1910, in the Bitteroot and Coeur d'Alene area. An estimated 3 million acres and 8 billion feet of standing timber were destroyed. Many towns, including the north Idaho mining center of Wallace, were wiped out. Seventy-eight fire fighters were killed. The only thing that stopped the fire was a downpour of rain and snow.

379. When did people wake up to the need for a fire protection code, new fire-fighting techniques and methods of control? In Oregon and Washington in 1902, fires swept through 700,000 acres on the west slopes of the Cascade Mountains, which caused timber owners, loggers, settlers, trappers and hunters to organize protective associations and set up forest fire codes, patrols and fire-fighting equipment without waiting for the slow process of law. Between 1905 and 1912 the codes were put into manuals and state laws. This laid the foundations for federal laws, climaxed by the Clarke-McNary Act of 1924.

380. Why is the Clarke-McNary Act a milestone in forest fire legislation? It made a three-way alliance for a cooperative attack on forest fires—federal, state, private owner. The earlier constitutional interpretation of federal interest in state and private forests was set aside. Forests became a national concern; the Clarke-McNary Act launched an all-out offensive to protect every acre of forest in the country.

381. Has the federal backing of forest protection paid off? Definitely. It has converted forestry from a daring pioneer enterprise into a national policy of conservation. It has been a continuing influence in establishing commercial tree farms in thirty states, and an expanding industrial investment of $5 to $50 per acre in forest planting.

382. Has any huge forest fire got out of hand since the passing of the Clarke-McNary Act? Yes. In dealing with elemental forces there are always surprises and something new to learn. The Tillamook Burn of 1933, on the west coast of Oregon, still shows part of its black scar as a reminder that there is no final security. A logger's ground cable fell across a dry log and the friction gave out sparks. As a result, in two hot August days over 300,000 acres of some of the finest Douglas fir of our land went up in smoke and 12½ billion feet of standing timber were destroyed. This happened despite the fact that the Oregon coast has an annual rainfall of over 75 inches and summer fogs sweep the trees. The region had been considered one of the safest.

383. How acute is the danger of forest fire today? The greatest destruction is not from big spectacular fires but from thousands of little fires all added together. These are set by the burning habits of landowners and by careless visitors and campers. The greatest danger is in late summer and fall when the woods and ground litter have been parched by months of dry weather.

As William B. Greeley, former Chief Forester and a great leader in forest fire-fighting, puts it: "The thirsty air is sucking moisture out of humus, leaves, twigs and shrubs. The great sponge of vegetable matter as well as the soil itself is robbed of its hoard of moisture. The dryness of the woods reaches an explosive quality when touched by a flicker of flame."

384. What was the Great Plains Shelterbelt Project? A bold experiment growing out of the drought and terrifying dust storms of 1933. The proposal was to plant a gigantic tree belt all the way across the eastern Great Plains from North Dakota to Texas. If this could be established where nature had always grown dry, grassy plains, it would (1) slow down wind speed close to the ground and thus reduce prairie fires, windbreakage, and blow down of crops; (2) prevent quick evaporation of soil moisture and cut down wind erosion and the loss of priceless top soil, which made billowing clouds of dust that dimmed the sun in New York City and sprinkled the decks of ships far out in the Atlantic; (3) prevent damage to orchards, gardens and field crops by reducing drifting dust smothering newly germinating seeds; and (4) provide winter protection to livestocks and their feeding grounds.

385. How was the Great Plains Shelterbelt Project to be carried out? First, by high-level planning between foresters, farmers, botanists, and soil scientists. Then by a cooperative program in which the government would supply the tree stock, plus guidance and help in planting. The landowners would make available the space and agree to take care of the young windbreak, keep down weeds, and protect it from grazing cattle and other local threats.

386. What happened to the Shelterbelt Project? By 1937 the project was in full swing. It continued for eight years, during which some 200 million trees and shrubs of forty different species were planted. This scattered pattern stretched from the Canadian border through North Dakota, South Dakota, Nebraska, Kansas, western Oklahoma, into the Texas panhandle. Windbreaks across 18,600 miles of open fields were planted on thirty thousand farms.

387. What is the condition of the Shelterbelt today? A survey made by the Forest Service in 1954 shows 48 percent of it to be in excellent or good condition; 29 percent, fair; 18 percent, poor; 5 percent, destroyed. This is based on 938 windbreaks sampled.

388. What is the average height of the trees of the Shelterbelt experiment? The same 1954 report shows that 16 percent of the breaks are 50 feet or taller; 38 percent are between 35 and 50 feet high. These are the fast-growing hardwoods. The evergreens average 10 feet.

389. What was the chief reason for tree survival and good growth? The condition of the site, which includes good soil and a not-too-deep water table, combined with cultivation in early stages to keep the seedlings from being choked with weeds, and the prevention of grazing and trampling by livestock. Perhaps the greatest single cause of damage was livestock, especially in the southern part of the Great Plains Shelterbelt.

390. What is the pattern of tree planting in the Shelterbelt? The pattern is a main belt of three to six rows, and two supplementary belts of one to three rows each, with 500 feet between, in which crops can be planted. Within the rows a carefully worked-out plan of tall, medium and short trees or shrubs is used to produce, when mature, a sort of slanting roof, oriented for the prevailing winds.

391. What kinds of trees have proved to be best for Shelterbelt protection? *Tall, fast-growing trees:* American sycamore, white willow, Siberian elm, and plains cottonwood (the last is good to get the shelterbelt going fast, but more permanent trees must replace it as cottonwood is a short-lived tree and already some of the tallest in the Shelterbelt are dying out). *Tall, slow-growing trees:* American elm, green ash, honey locust, bur oak, hackberry, black locust, black walnut, catalpa, Kentucky coffee tree. *Short, fast-growing trees:* box elder, Russian olive, mulberry, osage orange. *Shrubs:* wild plum, chokecherry, a very hardy pea shrub (*Caragana arborescens*), and one of the sumacs called skunkbush (*Rhus triloba*). *Conifers:* eastern red cedar, ponderosa pine, Austrian pine, Rocky Mountain juniper. The red cedar has proved to be the hardiest of this group.

392. Where can full information about shelterbelts and wind-breaks be obtained? For the 1954 Survey by the Forest Service, write: Rocky Mountain Forest and Range Experiment Station, Fort Collins, Colorado. For further information write for "Shelterbelts for the Northern Great Plains," *Farmers' Bulletin,* No. 2109 (Washington, D.C.: Superintendent of Documents, Government Printing Office).

393. How effective was the Great Plains Shelterbelt in slowing down the wind? Very effective for a distance of twenty times the height of the trees. Thus on the lee side of a screen fifty feet high, an area one thousand feet wide enjoys wind reduction which conserves moisture, cuts down drifting, and blowing away of soil and snow.

394. What is the ground-water table? Soil is formed with a series of layers resting on a dead, dry, impervious foundation of rock. The bottom layer consists of very fine particles of clay or silt that have gradually sunk through the porous layers above and formed a compact, sticky zone saturated with ground water that has seeped down with the material. This is called "gley" (derived from the same Greek word as "glue"). Air cannot penetrate, so the gley becomes a fairly permanent reservoir of water, which does not evaporate much, even in long, dry periods. It furnishes water to soil layers which lie above and which pull up the water into spaces between fine soil particles by capillary attraction. The upper edge of the saturated gley zone is known as the ground-water table.

395. What part does the water table play in the life of trees? The depth of the water table below the surface of the ground determines the kind of trees which grow above ground. A shallow water table (that is, one close to the ground) makes less soil nourishment available with higher concentration of minerals and more acid. This means that trees (and other plants) which are attuned to this kind of acid condition will grow there. A deeper water table (that is, one with more porous humus above it) is an area hospitable to other types of forest trees. Thus, by controlling the depth of the aerated soil in which roots thrive, the water table exerts a direct influence on the kind of forest and its distribution.

396. Why don't tree roots penetrate the saturated gley soil of the water table and enjoy lots of water? A good percentage of air in the soil is highly important. The gley layer is almost airtight, and this lack of air, plus a concentration of chemicals that may make it too acid, bars the penetration of roots into the water table. (It is not a pool of well-aerated water.) Only a few trees have evolved an ability to send roots into the gley.

397. What are some of the exceptional trees which can tap the water table? One of the finest is the ancient bald cypress of southern swap land. Another is pitch pine, which can grow in coarse, sandy soil where water drains through fast, by sending roots into the water table for water.

398. Can the depth of the water table be judged by the kind of trees? In a general way, yes, when it is near the surface. Balsam fir, white spruce and, to some extent, black ash and red maple indicate shallow root soil with the water table 1 to $1\frac{1}{2}$ feet below the surface. Rock elm, red maple, yellow birch, balsam fir, white spruce, and below-par sugar maple and basswood indicate a table 2 to 3 feet below. Flourishing sugar maple and basswood and white pine show a table 4 to 5 feet down. These indications are for gley derived from granite silt.

399. What is the best depth of water table to produce the finest timber forest? Four feet or deeper.

400. What is the depth of the water table in the Midwest where there are forest trees on the edges of the prairie? In this case the gley consists of limestone silt. Bur oak, black oak, a scattering of red oak, aspen and box elder indicate a table 2 or 3 feet below. White oak, red oak, a scattering of black oak, walnut, hickory, and white ash have found a deeper water table at 4 to 5 feet down, or deeper.

401. How much air is in the earth where roots thrive? The amount of air in soil depends on its texture. Together with the depth of the water table, this exerts an important influence as to what kind of trees will grow in a place. The forester speaks of "absolute air capacity"—found by measuring the amount of air held in soil after it has been saturated with water and allowed to drain for twenty-four hours. The lowest air capacity, tolerated by wet-place conifers such as black spruce, balsam fir, northern white cedar and bald cypress, is 7 percent by volume. The air volume in upland woodlands where sugar maple, beech and birch grow, is 20 percent or more. The best air content for the most flourishing forest is around 30 percent.

402. How much water is in the soil above the water table? This varies greatly according to soil texture. A measurement of water is based on "field capacity." This is the amount of water held in damp soil after the excess water of a drenching has drained away and the stable water supply of the soil is moving in all directions by capillary attraction, not just down by gravity. Field capacity ranges from about 5 percent in sandy soil to around 35 percent in clay soil, with good nourishing loam around 20 percent of water by volume. This field-capacity water clings to the surfaces of soil particles where it is picked up by root hairs and is the most important water supply of trees.

403. Is the water in the water table more important for trees than water in the soil? No, this rises only a few feet by capillary attraction. It supplies water for roots when the water table is near the surface. When it is deeper than fifteen feet, trees get along without the water table reservoir. The water table influences the kind of trees which grows above it by establishing the depth of the porous soil, more than as a water supply.

Sugar maple is as American as the pioneers who first saw it in rugged New England and learned from the Indians how to make sugar from its sap. Its leaf is a masterpiece of art; its winged seeds resemble buoyant little airplanes; its light golden wood makes beautiful furniture.

White pine silhouette has dark horizontal branches with bars of sky showing between. Its seedlings like sunlight and spread quickly over a meadow, as shown in this picture. Its name comes from the whiteness of its wood that is straight-grained and popular with carpenters and home builders.

American elm is well known as America's greatest tree decoration. Its trunk divides into long branches that mount up and then curve down forming a tree fountain. New England roads arched by elms planted by the first settlers are a proud heritage.

White oaks were the sovereigns of the virgin forest of the eastern United States. The great strength and beauty of oak wood have made it so popular for timber, shipbuilding, furniture and paneling that there remain few old monarchs with heavy bole and massive horizontal branches.

Apple is the best known of all orchard trees. The bole is often slanting and fluted. Children love the apple tree because it is so easy to climb and the fruit is so easy to pick.

All fruit trees have eye-catching flowers. A cherry tree is shown here in full blossom. This is a relative of the rose, as also are peach, apple and plum trees. Citrus trees, including orange, grapefruit and lemon, also have beautiful white flowers, which are very fragrant.

A hedge row along a country road is the best place to get close to trees and discover their details. Twigs, buds and leaves are easy to reach on young trees. Here also are the wildflowers that live in a tree community.

A Douglas fir forest is amazingly uniform. Tall straight trunks stand so close together that they may be likened to a wheat field. Two-thirds of the lumber from the Northwest comes from Douglas fir. These tall trees are so strong with their straight grain that they make fine masts and spars.

Picture shows the top of the General Sherman, a big tree sequoia, after it was sheared off by lightning. This tree is 3,800 years old. Its diameter is 36 feet. One horizontal branch is $6\frac{1}{2}$ feet in diameter and 150 feet long, dimensions greater than our loftiest American elm.

Saguaro is the giant cactus tree that may tower fifty feet or more. It is the majestic symbol of the southwestern desert, almost entirely in Arizona. The greatest concentration of saguaros is about ten miles south of Tucson, where there is a forest of some 15,000 to the square mile.

Joshua tree is a giant lily (*Yucca*) that grows in the deserts of southern California. Heavy branches end in big balls of leaves formed as sharp daggers, ten inches long. Beautiful white flowers bloom among these weird balls of daggers.

Washington palms are the only native palms of our Southwest. They are shown here in their natural place in Palm Canyon, near Palm Springs. This palm has been widely planted as a street tree in Phoenix and other cities of the Southwest.

Torrey pine is a very ancient pine ancestor with deep plunging roots and picturesque contorted branches. It has all but disappeared from the earth, its last stand being a small area known as Torrey Pine State Park, ten miles south of San Diego, California.

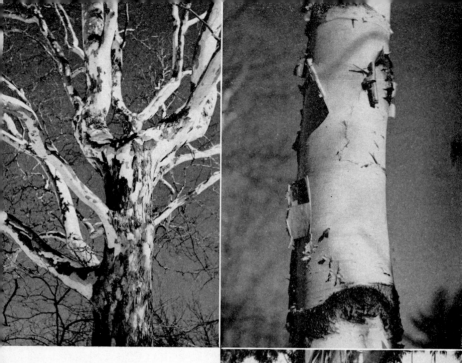

Bark is often overlooked in the shade cast by leaves, but it often has interesting patterns and colors. Compare the six tree barks on these two pages. *Above:* Sycamore, or plane tree, has bark like a patchwork quilt with tints of white, yellow and pink. *Upper right:* Paper birch bark is famous as the material used to make Indian birch bark canoes. *Right:* Eucalyptus, imported from Australia and widely planted in dry areas of California and the South, has bark that strips off with a play of many colors.

Above: Honey locust. Note the long thorns. This tree is unclimbable and immune to browsing animals and bark chewers. *Upper right:* Shagbark hickory. Note the plates of bark-like shingles of an old house that have become unnailed at the bottom. These appear loose but they are tough and hard to detach. *Right:* Smooth silvery gray, beautiful when it catches light in the winter woods. Beech bark is elastic, so it does not crack and break when the trunk expands with growth.

Two trees of bygone ages. *Above*: A fossil stump of solid stone from the dawn-seed fern tree that flourished on earth more than 300 million years ago. Bulbous base indicates that it grew in swampy places. *Left*: The fluted trunk of horsetail that is a small slender plant in our day but that grew as a giant tree in the Coal Age, some 250 million years ago.

404. Are the water table and the water that gravitates through the soil from snow and rain the only sources of water for tree roots? No, a considerable amount of water is condensed from the air on relatively cool surfaces in the shade of vegetation, boulders or hills. During hot, humid periods this may be a vital supply. A rough surface helps to get more moisture into the soil. This is automatically provided by the litter in the forest. The amount of water supplied in this way has been estimated to equal almost three inches of rainfall per year.

405. Is water condensed within the soil? After the gravitational flow has stopped, soil water is transported and delivered throughout the soil mostly in the form of water vapor. The relative humidity of the air circulating between the soil particles is normally around 100 percent in moist tree-growing soil.

406. Is it true that all forest lakes are disappearing? Yes, some imperceptibly, some before our eyes. The constant descent of vegetable matter—seeds, leaves, pollen, twig litter, bits of bark, fallen trunks—means that every pond and lake in the forest is getting shallower year after year. Pond weeds and water plants are evidence that the bottom is approaching the surface. Bogs indicate that the top has just been reached.

407. What is a "pure stand"? A forest in which at least 80 per cent of the trees are the same kind.

408. Is it true that the great pure-stand Douglas-fir forests of the Northwest are the result of forest fires of past centuries? Yes. Douglas fir does not reproduce in its own dense shade. In the absence of a catastrophe like a big wind throw-down or fire, Douglas fir would be succeeded by shade-tolerant western hemlock, western red cedar, and true firs. It is a good guess that the virgin Douglas fir forests came into existence by forest fires interrupting the natural succession.

409. Do big forests have a direct effect on climate? The shrinking of a vast forest changes climate. Even the great monsoon belt of Africa is now threatened with years of drought. Elephants and rhinoceros which used to forage in interior areas are gathering today along watercourses where crocodiles line the banks, while behind them the grass savannas and sparse, dry forest is burning. The process started when natives burned openings in the jungle, and then after a year or two of crops moved on and burned more. The world's richest primeval rain-forest is drying up. Reservoirs of water are disappearing and man must face the day when the great heritage trees with their fabulous animals will all be gone, and new life will only be maintained by the fortunate miracle of new trees.

410. What are "new trees"? These are trees that prosper vigorously after they have been transplanted from a different hemisphere. Such trees are eucalyptus from Australia that thrives today in California, Morocco, South Africa and India; poplar that grows in the United States and is today restoring tree life to the tree-hungry countries of Iran, Iraq, and to the deltas of Argentina, Uruguay, and New Zealand; ginkgo from central China that is bringing tree shade to the streets and parks of modern America; Monterey pine from a tiny sanctuary in southern California and has become the fastest-growing timber tree in the world in Australia, New Zealand, Chile. Other new trees are acacia, Australian pine (beefwood), piñon pine, Russian olive, London plane tree.

411. How does temperature in a forest compare with open areas in the neighborhood? The year-round average is almost the same, perhaps 2° cooler among the trees. But temperature doesn't reach the extremes of cold and hot in a dense evergreen forest, or among hardwoods when leaves are on the trees. If the canopy is light or branches are bare of leaves, the reverse is true. It gets hotter when the sun shines because radiating warmth penetrates to the ground at the same time that circulation of air is cut down. It gets colder in bitter weather when the sun is not shining. The average temperature of the open or leafless forest is warmer than outside it.

412. Which are apt to be the most damaged in a hurricane, conifers or hardwoods? In the New England hurricane of September 1938, a much higher percentage of pines and other conifers was blown down, than of hardwoods. The damage was greatest for trees over forty years old. Young stands of all kinds of trees were not seriously damaged.

413. What was the total damage to the forests by the New England hurricane of September 1938? About half of the timber was blown down in the hurricane path, totaling 3 billion feet on 600 thousand acres of forest land.

414. What nongovernment organizations offer information about forest planting and management?

> The American Forestry Association
> 919 17th Street, N.W.
> Washington 6, D.C.
>
> American Forest Products Industries Incorporated
> 1816 N Street, N.W.
> Washington 6, D.C.
>
> American Paper and Pulp Association
> 122 East 42nd Street
> New York, 17, New York
>
> American Pulpwood Association
> 220 East 42nd Street
> New York 17, New York
>
> Forest Products Research Society
> Box 2010
> University Station
> Madison 5, Wisconsin
>
> National Lumber Manufacturers Association
> 1319 Eighteenth Street, N.W.
> Washington 6, D.C.
>
> Society of American Foresters
> 425 Mills Building
> 17th Street at Pennsylvania Avenue, N.W.
> Washington 6, D.C.
>
> Forest Farmers Association Cooperative
> P.O. Box 7284, Station "C"
> Atlanta, Georgia

Industrial Forestry Association
1410 S.W. Morrison Street
Portland 5, Oregon

New England Forestry Foundation Incorporated
3 Joy Street
Boston 8, Massachusetts

Southern Pulpwood Conservation Association
1506, First National Bank Building
1224 Peachtree Street, N.E.
Atlanta 3, Georgia

Trees for Tomorrow Incorporated
120 South Mill Street
Merrill, Wisconsin

Western Forestry and Conservation Association
712 U.S. National Bank Building
Portland 4, Oregon

415. How can one become a forester?   The forester in the highest sense is a professional man with a degree from an accredited forestry school. This may be a Bachelor of Science with a major in forestry in an undergraduate college or higher degrees for graduate work in forest sciences and technical fields: Master of Forestry, Master of Science, Doctor of Philosophy, according to the program offered by the school.

416. What leading schools offer graduate degrees in forestry?
The School of Forestry, Duke University (Durham, North Carolina), offers a four-year graduate course leading to the degree of Master of Forestry or Doctor of Forestry. It offers no degree in forestry to undergraduates, but those headed for the graduate school can take a preforest curriculum in Trinity College of Duke University. The Duke School of Forestry has a 300-acre aboretum and a 6,000-acre forest, as well as a fine forestry library. Fellowships, scholarships, and research assistantships are offered at Duke to those who show promise of becoming leaders in the forestry profession.

The School of Forestry, Yale University (New Haven, Connecticut), is also on a strictly graduate basis with a Master of Forestry degree in two years. Candidates with undergraduate degrees from forestry schools of high standing may be able to qualify for a Master of Forestry in one year. Yale also confers the degree of Doctor of Philosophy in Forestry after three years of graduate work, if other special conditions are met. Yale has top-notch facilities and a great library with emphasis on tropical woods. In 1958 the new William B. Greeley Memorial Laboratory was opened. The school owns 9,800 acres of demonstration forests in Connecticut, Vermont and New Hampshire. A Bachelor of Arts degree is required for admission but classes may include members of the junior and senior classes, research and summer students.

The Harvard Forest, Petersham, Massachusetts, is a unit of the Harvard Graduate School. It is also a member of the Harvard University botanical group. The degree of Master of Forestry is offered candidates who have a bachelor's degree from a recognized undergraduate school of forestry. At Petersham, Harvard Forest has fine fireproof buildings in the midst of 2,300 acres of native New England forest used as a field laboratory and demonstration forest by the school. The general public enjoys visiting the Harvard Forest to see the Forest Model collection and the dioramas of New England land at different periods in American history.

New York State College of Forestry, Syracuse University (Syracuse, New York), has its own quarters on the campus, including a pulp and paper laboratory, greenhouse, forest insectary, woodworking shop, sawmill and wood preservation laboratory. Undergraduate courses lead to the degree of Bachelor of Science. The curriculum is broad, with courses in general forestry, landscape and recreation forest management, forest products, wood technology, pulp and paper manufacturing. Graduate work may lead to a Master of Forestry, Master of Science, or Doctor of Philosophy.

Various experimental and demonstration forests are used by the school. A collateral opportunity is the Archer and Anna Huntington Wildlife Forest Station of 14,800 acres near Newcomb in the Adirondacks. This is used for forest experiment and for research in the haunts and habits of fish, birds, game, food and fur-bearing animals.

417. What recognized forestry schools offer undergraduate courses? The following are accredited by the Society of American Foresters:

Alabama Polytechnic Institute, Department of Forestry, Auburn, Alabama

University of California, Department of Forestry, Berkeley, California

Colorado State College, Division of Forestry and Range Conservation, Fort Collins, Colorado

University of Florida, School of Forestry, Gainesville, Florida

University of Georgia, The George Foster Peabody School of Forestry, Athens, Georgia

Louisiana Polytechnic Institute, Department of Forestry, Ruston, Louisiana

University of Idaho, School of Forestry, Moscow, Idaho

Iowa State College, Department of Forestry, Ames, Iowa

Louisiana State University, Department of Forestry, Baton Rouge, Louisiana

University of Maine, Department of Forestry, Orono, Maine

University of Massachusetts, Department of Forestry, Amherst, Massachusetts

Michigan State College, Department of Forestry, East Lansing, Michigan

Michigan College of Mining and Technology, Department of Forestry, Houghton, Michigan

University of Michigan, School of Forestry and Conservation, Ann Arbor, Michigan

University of Minnesota, Division of Forestry, St. Paul, Minnesota

University of Missouri School of Forestry, Columbia, Missouri

Montana State University, School of Forestry, Missoula, Montana

State University of New York, College of Forestry, Syracuse, New York

North Carolina State College, Division of Forestry, Raleigh, North Carolina

Oregon State College, School of Forestry, Corvallis, Oregon

Pennsylvania State Forestry School, University Park, Pennsylvania

Purdue University, Department of Forestry and Conservation, Lafayette, Indiana

Utah State University, School of Forestry, Logan, Utah

University of Washington, College of Forestry, Seattle, Washington

West Virginia University, Division of Forestry, Morgantown, West Virginia. (See also Question 416.)

For more information on these and other forestry schools, write Society of American Foresters, Mills Building, Washington 6, D.C.

418. Is it necessary for a forest ranger to have a degree in forestry? A degree in forestry is not required except in certain cases. Many forestry schools offer special courses in range management. The New York State College of Forestry has a State Ranger School (Wanakena, New York) which gives practical courses for rangers. Students live at the school. Applicant must be physically strong, at least 17 years of age, and a high-school graduate.

419. What are the opportunities for forest rangers? All federal, state, county, city, and school forests need rangers. The big paper and logging companies which own forests must also have rangers, who are primarily the outdoor men of the forests. Ranger training also leads to work as managers of small forests or clubs or conservation society tracts, guards, nursery foremen, assistants to lumber companies, forest engineers.

Whereas the typical forest ranger might qualify with practical experience in woodsmanship and livestock handling, the career of district forest ranger of the National Forest Service calls for technical training and a forestry degree. The district forest ranger is administrator of 100,000 to 500,000 acres and is responsible for timber management, wildlife, water resources, and recreation facilities. He sees to road building, bridges, trails, telephone lines, and he must know how to fight fire.

420. Where are the opportunities for a man with a degree in forestry? The profession of forestry is so broad that it may lead in many and various directions. There is the wide field of government service in the U.S. Forest Service, National Park Service, and other bureaus. Openings in the teaching profession are available in the forestry and agricultural schools. In biology there is much work to do in silviculture, plant breeding, pest fighting, and conservation. The consultant forester is in great demand as an employee of a private company, or in federal, state, or county forestry. Also, forestry leads into wood utilization, conversion, and manufacturing. At least 150 firms, particularly timber and paper companies, employ foresters both in the maintenance and use of their own vast forest tracts, and also as consultants with farmers and landowners in the development of their woodlots. There are 50,000 forest-product industries in the United States that can use technical advice from independent consulting foresters to help increase their efficiency and profits. Today, cost accounting and air survey are opportunities for foresters.

III. HOME TREES

421. Is the typical home tree different today from a generation ago? Yes. This is a new day, for new trees, for new homes. The tree situation outside the house has changed as much as the furniture and electric equipment has changed inside the house.

Home trees of our grandparents had plenty of room, even "downtown." They were the native trees of the woods, planted along streets and around the yard. For the present generation the residential streets of older towns, vaulted with elms, are a great glory.

422. What were some of the typical shade trees of fifty years ago? American elm, oak, sugar maple, horsechestnut, linden, sycamore, ash, catalpa, walnut, cottonwood.

423. How is the home tree situation different today? Housing projects, suburbanization, faster living pace, smaller backyards, and more people in less space call for fast-growing small trees with decorative style.

424. On what basis should today's owner select his home tree? Before selecting a home tree the owner should ask himself what need he wishes his tree to fill. Does he want it for shade or for decorative flowering? For edible fruit or to attract birds? Does he want a standard-size tree or a dwarf? Evergreens or trees with colorful autumn foliage? Or trees with branch patterns to add interest to the solitude of winter?

Thought should be given to the location. Does it offer growing space or will the tree be confined in a small suburban yard? Is this tree to be planted in the city, on the street, or in the country? What are the demands of the tree for food, water, light and air? And once the tree is planted and growing, how much upkeep will the tree need?

425. What are the finest trees for landscaping? The question of what trees have high excellence was recently submitted by the Brooklyn Botanic Garden to a Selections Committee of horticulturalists, nurserymen, gardeners, and landscape architects. The criteria in making recommendations were: (1) Beauty of foliage, flower, and fruit; with special emphasis on those plants that are outstanding at more than one season of the year. (2) Tolerance of a wide range of climates and soils. (3) Ease of growth. (4) Relative freedom from pests and diseases. (5) Adaptability to various uses in garden or landscape. (6) Availability from nurseries or obtainable through special sources.

The replies of the Selections Committee, with details and photographs of the trees, were published in a handbook entitled *The Hundred Finest Trees and Shrubs for Temperate Climates* (Handbook No. 25). Copies are available from the Brooklyn Botanic Garden, Brooklyn 25, N.Y.

The trees named by the Committee are: Japanese maple, sugar maple, silk tree, shadbush. Katsura tree, Atlas cedar, cedar of Lebanon, eastern redbud, yellowwood. Flowering dogwood, Kousa dogwood, cornelian-cherry, Washington thorn. English hawthorn, cockspur thorn, Russian olive.

Franklinia, American beech, European beech, ginkgo, honeylocust, Carolina silverbell, witch hazel, goldenrain tree, English holly, and American holly. Goldenchain tree, crape myrtle, sweet gum, tulip tree. Southern magnolia, saucer magnolia, and star magnolia.

The Japanese flowering crabapple, Arnold crabapple, Sargent's crabapple, and red jade crabapple. Black gum, dawn redwood, eastern white pine, swiss stone pine, and Himalayan pine. Sourwood, Oriental cherry, Japanese weeping cherry, golden larch, white oak, willow oak, and scarlet oak.

Redwood, pin oak, big tree, Japanese pagoda tree, Japanese snowbell, bald cypress, Canada hemlock, mountain hemlock, American elm, and Japanese zelkova.

For other "home trees" see Questions 429–434.

426. What is the dollar value of shade trees in the United States? The Division of Forestry Pathology (U.S. Dept. of Agriculture) estimates that the investment value of U.S. shade trees is $600 million.

427. What is the value of a large street elm in a New England town? Arthur D. Little Co., Cambridge, Mass., estimates the value of a single large street elm at $700.

428. Is there a tree that owns itself? Yes. In Athens, Georgia, stands a white oak tree which nobody can legally cut down because nobody owns it or the land on which it stands. Many years ago a farmer who owned it stipulated in his will: "In consideration of the great love I bear this tree and the great desire I have for its protection for all time, I convey to it entire possession of itself, and all land on eight feet of the tree on all sides."

429. What home trees are characteristic of northeastern United States? Among many, the flowering dogwood, red bud, ginkgo, oriental cherry, oriental magnolia, catalpa, hawthorn, apple, pin oak, red maple, shadblow, and cedar.

430. What home trees are characteristic of the southern states? Yaupon, silverbell, crape myrtle, American holly, princess tree, flowering dogwood, redbud, peach, southern magnolia, loblolly pine, persimmon, and pecan.

Holly leaves and berries

431. What home trees are characteristic of southern Florida? This section of our country, generally free of frost the year round, has some very unusual trees. Among others are the cabbage palm, beefwood, royal poinciana, orange, grapefruit, albizia, papaya, crape myrtle, cypress, slash pine, sapodilla, and fig.

432. What home trees are characteristic of the Northwest? Bigleaf maple, Pacific dogwood, red alder, cottonwood, madrone, Oregon white oak, western red cedar, Sitka spruce, cascara, Oregon myrtle.

433. What home trees are characteristic of the Southwest? One-leaf piñon, piñon pine, saguaro, mesquite, blue palo verde, crucifixion tree, Russian olive, oleander, chinaberry, acacia.

434. What home trees are characteristic of California? California has an abundance of exotic trees that are difficult to surpass anywhere. The coastal strip is similar in climate to that of the Mediterranean and has come to be called the American "Riviera." Here, in particular, flourish some of the country's most beautiful trees. Among many interesting home trees are certain species of eucalyptus, cedar of Lebanon, camphor tree, jacaranda, California juniper, pepper tree, avocado, date palm, lilly-pilly, carob, deodar, lily-of-the-valley tree, almond, olive, and sweet shade.

435. Is there any home tree that can be grown from coast-to-coast? Yes, the trembling aspen. No other tree grows naturally from Maine to California. This tree, a form of poplar, can be easily identified, for its leaves flutter in the slightest breeze.

436. What is the difference between a large shrub and a small tree? No clear-cut distinction can be made. Sometimes plants under eight feet in height are called shrubs, and plants over twenty feet high are called trees. The clearest distinction is that shrubs usually develop several shoots from the root, growing from the base, while a tree develops a single stem or trunk and grows from its upper buds. Some trees, such as witch hazel, alder, and shadblow, may be a shrub in one place and a tree in another.

437. What are some attractive native deciduous trees for the home? Red maple and flowering dogwood are two of the best smaller trees. They are fast-growing and hardy, with red fall foliage. The American larch or tamarack is interesting, with needles that are bluish in spring and yellow in the fall before they drop off. Sassafras is a good choice because of its striking autumn foliage and odd horizontal branching.

The smoke tree, a close relative to sumac, is occasionally used as an ornamental. Among the more beautiful of our smaller trees are the thorns. Washington thorn is the most upright-growing of all. Its red fruit hangs on the tree most of the winter. Cockspur thorn is the most horizontal and has very firm, glossy foliage.

Magnolias with their large, showy, white, pink or purple flowers are excellent ornamentals. Hawthorn is a small, compact tree with eccentric zigzag branches. It has beautiful white or red flowers in the spring and little red "apples" in the fall which add to autumn landscapes.

Mountain ash in cool northern places has the most beautiful cascades of red berries of any of our flowering trees. But these are so bitter that even birds are restrained from eating them. Its leaves are like ferns eight inches long.

Dogwood blossoms

Redbud is best in the Middle West. A wealth of purple flowers springs out of branches and trunk. The leaves are round Valentine hearts.

Scarlet gum eucalyptus is one of the outstanding flame-colored trees for California. It flowers in January and again in the fall.

Goldenrain tree bursts out in great clusters of tiny golden flowers in July. Shadblow is a delicate puff of white flowers in the earliest spring before most other trees are in flower or leaf. Silverbell tree decorates itself in May with bell-shaped, snowy flowers which hang in great rows from the branches.

Among the decorative flowering crabapples, Japanese crabapple has red and white buds which make it particularly attractive. It flowers heavily in May.

438. What are some attractive evergreens for ornamental purposes? Arbor vitae, boxwood, firs, hemlock, American holly, junipers, and cedar. Austrian pine, mugho pine, Scotch pine, and

white pine are also good. Yews are among the most useful evergreens for ornamental use.

**439. What civic-minded association set out to spread the redbud
across two states?**   The Texoma Redbud Association whose aim is
to plant "beauty in hearts" by planting the beautiful redbud tree
through Texas and Oklahoma. In one year alone, 5,000 of the trees
were planted around Lake Texoma, on the state line. The redbud
trail now runs along major highways from Oklahoma to the Gulf
of Mexico.

Redbud leaf

Redbud pods

**440. What are some of the qualifications for the ideal city-street
tree?**   It is long lived and capable of reasonably rapid growth. It is
clean, neat, and resistant to damage by wind or ice loads, and fungus
and insect attack. It is tolerant to dust and smoke, upright in growth,
attractive in shape, and has attractive color foliage in autumn.
It does not raise or break up pavement and clog sewers with its roots.
Its light foliage permits grass to grow in its shade. Actually no tree
fulfills all the requirements of the perfect city-street tree.

**441. What considerations should influence the choice of a street
tree?**   Soil and atmospheric conditions, width of the street, proximity
of the planting area to buildings and overhead wires, density of
vehicular traffic, amount of impervious pavement, and size of planting area available.

**442. What trees best fulfill the requirements for the perfect city-
street tree?**   The pin oak is the most commonly planted and the best
species of oak for city streets. Its smaller size makes it more adaptable

than most other oaks to narrow streets. It is also easily transplanted and becomes established quickly.

Red oak is a good fast-growing oak for street planting in most sections of the country. Moreover, its open growth permits the passage of electric wires through it. Scarlet oak withstands droughts better than other oaks and requires less room than red oak.

American elm is easily transplanted and also becomes established quickly. It needs considerable room, however, so it must be planted on wide streets. London plane prospers in "downtown" areas better than any other standard shade tree. New York City has many in midtown streets, as, for example, in front of Rockefeller Plaza and in the small park behind the New York Public Library on 42nd Street.

The silver linden is especially desirable as a street tree. It grows into a compact specimen, withstands dry, sandy soils, and loses few leaves in summer.

Sweet gum grows well between the curb and walk in some cities. This is an excellent street tree except for the litter of prickly fruits.

The ginkgo, a native of Asia, is one of the most popular park, yard, and street trees—especially in large cities. Among its assets are ability to withstand city conditions, wide tolerance of soil types, ease of transplanting, and remarkable freedom from insect and fungus attack. No wonder this weird tree has come down to us from just after the Coal Age in the same form. Apparently it has become so used to surviving through those millions of years that it can take in its stride carbon monoxide and arid hot pavements and visits of male dogs, which are the chief afflictions of city trees. The narrow upright form (*Ginkgo biloba fastigiata*) is ideal for narrow streets and those bordered by tall buildings. Plant only the male ginkgo tree, for the female develops fruit that falls and has an offensive odor. (See Question 127.)

Honey locust, especially the thornless variety, is a good street tree for larger eastern cities. It is very hardy, grows fairly rapidly, and is resistant to ice, wind, and pests.

Yellowwood is another excellent tree for cities and town.

443. What kind of ordinances regulate the planting of trees on city streets? While similarity exists between the various municipal ordinances, there are also differences in detail. In some cities the planting of trees is undertaken exclusively by the city. In others, as

New York City, the planting of trees is the duty and at the expense of the adjoining property owner. The most common practice is a combination of the two methods.

When trees are set out by private individuals the city regulates what trees may be planted, the location of the tree pit, distances between individual trees, and distances between tree and intersections, traffic lights, street lights, and fire hydrants. There are also rulings against planting trees in front of major entrances to large buildings.

Once the trees are planted, most cities and towns assume responsibility for their care and upkeep, spraying them, pruning them, and removing them if they become a menace.

444. Are any trees forbidden in certain cities as street trees? Poplar, silver maple, box elder, black locust, horsechestnut, Chinese elm, mountain ash, beech, birch, sugar maple, American plane, dogwood, and hornbeam are among those trees which are classified as undesirable big-city street trees.

445. Why are these trees undesirable for city planting? Many of them do not survive in the face of extreme city conditions, such as polluted air, desert aridity of pavements, and adverse soil conditions. Others are not suited for city living because of their shape and susceptibility to disease, insect pests, or because branches of the tree are brittle. Still others cannot stand the pressure of high winds and are a menace to passersby as well as becoming a maintenance problems after storms.

446. Will evergreens thrive in a city? No. Evergreens are covered with an abundance of foliage the year round which demands a steady supply of moisture from the soil to replace water lost constantly through the leaves by transpiration. Evergreens cannot survive in desert-like concrete pavements or in an atmosphere which clogs their leaf pores with dust.

447. Do modern buildings need trees? Almost any type of planting enhances the appearance of a building. With the proper design and selection of trees the building achieves a setting. Trees are beneficial as eye-rests, contrasting softly with the sharp lines and unrelieved starkness of towering walls. Trees also serve to unify the building with surrounding areas when they are attractive, or to block out the surroundings when they are objectionable.

Major or large trees are generally used in front of buildings because they are in scale with it. Minor or small trees, like crabapple, hawthorn, cherry, magnolia, are often used near the entrances or corners of the building.

448. Should different kinds of trees be planted along the same avenue? No. The effect would be spotty and uncomfortable for there would be a series of accents competing with each other for attention. The best plan for unifying and beautifying a street is to plant trees of the same species at fixed intervals.

449. What great capital city is famous for its trees? Paris, France. Rows of horsechestnuts and lindens along with the historic avenues have made this city world famous as a center of beauty, especially in the spring. This is the direct result of imaginative and well-maintained tree planting. London and Washington also enjoy reputations for their handsome trees.

450. Are nut trees desirable street trees? No. Nut trees such as walnuts and filberts have a great nuisance value when their fruit falls. For the same reason fruit trees are poor street trees.

Flower of southern magnolia

451. What is the order of flowering of some popular home trees? In April: star magnolia, red maple, Japanese cherry, and sassafras, hornbeam and shadblow. May: flowering plant redbud, horsechestnut, flowering dogwood, tulip tree and goldenchain. Southern magnolia, sweetbay and American linden bloom in June, followed in July by goldenrain tree, sourwood, Japanese tree lilac. In August: Chinese scholartree, Java sumac; and in September, the *Franklinia* (called *Gordonia* in England).

452. What is the history of the famous cherry trees in Washington, D.C.? In 1903 the Division of Foreign Plant Introduction of the Bureau of Plant Industry received from Japan as a gift through David Fairchild and Barbour Lathrop thirty named varieties of flowering cherry. In 1912, through the generosity of the city of Tokyo more than two thousand trees were presented to the city of Washington by Yakio Azaki, Mayor of Tokyo.

453. How did we get our home trees that came from foreign countries? Botanical gardens and the United States Department of Agriculture sent plant hunters to remote corners of the world.

454. When did the profession of worldwide plant explorer begin? Around 1800 the development of big English and continental estate gardens awakened interest in the trees of other lands.

455. Who were some leading American plant hunters? Ernest H. Wilson (1876–1930) traveled on three expeditions to China and to Japan, Korea, Formosa, South Africa, Australia, India, New Zealand, and Tasmania. He was responsible for introducing the dove tree (western China), the tea crab apple (China), and the Chinese dogwood, among many others.

George Forrest (1873–1932) was another famed plant explorer. Between 1904 and 1932 he made seven expeditions to Yunnan and southeastern Tibet. He brought back and introduced to the Western Hemisphere the Forrest fir (China) and the Yunnan crab apple (western China).

Frank Nickolus Meyer (1875–1918) made four expeditions to Asia for the United States Department of Agriculture. He was responsible for bringing back the lace-bark pine from Shansi, China, and the dwarf or Siberian "Chinese" elm from near Peking in 1908.

David Fairchild (1869–1954) was a giant among the many worldwide plant explorers and is credited with having done more for American agriculture than any other single person. His travels girded the world's hemispheres. A few of the trees he introduced are the tung-oil trees from Hankow, China, in 1904; many varieties of the date tree from Egypt, the Persian Gulf, and Baghdad in 1901–1902; and many varieties of the flowering cherry from Japan in 1902.

456. What methods are used to propagate decorative trees? Seeds and various vegetative techniques, such as hard and softwood cuttings, layering, grafting, budding and mist propagation.

457. What is the most universal method of propagation? Growing plants from seeds. It is also the least expensive.

458. How does vegetative propagation differ from seed propagation? Seed propagation is basically a sexual process involving the union of sperm and egg cells produced in flowers before seeds are fertilized and formed. Vegetative methods use stems, roots and buds which take root without sex cells.

459. What is the principle behind vegetative propagation? The capacity of plants to regenerate themselves. Every plant is made up of living cells and each cell has all the characteristics (chromosomes) of the entire plant. Under the right conditions a slip from a branch or a piece of wood can regenerate the lost parts.

460. Why resort to vegetative propagation techniques? Vegetative methods offer a way to propagate trees that are sterile and bear no seeds. The resulting plants duplicate the plants from which they come. For example, there are some hybrids which cannot produce seed and other hybrids which have abundant seed. Yet plants grown from such hybrid seeds do not resemble the parent. They tend to revert to the wild ancestor. To perpetuate the hybrid characteristics vegetative methods are used.

The vegetative techniques also produce quicker results than would be obtained from planting seeds. Trees reach flowering and fruiting faster.

461. What is a hybrid plant? A plant produced by interbreeding or cross-fertilization, whose parentage is complicated and whose characteristics are not fixed. Thus hybrid plants must be propagated by asexual or vegetative methods, not by seeds.

462. Is there such a thing as natural tree hybrids? Yes. Many are known. For example, in the fir family there are 3 known natural hybrids, and in the maple, 9. The buckeye has 11; the alder, 8; hickory, 7; dogwood, 5; hawthorn, 5; cypress, 1; magnolia, 5; spruce, 6; elm, 6; and in the oak family 77 natural hybrid species have been recognized.

463. What is a cutting? Any part of a stem of twig severed from a tree is a cutting.

464. How are cuttings used in vegetative propagation? Cuttings, when properly taken from the tree and planted in moist soil or sandy loam (or merely water), will root and grow into a tree resembling the tree from which they were cut.

465. What is the advantage of using cuttings to propagate plants? Cuttings are a marvelously rapid method of propagating plants which root easily. It is also one of the oldest and simplest methods used.

466. What produces the new roots of a cutting? The food stored in the stem and remaining leaves stimulates cells constantly in contact with water to produce roots.

467. What is the difference between a "softwood" cutting and a "hardwood" cutting? The difference lies not in the type of parent plant used, but in the degree of maturity of the tissue in the plant part that has been selected for a cutting. It does not refer to the lumberman's division of trees into softwoods and hardwoods. Criteria used to distinguish between softwood and hardwood cuttings are the stage of growth as determined by the presence or absence of foliage, and the degree of lignification (conversion into wood) of the stems.

Softwood or "greenwood" cuttings are made from plants still actively making or just having completed growth, when tissues are still relatively soft. Hardwood or "mature" cuttings are made from the ripe wood of the past season's growth or even older wood.

468. When are softwood cuttings taken? In the spring and summer, when tissues are soft. Slips one to three inches are cut from the tip of a shoot, below a node. Growth activity is considered greater at nodes, and rootings at these points are more reliable.

469. What is a node? A node is the place on a twig where a leaf is attached to its stem, or a bud to its twig.

470. When are hardwood cuttings taken? Any time in the fall, winter or early spring when leaves have dropped and tissues are fully matured. Cuttings are usually about six inches in length, tied in bunches of 50 or 100, and stored over the winter before spring planting.

471. What is the advantage of storing hardwood cuttings? The chief advantage is that the cut surface at the base of the cane forms a callus before planting time. Possible winter injury is avoided, and the cuttings may be held for favorable outdoor weather.

472. Can hardwood and softwood cuttings be taken from the same tree? Yes, at the appropriate times of the year.

473. What are some home trees that can be successfully rooted from softwood cuttings? Cedar, red bud, false cypress, dogwood, hawthorn, olive, silverbell, sweetgum, tulip tree, magnolia, crabapple, poplar, arbor vitae, locust, willow, elder, elm, ginkgo, Asiatic maple.

Silvery dogwood bud can be seen in fall and winter

474. What are some home trees that can be rooted from hardwood cuttings? Japanese flowering quince, willow, alder, false cypress, dogwood, hawthorn, olive, poplar, willow, elm.

475. How are evergreens usually propagated? Many of the coniferous evergreens are propagated from cuttings since they do not come true from seed. But varieties of pines, hemlocks, firs and spruces that do not root easily from cuttings are best propagated by grafting.

476. What is layering? Layering is the technique of rooting plants while they are still attached to the parent plant. Separation does not occur until after the plant has been rooted. Layering is one of the oldest propagation practices and can be traced back to ancient China. This practice is used when neither seed, grafting, budding, nor cuttings are effective.

477. What is mist propagation? Mist propagation is a new type of vegetative propagation. It is a technique that roots softwood cuttings under a fine mist of water, with faster results than the ordinary softwood cutting method.

478. What is grafting? Grafting involves the transfer of a scion or twig of a desired variety to be propagated, to the stock or seedling plant which supplies the roots of the new plant.

479. Is the stock referred to by any other name? Yes. The stock or seedling on which the grafting operation is performed is also called rootstock or understock.

480. Why does grafting work? When the actively growing tissue of the scion is brought into proper contact with similar growing tissue of the stock, they unite, heal and grow as one tree. The root system of the stock will develop and support the scion, which grows into the trunk and branches.

481. When is it used? Grafting is used to propagate hybrids which do not reproduce true specimens from seeds, or do not readily develop roots from cuttings. This includes, for example, some evergreen and ornamental trees, nut trees, and most fruit trees.

482. Is grafting easy? Yes, particularly the method called whip (fresh young shoot) grafting. Grafting young nursery scions to root systems by whip grafting has a high percentage of success.

483. What is budding? Budding is a form of grafting whereby a bud instead of a twig is transferred to another tree.

484. What trees are usually propagated by bud grafting? The stone fruits—peach, plum and cherry tree.

485. Can new varieties be created through grafting? No. Rootstock and scion are known to influence one another and the relationship between the two is under extensive study, but no generic changes are produced by grafting.

In general, rootstocks exert more influence on scions than scions on rootstock. Use is made of this knowledge, for example, in dwarfing trees where certain rootstocks are known to have a dwarfing influence on the scions.

486. Is grafting successful between trees of different species? No. Compatibility between scion and stock of closely related trees is essential. For example, graft plum on plum, cherry on cherry, and so forth. For strong growth of apples, grafts may be made between varieties such as Red Delicious, McIntosh, Rome or Winesap.

487. Can large trees be grafted? Yes. The method used is called cleft grafting. The branches of the entire mature tree are eventually grafted, but the operation must be spaced the first year. The top of the tree is grafted at the outset, followed by working the sides and lower portion the following years.

488. What trees are never grown on their own roots? Cultivated fruit trees. In this case the rootstock is a small seedling from a tree which, if allowed to mature, would produce worthless fruit. The scion is of a desired variety that is to be propagated.

489. What is a dwarf fruit tree? One grown on rootstock which dwarfs it.

490. What rootstocks are used to dwarf a tree? They are selected from seedlings whose parents have shown definite dwarfing habits.

491. What are the advantages of dwarf fruit trees over standard trees in the home garden? Dwarfs are quick growing, usually beginning to bear fruit one to two years earlier than standard trees. Several varieties of fruit can be grown to give a succession of fruit ripening throughout the season in the space required for standard trees.

The size of the fruit is as large as, if not larger than, the fruit of standard trees, and dwarfs generally produce sweeter, better-colored, better flavored, and earlier-maturing fruit. They can be more easily protected by fungicide-insecticide dust; old-fashioned large standard trees are difficult to dust and spray.

All the work around dwarfs can be done without need of orchard machinery. They may be transplanted successfully at any age because of their relatively small size and the fibrous nature of their roots. Dwarfs may be grown on land that has not sufficient depth for the root systems of standard trees. Another great advantage is the ease with which dwarfs can be protected by windbreaks, wrapping and covers in cold weather.

Besides being desirable for their fruit, dwarf fruits blossom beautifully and make an ideal tree for the small home garden, where large standard trees are out of proportion with the limited space.

492. What are some of the dwarf fruits for a very small home garden? The most desirable varieties of dwarf apples, pears, peaches, apricots, nectarines, plums and cherries.

493. Which kind of dwarf fruit tree has the most varieties? The apple.

494. What apple dwarfing stock is in demand for growing dwarf apple trees? The Malling IX.

495. What varieties of apple can be grown on Malling IX stock? All varieties of apple can be grown as extreme dwarfs on this stock.

496. How did this rootstock come to be named Malling? The East Malling Fruit Research Station, East Malling, Kent, England, has done extensive research in the study of rootstocks. The station has developed and classified a series of rootstocks, among them the Malling IX, which give different degrees of dwarfing for apple trees.

497. What dwarf apple varieties are well-adapted for the northern states? McIntosh, Northern Spy, Rhode Island Greening and Wealthy.

498. What dwarf apple varieties are well adapted to southern and midwestern states? Delicious, Golden Delicious, Stayman Winesap and Jonathan.

499. What dwarf apple varieties have a wide range? Lodi, Yellow Transparent, Early McIntosh and Gravenstein.

500. How can the best variety of dwarf fruits be selected for a particular locality? Choose varieties developed for your locality and tested and recommended by your state agricultural station.

501. What are some of the best eating-apple varieties? The McIntosh, Delicious, Northern Spy, Sandow, Winesap, Jonathan. Also the Golden Delicious, Grimes Golden, Melba, Astrachan, and Lodi.

502. What apple has won awards as the best sweet apple? The Sweet McIntosh.

503. What kind of apple makes the best apple pie? The Newtown Pippin and Jonathan are classic pie apples because the cooked slices hold their form well.

504. What are some good cooking apples? Almost all varieties, except the Delicious. The Gravenstein is an excellent autumn cooking apple. The Rome Beauty, Fameuse, Melba, Lodi, Northern Spy, and Sandow are also good culinary apples.

505. What variety of the cherry is excellent for pie? The Montmorency variety is the most popular and important sour cherry grown.

506. Can many varieties of tree fruits be grafted into the same tree? Yes. A home gardener who wants to save space and at the same time grow many varieties of fruit trees in his garden can graft a number of varieties into the same tree. One branch, in fact, will supply the average person with an adequate supply of a particular variety.

507. Can many dwarfs be grown successfully north of the so-called "peach belt"? Yes. It goes without saying that the apple varieties "belong" in the northern regions. But peaches, nectarines, sweet cherries, apricots, and the tender varieties of plums and French pears can be grown many miles north of the peach belt also. To accomplish this, care must be given to the proper selection of rootstocks, the kinds and varieties of fruit budded into them, and measures taken for winter protection.

508. How do eating apples differ from crabapples? Eating apples are all grafted stock, running true to the species. The common cultivated varieties of the apple tree are directly descended from the crabapple.

509. What is a crabapple? It is the original, wild tree. Our native crabapples are stunted and produce small, sour apples better for jelly than for eating. For hybrids see Questions 519–522.

510. What is a good recipe for crabapple jelly? Here is a good recipe for crabapple jelly with purity, delicious taste and beautiful color: Select only whole crabapples. Remove overripe ones. If you wish, cut crabapples in half and remove stems, but this is not necessary. Wash thoroughly and place fruit in a large kettle. Cover with water. In an open kettle boil rapidly until fruit is tender, perhaps 15 minutes. Place fruit in a jelly bag, which can be a strong flour or sugar sack made of cotton. Hang the bag from towel rack or faucet so that the juice drips from a corner of the bag into a kettle. A good process is to let it drip overnight. For crystal clear jelly do not squeeze bag. However, this is not too important. A second dripping and squeezing for a second extraction can of course give more juice, even if it does become clouded. This is done by placing pulp in saucepan, adding more water, boiling about ten minutes, and putting in jelly bag for a second extraction.

For making the jelly add ⅔ cup of sugar to every cup of juice. Boil sugar and juice. Have glasses washed and sterilized because crabapple juice jellies quickly. With a jelly thermometer boil the juice until the thermometer registers 220 degrees. An old-fashioned method of testing to see whether the juice has jelled is to put a spoonful of juice in a flat saucer. Place in the icebox for a few minutes. To test, tip the saucer. If the contents seem solidified or adhere together in sheets over the saucer, the jelly is jelled. Pour into glasses and seal with paraffin.

511. Can trees be grown against a wall?   Yes. Gardeners use specially trained trees for decorative purposes grown flat against a wall. Light trellises may be employed, but generally the wall trees are either fastened directly to the wall or tied to a grid of wires fastened to nails in the wall. They are called espalier trees.

512. What are the shape and size requirements of an espalier? The espalier should be trained both in size and shape to add interest to the supporting wall. In general, it is wise not to cover the wall completely. Espaliers can be trained in interesting patterns, complementing and highlighting the texture and structure of the wall itself. Fan shape, for example, is simple and artistic.

513. What trees lend themselves well as espaliers?   Sweet bay and saucer magnolias are good. The small size and long, wandlike branches of the tea crab make it particularly adaptable, and viburnums in variety do well. Honeysuckle may also be used.

Dwarf peaches, nectarines and apricots lend themselves well to being trained in fan shape against walls. The Amsden June peach is one that is particularly ornamental as well as producing abundant fruit.

514. What is topiary?   Old-fashioned tree sculpturing made by clipping trees to form symmetrical or grotesque shapes, or the forms of animals and birds.

515. What trees are best for topiary?   Box and yew, and hemlock which thickens when it is clipped.

516. When was topiary in fashion?   It started in England in Tudor times, and this style of gardening was at its height in the reign of William and Mary, later adorning the gardens of the 18th century.

517. What great English poet thought that topiary was a violation of nature? Alexander Pope made the following satirical comment: "An eminent town gardener has arrived at such perfection that he cuts family pieces of men, women, or children in trees. Adam and Eve in yew, Adam a little shattered by the fall of the tree of knowledge in the great storm. Eve and the Serpent very flourishing; St. George in the boxtree, his arm scarce long enough, but will be in condition to stick the dragon by next April; a green dragon of the same with a tail of ground ivy for the present. A quickset hog, shot up into a porcupine, but it's being forgot a week in rainy weather . . ."

518. When was interest reawakened in the crabapple tree? During the first two or three decades of the 20th century interest in crabapples was scant. Since 1930, however, there has been a tremendous change, when the ornamental value of crabapples was recognized.

519. How many varieties of the crabapple are available in the nurseries of this country? Nearly 150 varieties.

520. What are some of the fine flowering crabapples? Japanese flowering crab was the first of the Asiatic crabs introduced into the western world about 1780, followed by Arnold crab, Manchurian crab, Sargent crab, Siberian crab, and tea crab.

521. What are some outstanding new crabapple varieties? Red Jade has slender, drooping branches with masses of small, red fruits. Katherine, with double white blossoms; Van Eseltine with large rose-pink blossoms. Liset (hybrid of Lemoine crabapple) has deep-purple red flowers; Red Bud, which is a red-fruited crab, and Winter Gold, a yellow-fruited crab.

522. Where do our most beautiful flowering crabapples come from? Some of the plants have originated in the wild here in America, for instance, the Bechtel crabapple. It was found in an old fence row near Staunton, Illinois, between 1840 and 1850. It had beautiful double flowers while all the other prairie crabapples had single flowers. Another, the Charlotte crabapple, was discovered in a pasture about 1902, in Waukegan, Illinois.

Some of our best Oriental crabapples were introduced directly from their native habitats in the Orient. Many were brought over to America by the Arnold Arboretum (Jamaica Plain, Massachusetts) as a result of trips made by E. H. Wilson and Charles Sprague Sargent. The Chinese flowering crabapple has not been found in the wild in China or Japan, but has come to us through the efforts of uncounted generations of Oriental gardeners.

The Siberian crabapple was brought to America from England as seed and was crossed with large, hardier apple types to produce an apple that could withstand the temperature of northern United States and Canada. Many hybrid varieties are now available that are the result of experimentation in the United States, Canada, and Europe.

523. What is a pleasant verse to memorize about an apple tree?
"The Wayside Inn—an Apple Tree." (Free translation of a German poem. Author unknown.)

> I halted at a pleasant inn,
>   As I my way was wending,
> A golden apple was the sign,
>   From a knotty bow depending.
>
> Mine host—it was an apple tree—
>   He smilingly received me,
> And spread his choicest, sweetest fruit
>   To strengthen and relieve me.
>
> Full many a little feathered guest
>   Came through his branches springing.
> They hopped and flew from spray to spray,
>   Their notes of gladness singing.
>
> Beneath his shade I laid me down,
>   And slumber sweet possessed me:
> The soft wind blowing through the leaves
>   With whispers low caressed me.
>
> And when I rose and would have paid
>   My host so open-hearted,
> He only shook his lofty head.
>   I blessed him and departed.

524. What very famous tree was cut down in 1820?   It was an old apple tree in England, cut down to preserve its wood from decay. Under its branches 150 years earlier Isaac Newton, observing an apple fall, was inspired to propound the universal law of gravitation.

525. When can sugar maple be tapped for sugar sap?   In early spring, while snow may be still deep in the sugar bush. Boiling it down we get American maple syrup and maple sugar. It is interesting to note that after the pipe which taps the sap is driven into the trunk, the wood itself acts as a pump by expanding during sunlit days and contracting during cold nights.

526. Are strains of the sugar maple bred to produce more or better sugar?   No. Trees tapped for maple sugar are just as they are found in the wild. No important effort has been made to select, breed, or graft better sugar trees because the wild trees are so good, and because it takes some forty years to get a good run of high-quality sap. (See Questions 600 and 601.)

527. What are some trees that grow well by the seaside?   Quaking aspen, paper birch, English hawthorn, honeylocust, red maple, red oak, sassafras, oleander, loquat, willow.

528. What trees make good hedges?   European beech, camphor tree, black thorn, arbor vitae, Japanese yew, hemlock, oleander, honeylocust, English hawthorn, European hornbeam. Osage orange is fine where thorns are wanted.

529. Can trees be patented?   A patent can be obtained under certain circumstances. For example, after they had worked for many years to produce a weeping crabapple called Red Jade, a patent was issued to the Brooklyn Botanic Garden.

530. Is there a flowering tree that blooms twice a year?   Yes, the Glastonbury thorn, planted from a cutting of the original English Glastonbury thorn on the grounds of Washington Cathedral, Washington, D.C., in 1901. It blooms in May and November.

Legend also has it that the Glastonbury thorn blooms whenever royalty is near. And so it did when the Prince of Wales visited Washington Cathedral, November 1919, and again when Queen Elizabeth II arrived in Washington in November 1951.

Trees grown from seeds of the Glastonbury do not bloom twice a year; only trees propagated from cuttings.

531. What is Bonsai? Bonsai is the art of dwarfing trees and training them to be replicas in everything but size of century-old specimens.

532. Can Bonsai trees be created at home? Yes, with patience and care. In a sense, Bonsai are pictures, created from a mental image and patterned after nature. Yet these pictures live, and need much attention to thrive and be trained.

533. In what are Bonsai trees grown? They are grown in comparatively small containers, simple in design, and are kept pot-bound always. There should be a hole in the base of the pot for drainage.

534. What is the correct proportion between size of Bonsai tree and size of container? Generally speaking, the ideal artistic proportion measures the tree four times the height of the container, or an 80–20 ratio. With certain lower and spreading Bonsai a ratio of 60–40 is good.

535. Do trees trained as Bonsai show the changes of the seasons? Yes. For example, the Japanese flowering cherry and flowering apricot bloom in the spring. Maples have green foliage in the summer and autumn colors in the fall. Other deciduous trees, as the elm, display their interesting barren branch structure in mood with winter.

536. Is there a particularly fine collection of Japanese Bonsai in the United States? Yes, at the Arnold Arboretum, Harvard University. This unique collection, known as the Larz Anderson Collection, numbers twenty-three trees ranging in age from 52 to 217 years and in height from 13 to 42 inches, with a spread of from one to six feet. The oldest, Hinoki False Cypress (*Chamaecyparis obtusa*), is 217 years old, with a spread of 6 feet and a height of 30 inches. The collection was donated to the Arboretum in 1937 by Mrs. Larz Anderson as a memorial to her husband's great friend, Charles Sprague Sargent, the Arboretum's first director.

537. What are some good books on Bonsai? *Bonsai: Miniature Trees,* by Claude Chidamian (Princeton, New Jersey: Van Nostrand, 1955. 96 pages). *Bonsai* (Tokyo, Japan: Sanseido, 1954. 172 pages). Though the text of this book is in Japanese, there are 116 pages of pictures of fine examples of Bonsai. *Handbook on Dwarfed Potted Trees: the Bonsai of Japan* (Brooklyn Botanic Garden Handbook, Vol. 9, No. 3). *The Art of Growing Miniature Trees, Plants and Landscapes,* by Tatsuo Ishimoto (New York: Crown Publishers, 1956). *The Japanese Art of Miniature Trees and Landscapes; Their Creation, Care, and Enjoyment,* by Yuji Yoshimura and Giovanna M. Halford. (Rutland, Vermont: Charles E. Tuttle Company, 1957.)

538. Can great forest trees be trained to grow in pots? Yes. Maples, elms, and others are the same species as forest trees. When trained this way they are called Bonsai.

539. Where did the art of Bonsai originate? In Japan. It is one of Japan's finest contributions to horticulture.

540. Is Bonsai an ancient art? Yes. The earliest authentic record of Bonsai is found on a Japanese scroll of 1310, with pictures of dwarfed trees in containers.

541. Is there a philosophy behind the Japanese art of Bonsai? Very definitely, and one deeply rooted in Japanese tradition and its love of truth, beauty and life as expressed through nature. Bonsai embodies an outlook, a spirit, the art of practicing patience and unhurried deliberation amid the rapid pace of daily life. Bonsai lovers feel such discipline is nobly rewarded by mental alertness, good health and peace of mind.

542. What kind of trees are used for Bonsai? Most woody plants can be used, including maple, bamboo, cherry, pine, holly, oak, azalea, juniper and many others.

543. How long does it take to create a Bonsai? In general, a genuine Bonsai takes from 50 to 100 years. However, by twisting the trunk and restraining growth of tops and roots, a comparatively young plant can appear aged.

544. What is the principle underlying all training of dwarf trees?
If branches and roots are vigorously restrained from developing
rapidly, the tree becomes dwarfed.

545. How long may a Bonsai live?   A Bonsai tree may well live
through three generations of man. Naturally dwarfed trees can be
seen in the Arctic or on mountain tops where bright light, cold winds,
shallow rocky ground dwarf trees that are hundred of years old.

**546. Are hardy young trees in the wild better for transplanting
than nursery seedlings of the same species?**   Nursery-grown stock
transplants better than wild stock because of the more compact,
bunchy, and well distributed root systems which result from nursery
care, such as transplanting at intervals, pruning roots, spacing and
cultivation.

   The root systems of wild trees have been allowed to spread at
random and when transplanted too much of the root system is broken.
In transplanting sassafras, for example, best results are obtained when
nursery trees are used because of its long, single taproot.

547. Why should special care be taken when transplanting trees?
Transplanting a tree can be likened to performing a serious operation. It shocks the tree and disturbs its normal, natural functioning.
The older and larger the tree, the greater the shock. Special attention
should be given to state of health, age, size, and adaptability, as well
as careful handling.

**548. What are a few important points to remember when trans-
planting trees?**   Effort should be made to save from injury as many
of the tender, cottony hairs at the root tips as possible. Since many
roots are unavoidably severed and lost in digging up, the crown of
the tree must be brought into balance with the root system by pruning
the branches or twigs back proportionately. The tree should be re-
planted at the same depth as it grew previously. Broken or bruised
roots should be pruned, and roots should have ample room to spread
out in their natural position. The phrase "Dig a $5 hole for a $2
tree" is good advice.

   Conditions must also be provided in replanting to make it as
easy as possible for the roots to resume their natural functions. Before

selecting a site, attention should be given to the light requirements of the tree. Does it, for example, grow best in full sunshine, partial shade, or shade with little direct sunshine? The best time of year to undertake transplanting is another question that should be asked. The soil requirements of a particular tree are important. Does it, for example, prefer sweet soil, acid soil or peaty soil?

549. What is the best size of tree to transplant?   The best trees are young trees: deciduous trees from 6 to 8 feet tall; evergreens 2 to 5 feet tall.

550. When is the best time to transplant deciduous trees?   These trees may be moved in the dormant periods of fall and early spring, but not during the active growing season. Early in the spring, however, before new growth begins, is the most favorable time to transplant large or small trees.

551. Are there any deciduous trees that should be transplanted in the spring only?   Yes. Certain trees, more difficult to transplant than others, should be moved only in the spring. The flowering dogwood is one common lawn tree that prefers springtime transplanting. This is because of its inherent difficulty to become established in a new site unless it has a chance to make immediate root growth.

Other difficult trees that should be moved principally in the spring are the American holly, beech, sweetgum, yellowwood, birch, black tupelo, chinaberry, crape myrtle, Japanese maple, dogwood, Eastern redbud, hickory, goldenchain, magnolia, sassafras, sourwood, snowbell, tulip tree, walnut. If these trees are root pruned a year prior to transplanting, and moved by the ball-and-burlap method, success is more certain.

552. What trees usually transplant easily?   Honeylocust, catalpa, hawthorn, willow, apple—including flowering crabapple—American elm, European linden, ginkgo, hackberry, most of the maples, red and scarlet oak, and honeylocust.

553. When is the best time of year to transplant evergreens?   Evergreens are best moved when root growth is most likely to take place rapidly, a period extending from late summer or fall until one month before heavy frost.

554. Why is it essential to transplant evergreens at a time when their roots can grow rapidly? The ever-present foliage of the evergreen demands moisture for evaporation which must always be supplied. New root growth at the time of transplanting is imperative to supply the demands of foliage for moisture constantly being lost through transpiration.

555. What are the two methods commonly used to transplant trees? The bare-root method, where the soil is removed from the roots leaving them naked, and the ball-and-burlap method, where the tree is lifted with its root system encased in a ball of soil held together by a strong, light material like burlap.

556. What trees are transplanted by the bare-root method? Only young and thriving deciduous trees up to four or five inches in diameter. The naked roots must be protected and not exposed to direct sunlight. Transplanting on a cloudy day is preferable.

557. What trees are transplanted by the ball-and-burlap method? This method is used for moving all evergreens, coniferous and broadleaf, and certain deciduous trees that are difficult to transplant. Older and larger trees with a trunk diameter of six inches or more should also be transplanted with a ball of earth.

558. What determines the size of the ball of earth? The size of the tree. A ball of earth eight to ten times the diameter of the tree trunk should be moved with the tree.

559. Why are evergreens always transplanted by the ball-and-burlap method? Evergreens are much more likely to dry out than deciduous trees because their foliage is always active and need a correspondingly larger and steady amount of moisture.

560. Can wild trees be successfully transplanted? A young tree can be transplanted. Avoid jerking it out of the ground, but trench around the roots and take care not to damage them more than necessary. Put it in a place with about the same amount of sunlight or shade as where it was growing, and mulch under it with the same kind of leaves until it takes hold. Trim back the top to balance severe root loss. Then wait patiently for several years for it to recover and look attractive. In the wild, trees have their roots entangled with many roots of surrounding plants. Nursery stock is much better because roots are bunchy, and the tree has been spaced and pruned with routine nursery care to make it transplant readily.

561. Why prune a tree?　Pruning is done for several reasons, but it should never be done unless the reason is valid. Proper pruning helps to keep a tree symmetrical and beautiful, an aid to bringing out and highlighting the natural characteristics of a tree. Broken, diseased branches must also be pruned in such a way as to promote healing and keep the tree in top health.

Proper pruning also promotes fruit production by invigorating the portion of the fruit tree that remains. Another function is to thin the canopy of a large tree to reduce wind resistance so that a tree may better withstand heavy storms.

Pruning is often necessary in transplanting to balance the crown with a root system reduced in size. Some tall, spindly trees need to be pruned at the top in order to produce new twig or branch growth.

562. What is the principle underlying good pruning?　The proof of a good pruning job is the absence of conspicuous evidence that any pruning was ever done.

563. When is the proper time to prune a tree?　Trees may be pruned at any time, but it is best to avoid severe winter weather and the short period in spring when the sap is rising rapidly before buds open.

564. What are the best tree fertilizers?　Many chemical elements are recognized as essential to plant growth. Most average soils have enough of these, except for nitrogen, phosphorous, potassium, and sometimes magnesium and lime. For fertilizers recommended for particular localities consult a United States Agricultural Experimental Station, the state department of agriculture, or a local forester.

565. Is overstimulation caused by excessive fertilizing harmful?
Yes. Overstimulation may cause vigorous soft growth which is more
susceptible than normal growth to disease. Rapid growth that does
not mature before freezing weather is subject to injury.

**566. Should evergreen leaves or needles be raked from under the
tree?** No. They should be permitted to rot. One of the most common
defects in soil of residential areas is deficiency in organic matter,
residue from decay of plant tissues. Litter of plant materials on the
ground is the foundation of fertile humus.

**567. Besides their cheery companionship, are birds desirable
among home trees?** In addition to the beauty, melody, and vibrant
life which birds bring, they add loveliness to flower, fruit and foliage
through their destruction of insect pests and weeds. It is well established that birds are of great economic value, helping nature achieve
and maintain a balance between vegetable and insect life.

**568. What is the figure placed by the United States Department of
Agriculture on the value of birds in destroying insects?** $350
million dollars annually.

**569. Has a monument ever been erected and dedicated in grati-
tude to birds?** Yes. It is said to be the only monument erected for
this purpose in the world. The Mormons had it built in Salt Lake
City after gulls by the thousands from the islands in Great Salt Lake
intervened in time to save a rich and needed harvest of potatoes, corn,
wheat, beans, peas, and oats from annihilation by grasshoppers. But
a good home tree is the kind of monument which the birds like best.

570. What makes a tree attractive to birds? Fruit and berry trees
attract the largest number of birds who look to the flowers and
fruit for food and foliage. Many seek out trees in search of insects.
Others depend on the seeds of trees for their food. Some birds, like
the vireos, feed exclusively on insects during the greater part of
the year and to some extent upon fruit and seed-bearing trees in
spring and autumn. Birds are also attracted to trees like the red
cedar, whose dense foliage offers concealment and an ideal site for
nesting.

571. What bird is extremely adaptable and feels at home almost anywhere?   The robin is known to eat at least forty different kinds of wild fruits, and nests in a great variety of trees.

572. Do any birds nest exclusively in one kind of tree?   The piñon jay nests in the piñon pine so exclusively that it takes the same name.

573. What kind of trees are apt to attract what birds?   The hemlock's low widespreading branches afford shelter for ground-feeding birds. Small hemlock seeds attract the crossbill in the winter, and also the sharptailed grouse, chickadee, pine siskin and ruffled grouse.

Red cedar (a juniper) is a valuable tree for a bird haven. Its dense evergreen foliage forms a snug shelter for birds in the stormiest weather. The blue berry-like fruit of the red cedar is eaten by many birds, among them the most valuable in the garden: robin, bluebird, mockingbird, cedar waxwing and flicker. Winter birds such as the myrtle warbler, purple finches, or that rare northerner, the pine grosbeak, also seek out the red cedar.

It is said that ninety-three kinds of birds are attracted to flowering dogwood. Its brilliant red fruits last late into the fall. Watch for song sparrow, thrushes, catbird, and brown thrasher.

The snow-white flowering of the shadbush in the spring, followed by purple apple-like fruits later in the season, attracts a long list of birds. A few of these are the flicker, oriole, cedar waxwing, veery and robin.

If only two trees can be planted to attract birds in the home yard, plant red cedar and the mulberry fruit tree. The mulberry has such a bounty of fruit that it can feed numerous birds. Over fifty species flock to it, including all the fruit-eating species and several which seldom eat fruit, including the vireo, song sparrow, yellow-billed cuckoo and cardinal.

Excepting mulberry, the tall elder shrub is about the best of the wild fruits to attract birds. It beckons the flicker and woodpecker, bluebird, and thrush, among the more than one hundred different kinds of birds known to eat at this table.

American elm has a favorite tenant, the Baltimore oriole, which usually builds its nest near the end of a swaying branch. A few other birds, such as the prairie hen and the rose-breasted grosbeak, feed to some extent upon the buds of the elm, which serves as a natural, and in many cases advantageous, pruning process.

Crabapples, particularly Asiatic crabs which are more immune to disease than the native crab, hold their fruits well into winter, and therefore make a most desirable refuge for winter birds, including cedar waxwings. Hackberry bears fruit greatly loved by more than fifty different kinds of birds.

Hackberry leaf and seed

Mountain ash (a northern tree) also carries its fruit a long season, from July to late March, and attracts among others the cedar waxwing, catbird, robin, redheaded woodpecker, several grosbeaks, thrasher, Baltimore oriole.

Seventy-four birds are listed as eating the fruits of wild cherry, which seem to be preferred to cultivated cherries. The wild red cherry (*Prunus pensylvanica*) fruits early and attracts birds which, in turn, afford protection to other cherries in the orchard.

Fruit of black cherry

Hawthorns have little red apples in the fall which the goldfinch, cardinal, cedar waxwing and robin are crazy about.

Norway spruce's best bird friend is red crossbill. The Purple finch, goldfinch, and pine siskin flock to it in the spring. Myrtle warblers may be seen there all seasons, but most frequently during spring migration. Robins and chipping sparrows nest there. Cape May warblers hunt out Norway spruce the last weeks of September, followed by the chickadee, brown creeper and golden-crowned kinglet who stay the winter.

American holly's red berries catch the eyes of kingbird, catbird, bluebird, orchard oriole, and hermit thrush. Sassafras beckons to bobwhite, catbird, kingbird, red-eyed vireo, woodpecker, and flycatcher, all of which like its fruit. Both holly and sassafras are trees of thickets which enhance their appeal to birds.

The arbor vitae, alder, birch, red maple, oak, persimmon, white pine, red bud, tulip tree, sweetgum, and sycamore are also good bird trees.

574. What bird walks down a tree trunk head-first? The white-breasted nuthatch, the only bird with this accomplishment. He also walks sideways and upward, too, searching every part of the bark with his sharp-pointed bill for insects, larvae, and insect eyes.

575. Why is it especially important to plant trees to attract birds in winter? In summer birds usually have no feeding problem. In fall and winter, however, the food supply diminishes, and late winter brings actual scarcity. This is the critical time of year for many birds.

576. What trees retain fruits and berries long into the winter? Red cedar, hackberry, thorn apple, flowering apple, mountain ash, holly, dogwood, sour gum and persimmon.

577. What trees are attractive to birds strictly for their seeds? The alders and birches have seeds in their cones which are eagerly sought by the red poll, siskin and goldfinch.

The winged seeds of ash and boxelder are eaten by pine and evening grosbeaks, while early seeds of the elm are spring cafeterias for goldfinches and purple finches. Larch, pine, and other conifers attract piñon jay, crossbill, pine siskin and pine warbler.

Acorns and nuts of oaks and beeches are so important to woodpeckers and jays as often to influence the distribution of these birds, especially in winter.

578. What family of birds is particularly valuable in the amount of weed seeds they eat? The finch family, which includes the sparrow, grosbeak, goldfinch, bunting. Finches have short, conical bills designed for eating little seeds.

579. What birds go after insects in trees? Brown thrasher destroys May beetles, army worms, cankerworms, cutworms, tent and gypsy-moth caterpillars, and grasshoppers. Cardinal eats cutworms, codling moths, rose beetles, cucumber beetles, plum scale, and other plant scales, besides leaf hoppers and plant lice. Kingbird goes after caterpillars of all kinds, especially gypsy-moth larvae which feed on fruit and shade trees. It also eats June bugs, click beetles, crickets, weevils, and grasshoppers. Baltimore oriole feeds principally on leaf-eating caterpillars, May beetles, grasshoppers, and click beetles.

Grosbeak devours many garden pests. W. L. McAtee of the U.S. Biological Survey says of the grosbeak, "Few birds have so good a record."

The swallow, swift, warbler, chickadee and vireo consume a multitude of insects. Nuthatch, hummingbird, tanager, wren, waxwing, bluebird, robin, mockingbird, catbird, and cuckoo are other valuable aids in checking insect populations. Hawks and owls prey on moles, fieldmice, grasshoppers, and beetles.

580. What tree dyes were used by American Indians? The Cree Indians made reds and yellows by using roots and moss growing on fir trees, boiled with currants and gooseberries. The Blackfoot Indians obtained black from alder bark, and a beautiful shiny black from a chocolate-colored stone which, burned and powdered, was boiled with hazelnut bark. Yellows were obtained from sassafras bark and speckled alder bark.

The Ojibway Indians of Georgian Bay (near Lake Huron) got a medium red from tamarack bark, a darker red from spruce cones, another red from sumac berries, yellows from the roots of our common black willow, and scarlet from the roots of the sandbar willow. They secured brownish-red dye from the inner bark of the hemlock.

The Ojibways boiled very old, rotten wood of maple trees, with a little sandstone dust added, to get blue and purple.

The inner bark of the paper birch was boiled by the Ojibways of Wisconsin to obtain a reddish dye. Black oak produced a reddish-yellow dye, and butternut supplied their best brown dye.

The Navajo Indians combined the root bark of the chokecherry and wild plum to obtain a purplish-brown dye, and the root bark of the osage orange made a beautiful strong yellow dye.

581. How did Indians make their tree dyes color fast? The word "mordant" comes from the French word *mordre,* meaning "to bite." Mordants are substances added to dyes enabling them to "bite" into the fabric. This improves the fastness of the dye and its resistance to fading. The inner bark of such trees as the red oak, black oak, bur oak, speckled alder, and wild plum made good mordants. The Navajos also used ashes of juniper trees as a mordant.

582. Did primitive American Indians plant crop trees before the white man came? The pecan tree may be the only native tree they planted. This is the oldest cultivated nut tree native in America. It grows in Louisiana, Oklahoma, Texas and the Mississippi River Valley. The Indians also enjoyed the crops of wild acorns, walnuts, hazel and pine nuts.

583. Did the Indians plant fruit trees? Yes. After the white man came they planted peach trees. The peach was introduced into America by the Spanish who first visited Florida and the Gulf region. In 1682 William Penn wrote: "There are good peaches in Pennsylvania, not an Indian plantation without them."

584. Did the English colonists plant crop trees? Extensively. The earliest settlers brought trees from Europe. The Pilgrim, Francis Higginson, wrote in 1629: "Our Governor hath already planted mulberries, plums, chestnuts, walnuts."

585. What trees are used for Christmas trees? Practically all species of the evergreens are used, but some are more popular than others. Balsam fir is the most common, along with Douglas fir, black spruce, Eastern red cedar, white cedar, Scotch pine, red pine, and white pine. (See Question 362.)

586. Which evergreen makes the best Christmas tree? This must be a matter of personal choice. High on the list, however, is the Balsam fir. Firs hold their needles better than other evergreens, and are noted for their pleasing fragrance. (See Question 352.)

587. How can a Christmas tree be kept green and fresh throughout the holiday season? It must be remembered that Christmas trees of all types lose moisture through their needles when placed in a warm room, and this moisture must be replaced in the tree by allowing it to soak up water through the trunk. When buying a tree, make sure it is fresh and green. Then saw off the butt end of the tree at least one inch above the original cut. Keep the butt end standing in a container of water during the entire time the tree is in the house. Refill the container daily.

588. Which trees have the finest fall colors? The foliage of the flowering dogwood turns a brilliant red. The ginkgo bears gold leaves in autumn, and the Norway maple is noted for leaves that turn dark, golden yellow. Scarlet oak, sassafras, and sweet gum have brilliant red leaves in the fall. Sugar maple is flame red and orange.

589. What are some of the most notable native American shade trees? Among many that rate high are the American elm, red and pin oak, beech, linden, and sugar maple. Also the honeylocust, sweetgum, tulip tree, and ash.

590. What are the rules for planting and growing shade trees? If shade trees are to enjoy normal tree growth, never plant trees too close to buildings, sidewalks, driveways. Don't plant trees too deeply in the ground. The roots should be put the same distance in the ground as they were in their original location. Newly planted trees need water. Keep the soil moist but not soggy for a week after planting.

Spray the trees at the right time with the right solution to keep insects and diseases from despoiling the foliage. A balanced tree food should be applied when necessary. Use one with an organic base. Don't overfeed. (See Question 904.)

If a tree is to be moved, remember there is no better time than spring to do so. Certain trees may be transplanted in September or October if it is impossible to do so in the spring. The tops of deciduous trees must be pruned back to correspond to the amount of root system removed when transplanted.

Determine what trees will tolerate shade, as hemlock, and those which need full sunlight, as juniper. If possible, keep a mulch around the base to insulate roots against freezing or drying out. Keep so-called "weed killers" away from areas where trees grow.

591. Can trees be sunburned? A type of damage comparable to sunburn due to direct rays of the sun will affect trees with thin and delicate bark. Most such trees grow naturally in woods or shady places. For example, holly is quickly sunburned if surrounding trees are cut or if it is transplanted to the sunlight because its native habitat is shady. Paper birch which seems to have such thin, delicate white bark will not sunburn because it grows naturally in full sunlight, and is protected by layers of cork beneath the outer bark.

SOME REFERENCES FOR HOME TREES
BOOKS

Chapman, A. G., and R. D. Wray, *Christmas Trees for Pleasure and Profit*. Rutgers University Press, New Brunswick, N.J., 1957.

Fenska, Richard R., *The Complete Modern Tree Expert's Manual*. Dodd, Mead & Company, New York, 1956.

Hottes, Alfred C., *Practical Plant Propagation*. Dodd, Mead & Company, New York, 1927.

Hottes, Alfred C., *The Book of Trees*. Dodd, Mead & Company, New York, 1932.

Johnson, Loyal R., *How to Landscape Your Grounds*. Dodd, Mead & Company, New York, 1950.

Kains, M. G., and L. M. McQuesten, *Propagation of Plants*. Orange Judd Publishing Company, New York, 1938.

Levison, J. J., *The Home Book of Trees and Shrubs*. Alfred A. Knopf, New York, 1949.

Lucas, I. B., *Dwarf Fruit Trees for Home Gardens*. Dodd, Mead & Company, New York.

Mahlstede, John P., and Ernest S. Haber, *Plant Propagation*. John Wiley & Sons, New York, 1927.

McKenny, Margaret, *Birds in the Garden*. Reynal & Hitchcock, New York, 1952.

Pellett, Frank C., *How to Attract Birds*. Dodd, Mead & Company, New York, 1949.

Pirone, P. P., *Maintenance of Shade and Ornamental Trees*. Oxford University Press, New York, 1941.

Platt, Rutherford, *American Trees, A Book of Discovery*. Dodd, Mead & Company, New York, 1952.

Solotaroff, William, *Shade Trees in Towns and Cities*. John Wiley & Sons, New York, 1911.

U.S. Dept. of Agriculture, *Trees: The Yearbook of Agriculture, 1949*. U.S. Govt. Printing Office, Washington, D.C., 1949.

PAMPHLETS AND ARTICLES

Anthony, R. D., "Asiatic Crab Apples—Dual-Purpose Ornamentals." *Garden Journal,* December 1957.

Arnold Arboretum, Harvard University, "Japanese Dwarfed Trees." Bulletin of Popular Information, Vol. 14, No. 1. March 12, 1954.

Brooklyn Botanic Garden, *Plants and Gardens*.
  a. "Handbook on Dwarfed Trees: The Bonsai of Japan." Vol. 9, No. 3. Autumn 1953.
  b. "Handbook on Propagation." Vol. 13, No. 2. Summer 1957.
  c. "How to Prune Trees." Vol. 2, No. 1. Spring 1946.
  d. "How to Transplant Trees." Vol. 2, No. 1. Spring 1946.
  e. "Plants for Decorating Blank Walls." Vol. 9, No. 4. Winter 1953–1954.
  f. "The Hundred Finest Trees and Shrubs for Temperate Climates." Vol. 13, No. 3. Autumn 1957.

Everett, T. H., "Tree Pruning Pointers." *Garden Journal*, January–February 1957.

Garden Club of America, "Plant Hunters." (Reprinted from *Plants and Gardens*.)

Mann, Roberts, "Indian Dyes." Forest Preserve District, Cook County, Illinois. 1950.

McAtee, W. L., "Attracting Birds." Conservation Bulletin No. 1. Fish and Wildlife Service, U.S. Dept. of the Interior.

Muirhead, Desmond, "The Trees on Your Street." Portland General Electric Company, Portland, Oregon.

U.S. Dept. of Agriculture
    a. "Chestnut Blight and Resistant Chestnuts." Farmers' Bulletin No. 2068. June 1954.
    b. "Dwarf Fruit Trees: Selection and Care." Leaflet No. 407. October 1956.
    c. "Transplanting and Care of Evergreens." Beltsville, Maryland.
    d. "Transplanting and Care of Ornamental Trees and Shrubs." Beltsville, Maryland.

IV. TREE PRODUCTS

592. Why are trees the most all-around and useful of our natural resources? Trees supply almost everything: food, heat, construction materials, chemical products, paper, clothing, plastics, photograph film. They gather and guard our water, decorate life, make homes for animals. All this production is conjured out of air, sunlight, water and rocks, and the supply will be renewed and multiplied when given half a chance.

593. What is the most all-around useful kind of tree? The coconut palm, growing along tropical rivers and shores. It provides food, drink, clothing, shelter, shade and beauty.

594. Does cocoa come from the coconut palm? No, cocoa or chocolate is made from the seeds of *Theobroma cacao,* a native tree of tropical America, but now planted widely in the tropics. It is not a palm tree but belongs to the same order of trees as the linden. The similarity of the words cocoa and coconut is purely coincidental.

595. How many different products come from trees? The products from trees are countless—it is estimated that there are over nine thousand uses for paper and paper pulp alone.

596. What is the most valuable tree product? The wood of the trunk is the most useful of all natural substances, but important products come from all parts of the tree.

597. What else do roots provide besides a great service to the living tree? Handsome smoking pipes from briar roots, tea and oil from sassafras roots. Southern pine stumps, which include the heavy crown roots, are used in certain fine chemicals as high-grade turpentine, pine oil, raw resins for adhesives, paints, textile finishing, soaps, cement, insecticides, phonograph records, varnishes.

598. What do we derive from the canopy of a tree besides shade and beauty? People who have orchards think the canopy is the most generous part of the tree. This is the source of nuts and fruits, as well as oils, extracts and decorations from the foliage.

599. What product comes from tree sap?   Maple sugar is a product of true sap. Other products such as resin, turpentine and rubber are from special pockets and not from the sap system.

600. Are maple trees cultivated to produce superior maple sugar? No. This is one product which nature has produced better than man. It is a mysterious fact that trees must be grown from seed to produce good maple sugar. Second-growth wood has poor sugar sap.

601. Are superior maple trees grown by grafting and budding? Many maples such as Japanese cutleaf and bronze leaf Schwedler, for example, are cultivated for their beauty.

602. How old must a maple tree be before it produces?   Twenty years old for profitable tapping. At that age a single tap may be made. The foundations of maple sugaring rest on hundred-year-old maples, perhaps seventy feet tall and with diameters of 2 to 4 feet.

603. How many taps can be made on a mature maple?   Two to four, depending on the size of the tree, but buckets must be about the same height above the ground, and never one above the other. Sap flows up and down—not sidewise.

604. Why are sledges drawn by teams of oxen the traditional way to collect maple sap from the buckets?   These animals are strong enough to pull a sledge with a giant wooden tub through rough woods, up and down hills, across thawing brooks, close to each tree where the buckets are suspended. Today farm tractors are supplanting oxen, except where a few northwoods families still have a team and gather the sap in the way they always have. However, the ability of oxen to go through deep snow still makes them valuable today.

605. Is sugar maple the only tree that delivers sugar sap?   Silver maples and red maples are sometimes tapped but sugar maples have the highest yield. Butternut is often tapped, too, for its distinctive flavor.

606. Does tapping for maple sugar hurt the tree? Not if it is properly done. In pioneer days trees were tapped by "boxing." This gouged out a receptacle in the trunk to hold a pint or more of sap. Later the tapping-iron method made a slanting slice with an axe and a half-circle iron was driven in like a wedge to hold the spout. Both these methods seriously damaged the trees, but in those days there were so many maple monarchs that destruction of trees after a few years of sugaring didn't seem to matter.

Collecting maple sugar

607. What is the right time of year to tap for maple sugar? About the middle of March. The snow may still be deep in the northern woods. When cold nights are followed by warm days pressure is set up in the wood and sap begins to flow.

608. How is maple sugar made from the sap? By boiling it down. Sap, as it comes from the tree, is about 97 percent water. After this is boiled off, it leaves 3 percent sucrose (maple syrup). 3½ percent is a high yield. Further boiling of the maple syrup reduces it to maple sugar.

609. Where and how is boiling maple sap carried out? Sap from a few trees for family consumption can be boiled in iron kettles on the kitchen stove. Farmers who operate commercial sugar groves haul the sap to a nearby sugar house, a modest shed with a storage tank outside. The sap is piped from the tank into a shallow, rectangular corrugated pan that rests on a brick or cement foundation with iron doors and draft controls. In this the fire roars from end to end of the pan.

610. What is the proper way to tap for maple sugar?   Bore a ⅜ inch hole, no deeper than 3 inches, and between 2 to 4 feet above the ground. The sunny side of the tree trunk is best. Insert a metal spout which fits tightly in the hole so the sap can flow through it, and hang a bucket on the spout. You may have to wait days or even a couple of weeks for the clear sap to begin dripping off the end of the spout into the bucket. The bucket must be cleared every day. Sap allowed to stand loses its quality.

The latest device is plastic tubing which runs from tree to tree and on to the sap house, eliminating taps, buckets and gathering. This tubing is so rigged that the pressure of the sap from the tree even forces it to flow uphill to the sap house.

611. How fast does maple sap drip?   If the day is cold and overcast, very slowly, if at all. If a warming sun appears after a cold night, it flows faster. But it always drips, never runs. The drops may come in rapid succession, as many as 100 per minute.

612. What is the average yield of maple sugar per tree?   Two or three pounds per season. Fine trees in exceptionally favorable weather may yield five or six pounds.

613. What is a "sugar bush"?   The name for a grove of sugar maple trees.

614. Where is maple sugar mostly produced?   Vermont leads in the production of maple sugar. After that, in order of importance: New York, Ohio, Michigan, Pennsylvania, New Hampshire. The sugar maple tree is a native of northeast America and is found nowhere else in the world. Maple sugaring is a truly American industry, with some production just over the border in Canada.

615. How old is the maple sugar industry?   The tapping of maple trees was the chief source of sugar of the American Indians. Yankee settlers learned the art from the Indians. Earliest historical reference is in *Philosophical Transactions of the Royal Society* published in London in 1684. "The savages of Canada in the time that the sap rises in the maple make an incision in the tree by which it runs out. After they have evaporated eight pounds of the liquor there remains one pound as sweet. The savages here have practiced this art longer than any now living among them remember."

616. How long does a maple go on producing sugar sap? Box-tapping scars in old trees show that some were tapped for over a hundred years. One grove just west of the Connecticut River in Dummerston, Vermont, was tapped by members of the Kathan family for 98 years.

617. Can any use be made of bark? Cork is the most remarkable product of bark and it has a thousand uses. The chief source of tannin, used for tanning leathers, is bark. Forty percent of the dry weight of oak bark may consist of tannin. Lumps that grow on bark, galls or burls, may be 75 percent tannin.

618. What and why is tannin? It is a complex chemical compound with its own chemical classification, although remotely related to the glucosides which contain sugars and acids. In addition to bark, it turns up in leaves, wood, unripe fruits, black walnut hulls. It is 15 percent of the dry weight of tea leaves. It seems to have little usefulness in the life of a tree except that it is so astringent insects may find it unpalatable, and it may be an antiseptic against fungus diseases. Tannin is considered by botanists a waste product of energetic growth as it is produced especially in galls, unfolding leaves, germinating seeds and green fruits, to which it gives a puckery taste. The inner bark of black oak, where the most active growing is taking place, is bright yellow with tannin.

619. What is the world's chief source of tannin? Tannin extract is one of the most important industries of Argentina and Paraguay, where it comes from the heartwood of one of the heaviest and hardest woods in the world called quebracho (ax-breaker). Another important source is the bark of certain acacia trees (wattles) in Australia and South Africa.

620. Is tannin extract produced in the United States? Some from oak and hemlock barks, but the chief source of United States tannin was American chestnut wood. When chestnuts were killed by the blight, the tannin industry kept on for a while by extracting from dead chestnut trunks, but this has been about used up. Thus domestic production has fallen from 56 percent thirty years ago to 15 percent. Most of our tannin today comes from the quebracho tree in South America.

621. What kind of tree does cork come from?   Useful cork comes from the cork oak, *Quercus suber*.

622. Where do cork oaks grow?   The oldest and most productive of these remarkable oak trees are growing around the western Mediterranean Sea. Cork is exported from Italy (Sardinia, Tuscany, Sicily), France (Corsica, eastern Pyrenees), Tunisia, Algeria, Morocco, Spain (Andalusia, Estremadura, Catalonia), and, most important of all, Portugal, which is the leading cork producing country of the world. The biggest concentration of cork oaks is in Alentejo and the central areas south of the Tagus.

623. Does stripping cork bark kill the tree?   No, it does not hurt the tree if the stripping is done at intervals of ten to eighteen years, and carefully, so as not to damage inner bark which is left alive and intact to form more cork. The first stripping is made when the tree is twenty years old. This is called virgin cork and its surface is rough and gray. It is good only for grinding to make cork insulation and composition boards, and to make veneer siding for rustic picturesque houses. Ten years later the second stripping gives better cork, good for fishnet floats; but much of it is ground for insulation boards and linoleum. Finest cork comes from the third stripping when the tree is fifty years old. This is champagne quality cork, unique in the vegetable kingdom for compressibility, elasticity, frictional against glass yet smooth and impervious to air and water.

624. How long does cork oak continue to produce cork?   Trees continue to bear cork for 200 years.

625. Is cork produced in the United States?   The cork oak is an evergreen oak that grows beautifully in southern California as a healthy, broad-headed shade tree with glossy, dark-green, oval leaves, white hairs on undersides. The older trees build up superb casings of cork, but American impatience is a stumbling block to an important cork-producing industry, although quality gets better and better after each stripping. Four thousand cork oaks are now mature in California—the biggest one is on the grounds of the Napa State Hospital, a few miles north of San Francisco Bay, where the heavy coat on trunk and limbs totals a thousand pounds of cork. The big American cork industry converts cork into many products.

626. Does any other kind of tree develop cork? All bark contains cork in a botanical sense. It is a marvelous insulating material that nature invented and uses universally on trees. Thin layers of cork can be seen as the beautiful tan lining of birch bark. Cork is apparent on the roots of all trees, giving them the red-brown color, making

Corky ridges of sweet gum

them waterproof and bacteria-proof (roots collect water through myriads of soft hairs near their tips), and leaving the roots soft and flexible, though tough, for twisting and turning in their tortuous journeys underground. But only cork oak lays on deep coats of pure cork cells. Many substitutes have been flashes in the pan, such as the bark of the pau santo tree of Brazil—the supply was limited and transportation costs high—and the bark of a Japanese tree, abemaki, which makes an insulating board resembling corkboard.

627. How does cork help its tree? Cork is a wonderful insulation. *Quercus suber* grows in a climate of long summers so hot and dry that other kinds of trees cannot live unless assisted by man. There cork oak faces the full fury of the sirocco, a searing, hissing lethal wind with sharp grains of sand off the Libyan desert, week after week. Yet it has lived through centuries with its delicate cambium cylinder of life kept fresh and vital beneath the quiet insulation of pure cork.

628. How does a tree make cork? The thin layer of inner bark called cambium, that encloses the trunk and limbs of trees, is endowed with a capacity for making those parts of the tree expand in diameter. Cells facing inward lay on new cells which are impregnated with a binding substance called lignin. (See Question 750.) When these cells die and harden, they are wood. Cambium cells facing outward lay on new cells whose walls are impregnated with suberin, an oily chemical compound that makes them waterproof and also keeps them soft and flexible. (Oil or grease rubbed into leather does the same thing.) When these cells die they are cork. The peculiar oily substance, suberin, does the trick. It is made and supplied at the right time and the right place.

629. Why is cork-oak bark "pure" as compared to other barks that contains cork? The structure is different. Ordinary bark often contains, in addition to cork cells, long fibers running lengthwise of the tree like strands in a cable. These tend to split off either in transverse strips as in birch bark or in irregular flakes as in sycamore, or in long shreds as with shagbark hickory. But in cork oak all bark cells are suberized and pressed together so that there are no strands. Pure cork bark is all cells, each imprisoning a speck of air within elastic waterproof walls.

630. Is there any lignin binding together the cork cells? Bark with fibers has lignin which makes it more rigid and woody, but there is no lignin in pure cork. In fact, there is no space between cork cells, so cork is not porous. It is often called porous but that is only a surface appearance where cells are cut across. This is what makes it utterly waterproof, combined with the waterproofing of each cell wall with oily suberin.

631. How can cells that are oval or roundish be put together without spaces between them? The growing process presses them together uniformly in all directions so that they loose any roundness which they may have in the beginning. Their shape is a precise geometrical figure. It is the only shape which allows them to be assembled without any space between, and with minimum surface dimensions. Mathematicians call this remarkable form a tetrakaidecahedron (first discovered by Lord Kelvin). It has the same property as soap bubbles that cling together, obeying a law of nature operating on flexible and elastic material with uniform tension from every direction. It is also akin to the hexagonal shape of beehive cells except that these are elongated by the bee pushing down into the wax with its head. Thus the pressure is not uniform. This perfection of cork cells is hidden except through a high-power microscope. One cubic inch of cork has 200 million of these tiny dead air tetrakaidecahedrons.

632. How long has cork been used by man? About 300 B.C. Theophrastus referred to cork in a botanical work. Ancient Greece and Rome made wise use of cork. Pliny mentions its use for stoppers, floats and shoes. The use of cork for floats and buoys was so common in Roman days they had a slang expression for "needing no assistance": *nare sine cortice* ("to swim without cork").

633. What important products, other than tannin and cork, come from bark? Many, especially dyes, drugs, rubber and cinnamon, which come from various peculiar chemical compounds produced in bark.

634. What kinds of tree barks yield good dyes? Osage orange is the most important domestic dye tree and next comes the crushed bark of the black oak (a substance called quercitron), followed by the crushed barks of black walnut, butternut, sumac, yellowwood, mesquite, red gum, dogwood. Commercially, these dyes have been superseded by aniline and other synthetic dyes.

635. What tree barks did the Indians use for their brightly colored clothing? Each tribe had its favorite kind of dye bark from which they extracted countless color combinations. For example, larch bark gave them red dye; hemlock, brown and red; yellow came from sassafras; red oak produced bright red; red cedar bark mixed with crushed berries from the same tree dyed wools green, but the bark fibers alone made them orange or yellowish-tan. (See Question 580.)

636. What important drugs come from bark? An alkaloid from the thick hard bark of *Cinchona,* a tree of the high slopes of the Andes Mountains, is known as quinine, the universal remedy for malaria. The seeds of the South American tree were taken to Java where they flourished, and for many years the Dutch had a monopoly on world supplies of quinine, when plantations of the East Indian colonies entirely superseded the native source. In World War II, when the East Indian supply was cut, the search for cinchona bark swung back to the Andes, but today quinine can be synthesized from antibiotic drugs.

Another important drug is cascara, the laxative from the bark of the cascara tree that grows along the coast of Oregon and Washington, and nowhere else in the world. Fortunately, cascara stumps send up vigorous sprouts which develop into new trees when the old one is cut down, so that tree bark and medicine keep coming. (See Question 147.)

637. How was the unique antimalarial power of the remote cinchona tree bark discovered? Sometime before 1630 a cinchona tree fell into a pool of water, and an Indian drinking the water found his fever mysteriously cured. The tree bark with its ability to kill the malarial parasite in man became a fetish of the natives. In 1630 (the first recorded use of quinine) a Spanish official was cured of his fever. In 1638 the wife of the Spanish viceroy of Peru fell desperately ill, and the official urged her to try a broth made from steeping bark. So great was the rejoicing when it worked that the tree was named after the Countess of Chinchon. She carried the product and news back to Europe and knowledge of it spread rapidly. For two hundred years wild cinchona trees were cut down to strip the bark with no attempt to replace them. By 1850 the supply was almost exhausted—with 100 million people suffering from malaria, especially in the Far East. Then seeds were taken to India and the Dutch East Indies, and plantations for producing quinine became big industries in those countries. India needed all it could produce for its own sufferers, so the Dutch captured the export markets.

638. What is an alkaloid? It is a remarkable chemical of the plant kingdom, never produced in the animal kingdom, often found in bark but also in leaves, seeds, roots and stems. What alkaloids do for plants is a mystery, but since they are bitter or poisonous, perhaps they are protective. Not only quinine, the great tree bark alkaloid, but many others have shaped human history. Conium, in poison hemlock, killed Socrates. Another makes pepper seeds hot. Atropine gives belladonna. Nicotine in tobacco is an alkaloid. So are opium, cocaine and strychnine. There are many others.

639. What is the bark source of cinnamon? A tree of the laurel family (*Cinnamomum zeylanicum*), native to Ceylon. The spicy flavor is due to an essential oil in young bark. This is peeled, tightly rolled and dried, in which form it is a cinnamon stick. Or the young bark may be ground up for shaking out of a tin. At first slender young twigs were taken off big old cinnamon trees in the jungle, but now cinnamon is cultivated by raising it in orchards, then cutting off the main trunk and letting the stump send up suckers. They grow fast and their bark is rich with cinnamon. In forestry this is called coppicing.

640. What is an essential oil? It is not an oil or fat in a chemical sense, but another kind of chemical compound created in the living plant cell. Essential oils, unlike true oils, evaporate on contact with air, and for this reason they are sometimes called volatile oils. True oils are reserve foods that can be oxydized to stimulate growth and life, and they alternate with carbohydrates in that function. Essential oils seem to have no usefulness in the life of a plant and are considered excretions or waste products stored in their own compartments in the plant. In the life of man, however, essential oils are the source of many exciting products. In one form, a hydrocarbon called turpenes gives us turpentine, lemon oil, eucalyptus, and pennyroyal. Turpenes with oxygen produce Canada balsam, hard resins, camphor, rubber, menthol, bitter almond, thymol, and cinnamon. If sulphur gets mixed in the essential oil, it makes garlic or mustard.

641. Do all these essential oils come from bark? No, they may appear in any part of the plant. Camphor comes out of the wood of a cinnamon tree. Others come from leaves or green stems. Turpentine and resin come from the sap wood, although some of it may seep through cracks in the bark. Cinnamon and Canada balsam come from bark, and rubber from inner bark. Seeds are often the source of important oils (for example: coconut, tung, peanut, sweet almond, olive, soybean, castor bean, cotton seed, flax), but such oils associated with seeds are mostly true oils usable in the plant's metabolism, and not essential oils.

642. What kind of a tree does Canada balsam come from? In eastern United States from the balsam fir, and in western United States from true firs. The balsam can be secured without hurting even the bark of the tree because it forms bubbles, making blisters which can be punctured to get the pure balsam.

Balsam fir cone stands upright on twig

643. What is the great value of balsam? It is perfectly clear with an optical refraction the same as air so that it can be used to mount microscopic material and as an oil immersion necessary in high-power microscopic work. This remarkable product that bubbles out of the bark of fir trees is a tree product little talked about, but one of the most interesting and wonderful.

644. What kind of tree does carnauba wax come from? Carnauba wax (not from an essential oil, but a true wax) is another peculiar tree product with a special use in modern times. It grows on the leaves of a palm tree (*Copernicia cerifera*) native in Brazil, Paraguay, Argentina. It is so crusty that it can be shaken off, and it is then wadded up for world markets. A very hard wax with a high melting point, it is made into wax varnishes, phonograph records, candles, and is used in cold cream.

645. What is amber? The hardest resin known, it makes a very fine but expensive varnish. It comes from the fossils of extinct pine trees that once grew on the shores of the Baltic.

Another very hard resin that comes from fossil trees and from a few living trees is copal. It is usually dug out of the ground from extinct trees, but copal has been taken from kauri pines in New Zealand. Both amber and copal are tough and brittle but dissolve in alcohol and make varnish with a hard elastic finish that is excellent for outside varnishing on ships.

646. What kind of a tree produces lacquer? A sumac, *Rhus vernicifera,* native of China but cultivated in Japan, hence the name Japan lacquer. Milky juice from the tree hardens and darkens on exposure to the air so it is a natural varnish, resistant to heat, unmarred by alcohol, acids or alkalis. With the Chinese, lacquering is thousands of years old; and the way they applied the famous heavy coats of lacquer to their ancient works of art took several years and hundreds of coats.

647. Do any of our American sumacs produce lacquer? Yes, the latex of poison sumac, *Rhus vernix,* is lacquer and has the fragrance of old China. This slender little tree grows in wooded swamps from Texas to Maine, and has not only fine lacquer but also flame red leaves in the fall. It can be distinguished from other sumacs by its small waxy white berries. Avoid touching it; leave its lacquer alone, it makes the skin break out with flaming eruptions. (See Question 55.)

648. What is incense and where does it come from? Incense is related to the resins and essential oils. Burnt in censers, it comes from a mixture of fragrant resins. True frankincense seeps out of a small tree (*Boswellia Carteri*) in arid regions of Arabia and Somaliland. Other species of *Boswellia* are important incense trees on dry hills in India. The chief source of incense for the churches of Latin America is a 60-foot tree growing in patches in dry areas of Argentina and Paraguay called Palo Santo (*Bulnesia Sarmienti*). Incense comes from the heartwood permeated with fragrant resin. The timber of the same tree, exported as Palo balsamo, yields an oil for the perfume industry.

649. Are tree gums related to resins and essential oils?   No, gums are contained in cell walls (they are carbohydrates like cellulose) instead of collecting in separate compartments in the wood or bark like turpenes and essential oils. Whereas resins are soluble in alcohol but not in water, the reverse is true of gums—they are soluble in water but not in alcohol. They are akin to pectin, the jelly maker.

650. Where does gum arabic come from?   After dates, gum arabic is the most important tree product of the Sahara Desert. It exudes from the branches of several species of acacia trees of the oases. Thin strips of bark are torn from the trees which stimulate the ooze, and three to eight weeks later the gum is collected. This pure gum makes binders for pills and candy (gumdrops!) and in liquids it keeps powders suspended (chocolate milk). This property is like that of another plant, a seaweed of our Atlantic coast, *Chondrus crispus,* which, when pulverized, makes a gelatin of puddings and jellies, as well as for stabilizing chocolate milk.

651. What is the most valuable product of tree bark?   Rubber, from the latex tubes of the Para rubber tree (*Hevea brasiliensis*), a member of the big spurge family which has only weedy shrubs in our country, but many valuable species in the tropics. *Hevea* is native to the Amazon Valley where it may be 100 feet tall. Its timber is pale brown, lightweight, brittle, coarse and perishable. But the tree is a gold mine. Its remarkable latex helped make the age of the automobile possible, and found its way into thousands of things we consider necessary to our everyday life.

652. Where does most natural rubber originate?   Most of the world's natural rubber comes from plantations in Malaya and other regions in the Far East. The transfer of trees from South America is a remarkable exploit of British and Dutch colonial history, and a dramatic horticultural triumph. It parallels, on a larger scale, the transfer of the quinine trees industry from the Andes to the Dutch East Indies.

Until 1910 the world's rubber supply came from Brazil, but in that year vast rubber plantations in the Far East were coming into production. In 1938 almost all the world's rubber (98 percent) was coming from British Malaya and the Dutch East Indies.

In 1875 Sir Henry Wickham fought heat, insects and jungle perils to collect seeds of the wild Para rubber tree. His troubles and courage are a classic story, but he finally succeeded in getting baskets of fresh seeds down to the nearest port. Since this was before airplanes, the problem of transporting soft tropical seeds overseas and keeping them alive was a difficult one. He chartered a ship and loaded her decks with cargo declared to be "delicate specimens for Queen Victoria's gardens at Kew." He reached London with 70,000 seeds on the night of June 14th, the steamer having strained her boilers almost to bursting. No radio could announce the arrival, so Wickham took a cab, insisting the cabby whip the horse to a gallop, to the home of Sir Joseph Hooker, the famous Director of Kew Gardens. They worked all night clearing areas in greenhouses. In a short time all the rubber seeds were planted in an area of about 300 square feet where conditions were kept moist and tropical. Less than 5 percent of the seeds germinated. That was enough. Two months later 1,900 seedlings, in 38 portable, miniature greenhouses, each carried by two men, were loaded on a steamer for India with a gardener to tend them on the long voyage. The little rubber trees were finally landed in Ceylon with 90 percent of them in good condition. That was the cornerstone on which the great rubber industry of the Far East was built. Sir Henry and Sir Joseph were men of great horticultural skill, with devotion and vision. Yet it would have been impossible for them to know what a great benefit their experiment would bring to mankind, and that it would in the next generation produce a million tons of rubber per year.

653. Is *Hevea brasiliensis* the only tree ever discovered that produces rubber latex? No, although it is by far the most important because of the high rubber content and fine quality of its latex. It grows well in plantations where it is more economical to collect rubber.

The India rubber tree, *Ficus elastica,* is a big old tree which drops aerial roots from branches like the bombax or kapok tree. The aerial roots look like pillars holding up the branches. Both pillars and trunk exude latex from which rubber is made. The India rubber tree is well known as a house plant, with beautiful oval leaves which are dark green and glossy.

Gutta-percha is a firm, nonelastic kind of rubber from a sapodilla tree in Malaya and Indonesia, *Palaquium Gutta*. It is extremely resistant to salt water, which ordinary rubber is not, so it has a big-volume use for insulation of submarine cables. It is also well known in dentistry where its pliable, nonelastic nature makes it excellent for taking impressions. This is also the rubber used for telephone receivers, pipe stems, golf balls, electric connections, adhesive tape. The sapodilla trees of the Far East have been widely destroyed by wasteful methods of felling them. It is quicker to get the latex by boiling out the bark, than by waiting for it to seep slowly out from the living tree. A plantation method using a shrub form of sapodilla is being developed. Twigs are fast growing and even leaves have the valuable latex.

All members of the sapodilla family have milky latex. One of the most famous is *Achras sapota* of the West Indies and tropical America. The "gutta-percha" of this tree is pliable between the jaws, with no elastic pull, and is known as chicle—the heart of chewing gum.

654. Is rubber produced from plants in Mexico and in our southwestern deserts? Yes, from guayule which is a shrub and not a tree. It is inferior rubber but attracted interest when Para rubber was scarce during the war. Some rubber has also been secured from the milky juice of desert milkweed.

655. Do many plants have latex? Yes, many plants exude a milky fluid when the bark or stem is broken, including sumac, fig, mulberry, and Osage orange. Latex is also found in many herbs; for example, milkweed, dogbane, chicory, dandelion, poppy, oleander, bloodroot.

656. Is latex the same as sap? Latex is a juice of living cells but it is not sap in the ordinary use of the word. Latex is contained in its own cells called laticifers, which are often joined together to form pockets or systems of tubes, but are unconnected with the sapwood system. In guayule, mentioned above, the laticifers are separate cells scattered through the plant so that in this case rubber latex is secured not by tapping but by pulverizing leaves and wood.

657. How is latex from *Hevea brasiliensis* obtained? By diagonal notches in the bark which must be skillfully made by a small hand axe to get the most out of the tree. The laticifers are cylindrical networks in concentric layers. The art consists in slicing a few layers at a time; that is, cutting a precise depth into the inner bark but without cutting into the cambium which is the lifeline of the tree. Trees are tapped in the early morning when pressure is at the highest, and the latex oozes out into cups. Several cuts may be made on various sides of the same tree. Twice a week they are cut again with a deft stroke to tap deeper networks. This may go on for six months, after which trees are let alone for several years to rebuild their networks of laticifers in the bark.

658. Is latex always milky? Latex may be any color. In oleander it is clear. In the drug plant marijuana it is yellow-brown; in poppies it is bright yellow or orange; in bloodroot it is blood red. In milkweed, fig, spurge, and rubber trees it is milky white. Because the last named are so well known, and due to the coincidence of the word latex resembling *lac,* the Latin word for milk, it is often referred to as milk. Latex is derived from the Latin word for fluid. Laticifers are "fluid carriers." The error of language has led to these vessels being wrongly called lactifers. Latex is a fluid in which many kinds of substances are suspended. It may carry carbohydrates, acids, salts, alkaloids, true oils and fats, essential oils, tannin, mucilage—or turpenes like resin and rubber. Thus, this interesting substance gives us many widely different and important products.

659. How is latex important to a tree's life and growth? It is a remarkably clean and sanitary disposal system. The function of latex has long been a mystery. It has been termed a food-conduction system because it often carries food in the form of fat and carbohydrates; but no movement of these substances has ever been detected. It has been called a food reserve; but when plants are deprived of other food latex is still left untouched. It has been called a transporter of oxygen, and a regulator of the water balance in a tree; but there is no proof. It may be said that latex functions as an excretory system. As it often contains poisonous, bitter, stinging, puckery, or sticky-elastic substances, it may be valuable to the tree's life as a protection against animals and bacteria.

660. Is maple sugar derived from a latex? No, it comes from the true sap of the tree. To get it you have to tap through the bark into the sap wood, and it comes out when sap pressure is created by the sun warming cool tree trunks. Laticifers may be formed inside the sap wood, in roots, leaves, or, commonly, in the bark just underneath the outer corky surface. The contents are under turgor and their flow is a pressure flow, like that of toothpaste coming out of a tube.

661. Does ordinary bark from native American trees have any economic value? The twenty million tons of bark from forest operations in our country has long been considered a nuisance and problem of waste disposal. A little of it was used as fuel in steam plants and powerhouses, but today the sheer mounting volume of the material has spurred research into the use of bark chemicals and its processing for other uses. Bark is now incorporated into insulating felt, battery separators, mattress stuffing, reinforcing agents in magnesite flooring, and insecticide dusts. Although the chemical composition of each kind of bark varies, the average for essential oils, resins, pectins, gums, sugars, tannins, and nitrogen compounds is about 25 percent.

662. What are some of the latest discoveries of bark products? Silvacon, from Douglas fir bark, makes cement nailable, rubber more flexible and longer lived, keeps fertilizers from caking. Rayflo from western hemlock bark is used to make oil-well drilling muds more efficient. Wax from Douglas fir bark for furniture, floor and shoe polish, seems to be as good as carnauba wax scraped from the leaves of the Brazilian palm. Ground-up redwood bark is used for soil conditioning and for moulded pulp products and packaging materials.

663. Have stumps from trees felled for timber and pulpwood any value? Like bark of the big timber forests, stumps have long been considered a tough problem of disposal, especially in the South where pine stumps fail to decay like hardwood stumps, because of their high resin content. But today's chemists are finding chemical materials in them and bulldozers are salvaging old stumps out of a million acres of valuable land per year.

664. Is sawdust of any use? Mounds of sawdust at every sawmill have been a challenge. Here is the pure granulated substance of tree trunks, with no cost of production as that is written off in the lumbering operation. People have pressed sawdust into bricks for fuel, but it is cheaper to pick up kindling around the sawmill. It has been used as bedding for cattle, doll stuffing, packing material, and as a cleaning absorbent for barroom floors and butcher shops. It is stained dark green for the floors of steakhouses. These uses are limited by cost of transportation and handling. Recently sawdust has been treated with acid to extract the wood sugar and when this is fermented it becomes high-grade ethyl alcohol. Other treatments by water and fermentation (hydrolysis) produce acetic acid, baking yeast, carbolic acid, glycerine, and plastic for ash trays, battery boxes, dishes, electrical appliances, handles, and plastic board for construction and telephones.

665. What is wood flour? Wood flour is powdered sawdust used to make bowling balls, floor tiles, doorknobs, linoleum, phonograph records and wallpaper. With scientific treatment sawdust is coming into its own with new and wonderful modern products.

666. What were the first tree products used by man? Fruits, nuts, fuel wood.

667. What are the most important food trees today? That depends on the country and even the part of the country. In the northern United States, apple; in the southern United States, orange. Cherry and peach trees are most important in some localities. In the Mediterranean countries, olive and date are first. In some tropical countries, coconut. In the West Indies and parts of South America, the banana.

668. What are citrus trees? They are a genus of tree belonging to the rue family, which bears fruits with a thick and fleshy skin filled with tiny pockets of citric acid. This phenomenon consists of some cells dissolving in the rind, leaving minute cavities which contain glands that exude the citric acid. When a lemon or orange peel is twisted, the citric acid oozes out.

669. What are the fruits of the citrus genus? Orange, *Citrus aurantium*, meaning golden citrus. The orange has variety: *bergamot*, from which perfume is made; *amara*, the bitter Seville orange which makes good marmalade; *sinensis*, Portugal orange, an important sweet orange; *nobilis*, tangerine, or mandarin orange.

Citron, *C. Medica*, unlike the others, has a thick rind while the pulp is small and bitter. But citron is the parent of a variety: *Limonum*, the lemon; *acida*, the lime; *Limetta*, sweet lime.

Pomela, *C. decumana*, is the parent of the grapefruit.

Kumquat, *C. suntara*. (This was formerly listed under a different genus, *Fortunella*.)

670. Where did our citrus trees come from? Oranges are native to southeast Asia. They were grown in ancient China as ornamental trees, and mentioned in Chinese writings of 2200 B.C. They were brought overland to Europe around the end of the 9th century. The lemon came a little later. It is reported in Italy in A.D. 1260. It is thought that the sweet orange, *C. sinensis*, was brought from China, *via* the Cape of Good Hope, by Vasco da Gama. Orange trees became widely established around the Mediterranean after the trees were brought to Persia by the Arabs. Sour Seville oranges were brought to Florida by the Spanish. Indians of the Everglades spread the species and that is why wild orange trees are sometimes reported from Florida. Sweet oranges were also brought by the Spanish. The orange grove said to be the origin of the Indian River oranges is supposed to have been growing in 1823.

In California the navel orange, shipped in winter, was bred by the wizardry of Luther Burbank; the Valencia orange, shipped in summer, was introduced by a tree imported from Latin America in 1873. That tree, the father of nine million orange trees lined up in a half-billion dollar industry, still grows with regal rights behind an ornamental iron fence at Riverside, California, and was bearing good oranges at last report. An impressive outcome of the cooperation of one living tree with man.

671. What is the oldest known tree food used by man? Walnuts. Shells of walnuts were found in the Swiss Lake dwellings of Neolithic man, dating from about 7000 B.C. They were found with his bones and the bones of the animals he snared for food. These were the Persian-walnut type, *Juglans regia,* which we call English walnuts because they were first brought to America by the English settlers of Virginia.

672. When did the Persian walnut reach England? There is no precise record but an educated guess would be that the Romans, during their long occupation of Britain, introduced their favorite tree. The English originally regarded it as a foreign tree, as seen in the word "walnut." *Wal* is derived from *wealh,* an old English word for "strange."

673. Is the Persian or English walnut cultivated in England today? Yes, ever since Roman days, and especially in Wales. A superb avenue of these trees at Gwernyfed Park is a quarter of a mile long with tree trunks averaging ten feet in diameter.

674. Where do the English walnuts come from that we buy in the market? California. A hundred thousand acres of walnut orchards stretch from Los Angeles to Oregon.

675. How is the brand name of walnuts printed on such a rough surface? A unique machine was invented that stamps the brand name on the rough surface of each nut in such a way that the printing is clean and clear—at the rate of two thousand nuts per minute.

676. What part did the walnut play in Greek and Roman history? It was one of the outstanding foods of those days. Walnuts were thrown at brides and grooms for good luck. It was given its present scientific name, *Juglans,* by the Romans, meaning "the nuts of Jove."

677. Did the original Persian trees produce thin-shelled nuts? Sargent in his classical book, *Silva,* says "the nut of the wild tree is small, with a thick, hard shell and a small kernel, and is scarcely edible."

678. How were the thin-shelled English walnuts produced before the days of scientific plant breeding? The answer is speculative but highly interesting. J. Russell Smith in his book *Plant Breeding* puts it like this: "In the beginning a villager brought from the woods the very best nuts he could find and planted them on his farm. The next generation took the best nuts they could find from the older plantations and planted them. The next generation did likewise. This brought the best trees into village plantations where wild nut trees were scarce, and the pollen crossed from parents which were both from good stock. This went on for many centuries and over a wide area. The result was a selection combined with an ever better cross-breeding. Thus excellent varieties of Persian-English walnuts were created with thin shells and fine meat."

679. Was the American black walnut a food of primitive man?

No doubt the primitive inhabitants of the Middle West, where the black walnut flourishes, enjoyed the meat of these tasty nuts. Black walnut shells have been found crudely carved in the form of birds and pierced to serve as earrings, they were discovered among the bones and pottery fragments of the Mound Builders of Ohio and Indiana.

680. Can black walnuts be bred for thinner shells?

Yes, by beginning with "sports," wild trees which accidentally in nature produce nuts with exceptionally thin shells. This is the way brand names of good apples were started. Then buds or young shoots (scions) from the wild trees are grafted on to ordinary roots of the same genus which are grown in a nursery.

681. What are some brand names of thin-shelled black walnuts?

Thomas, Stabler, Ohio, Ten Eyck. Of these Stabler has the thinnest shell; Thomas is the hardiest. Best choice depends on location.

682. Can grafted nut trees be secured for growing on a small commercial basis?

Yes, there are nurserymen who specialize in nut trees. This includes not only black walnut but also grafted pecan, hickory, and English walnut on black walnut roots to make the trees hardier.

683. Is there a book that describes this unusual kind of orchard?

Nut Growing by R. T. Morris (New York: Macmillan, 1921), is a classic work on this subject.

684. What is the market for black walnuts? Candy makers, bakers of bread and cake, and ice cream manufacturers who have tried to buy black walnut meats in twenty thousand pound lots. Black walnut, unlike other nuts, retains its flavor when cooked.

685. Is there a machine to pick out the kernels? No, the commercial supply has come mostly from wild trees, and picking kernels has been a home industry in the southern Appalachians. The picking problem will be solved by thinner shells. A good start has been made. The search for thinner-shelled wild trees goes on; and growers are cross-pollinating the name brands. Black walnuts with shells as thin as English walnuts is the goal.

686. What is the food value of black walnuts? In calories per pound, they exceed beefsteak by more than three times. Moreover, black walnuts have 27.6 percent protein, as compared to beefsteak's 19.8 percent.

687. Are coconuts bred for quality and cultivated in orchards? No, the chief reliance of this primary source of food for millions of island people is from wild rather than from cultivated trees. In this respect coconut palm differs from all other important food trees. Coconuts are planted in groves in the Philippines and Puerto Rico as an organized supply for the confectionary trade, but even these plantations are not tended in the way that other food crops are cultivated.

688. Do bananas come from wild trees? Bananas come from a huge herb which is not a true tree. It dies back to the ground after it has fruited, and comes up from the crown of the roots to produce fruit for the next season. This unique tree had its original home in the hot jungles of Malaya and the East Indies, and was cultivated by man as far back as 4000 B.C. It was known to the Romans and Greeks, and was carried by man around the tropics. "Wild bananas" have probably escaped from ancient cultivation.

689. What is the family and species of the banana tree? It has its own family, the banana family (*Musaceae*). This includes the weird bird-of-paradise plant, the traveler's tree of Madagascar, and the tree which gives us Manila hemp. The basic species of edible bananas is *Musa paradisiaca,* but this species (which is presumably the wild tree) produces a small, fairly hard and often twisted banana known as the plantain, which must be cooked before eaten. There are three important varieties: *M. sapientum,* the Cavendish or Canary Island banana; *M. rubra,* the red banana; *M. gros michel,* the source of all our fine yellow bananas.

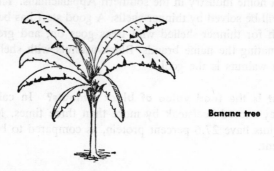

Banana tree

690. Where and when was the original *M. gros michel* discovered? In 1836 a French planter, Jean François Pouyat, of Jamaica, West Indies, was on a vacation trip to another island when by sheer luck he came across a banana tree with wonderful bunches of bananas. Not only were they bigger and more delicious, but grew in compact curves so they could be packed tightly without damage, instead of sticking out stiffly from the stem like Canary Island bananas which have to be packed in separate crates. He dug up the root and brought it back to his plantation where it continued to send up shoots that developed the same wonderful bananas.

691. Can banana trees be grown from seed? No, the banana tree has grown so long from root buds that its seeds have become worthless as seeds, residual, and almost nonexistent.

692. Have all the millions of banana trees producing yellow bananas for our markets been budded from that one *gros michel* tree? Yes, but it is easy because no grafting or budding in the usual horticultural sense is necessary. The underground stem on the crown of the root sends up shoots, each of which develops a banana-bearing tree the first season. Stems can be divided into chunks *ad* *infinitum.* Anybody who wants to grow a banana tree can buy a bud-bearing chunk or get one from the roots of a neighbor's tree, and start raising good bananas.

693. What family of trees gives us the most number of edible fruits? The rose family, which gives us apple, cherry, pear, peach, quince, loquat, plum, apricot, almond, and prune.

694. How can almond, a nut, be so closely related to plum, cherry and peach? In the botanical sense almond is not a nut at all; it is the stone of a peculiar kind of peach with a thick skin, almost no pulp or juice, and a stone with a large kernel that is not bitter like the seed in a true peach.

695. Where do almonds come from? *Prunus amigdalus,* the almond, grows wild in scrub oak forests with *Pistacia,* in dry, eastern Mediterranean countries such as Iraq, Jordan and Turkey. It has been planted in commercial orchards throughout California where five million almond trees, started since 1900, produce more than our imports from Mediterreanean wild trees.

696. Is the almond flower like that of a peach? Yes, a beautiful pink peach flower. The almond flowers come out very early; branches may be covered with blossoms in February, making a breathtaking display.

697. Do we have other nuts that are the stones of fleshy fruits? Yes, the pistachio nut is the stone of *Pistacia vera,* a close relative of sumac. It grows in dry, scrub oak forests of the eastern Mediterranean with the almond trees. It produces on the roughest agricultural land in the world. It survives on stony ledges where there is almost no soil, and so steep that only man and goats can climb there. For centuries farmers of the Near East have been grafting and budding and improving the strains of pistachio nuts.

698. Are pistachio nut trees cultivated in the United States? A few small plantations have succeeded where the owners have been willing to experiment and work over the trees on a nonprofit basis. In our hurried land, we are not temperamentally prepared, as are the Turkish growers of pistachio nuts, to build up an industry with an orchard tree that takes fifteen years to produce a commercial crop after planting grafted stock. Even then the trees may be loaded with fruit only once in five to seven years.

699. What is the source of the cashew nut?   The cashew tree, *Anacardium occidentale,* is a native of the Caribbean area but naturalized widely in South America and in the Far East. This is one of the most interesting trees of our hemisphere. The bark exudes a gum-like substance similar to gum arabic, used for varnish and bookbinding to prevent bookworms from eating the books. When the fruit reaches the ripe stage the stem to which it is attached swells up, becomes fleshy and juicy, making a cashew apple. The weight of the apple causes it to dangle and below this "apple" the true fruit of the tree, the cashew nut, dangles upside down. Mary Barrett in her book, *Common Exotic Trees of Florida,* says that this set-up looks like "a brown lima bean hanging down from a bright red or yellow pepper." The cashew apple (the stem) can be eaten fresh or cooked and it makes delicious cold drinks and wine. The shell of the nut is laden with a caustic oil. (The cashew tree is in the same family as sumac which also includes poison ivy.) This is driven off by heat but one must be careful not to let the fumes touch the face and eyes. In India this caustic oil from the nut shells is used to paint floors and rafters to preserve them from insects—but the practice is considered dangerous. The roasted kernels are the popular nuts with the pleasant milky flavor.

700. Does alligator pear come from a pear tree?   No, it comes from a tropical tree that is a member of the laurel family. It is in no way a true pear, and gets that name only from its shape and leathery hide. A better name is avocado. The tree is *Persea americana.*

701. Where did the name avocado originate?   The tree is the oldest fruit crop in Florida, where it was introduced by the Spanish. Its Spanish name, "aguacate," sounds like "avocado" when it is spoken fast.

702. Is avocado an important crop tree in our country?   In California it is a crop of increasing value with rising popularity. This nourishing salad fruit must always be served fresh; it cannot be cooked, canned, dried or frozen. Air shipping for quick delivery extends the markets and modernizes this style of fruit, yet avocado is the oldest American tree crop, a legacy from the Aztecs.

703. How does one choose avocado trees for home planting?
There are three horticultural races: (1) West Indian; chief source is the lowlands of Central America. As it is susceptible to frost, it can only be grown in farthest-south places of California and Florida. It has special aesthetic appeal, with nice smooth skin. Fruit matures in summer and fall. (2) Guatemalan; originated in the highlands and can stand temporary frosts, even as low as 21° for a brief time. The fruit is lumpy and warty. (3) Mexican; also from the highlands and is even more frost resistant, and more lumpy and warty. The trees can grow on a variety of soils but need good air drainage and are killed by standing water. Avocado is a handsome tree around home grounds, with large, oval rich green leaves, typical of other laurels, such as Oregon myrtle, camphor tree, and eastern sassafras. The fruit brings such a good price that it pays to plant even a few trees. A single avocado tree averages 150 pounds of fruit, sometimes more, in one season when it is mature and healthy. Usually grafted stock is planted, using West Indian roots and Guatamalan or Mexican scion.

704. Is there any use for the huge purple seed of an avocado?
This is a source of an oil used in cosmetics. The seed contains a red indelible stain useful as ink in primitive circumstances. Ground up and mixed with meal, it serves as rat poison.

705. Are there any other products, not food and drink, that come from the fruit and leaves of trees? Manila hemp is made from the fibers of the leaf stalks of a banana tree, *Musa textilis*. Its cultivation is a chief industry of the Philippine Islands where it is called abaca. The remarkable fibers discovered in the leaf stems of this tree are so strong, flexible, and impervious to salt and fresh water, that they make the great ropes of world shipping, burlap bags, and binding twine for protecting submarine cables.

Panama hats are made from pliable, thin strips of leaves of a palm tree, *Carludovica palmata*, which goes by the spirited name of Jipijapa in Ecuador and Colombia.

Kapok grows as hairs lining the seed pods of the silk-cotton tree, *Ceiba pentandra,* native of Latin America but cultivated in Java, which is the chief producer of kapok. The hairs spring from the inner wall of the pod and are not attached to the seeds, making it easier to separate than cotton. The cells of the hairs are hollow and air-filled and impervious to moisture. This last quality keeps a wad of kapok from soaking up water as does cotton, and makes it wonderful for buoys, life jackets, and stuffing pillows, mattresses and dolls. Today, foam rubber is taking some of the kapok markets.

Buttons are made from the extremely hard berries of a tropical South American palm, the ivory nut tree, *Phytelephas sp.* The wood of the same tree is hard and takes such a polish that it is called vegetable ivory and is used in the making of billiard balls. It is an arresting fact that certain tree bodies have unique chemicals or qualities found nowhere else.

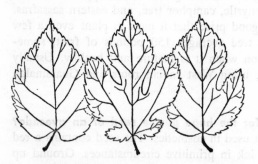 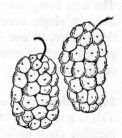

Three kinds of white mulberry leaves   **Fruit of white mulberry**

706. What tree does silk come from? The white mulberry tree, *Morus alba,* is responsible for silk, but unlike the kapok tree it does not produce the threads by itself. First a certain caterpillar, the larva of the silk moth, *Bombyx mori,* must eat the leaves and mix the mash with chemicals from its glands, then squeeze out the mixture through tiny nozzles. The silk stuff hardens when touched by air to form silvery threads. The caterpillar or silkworm is building itself a cocoon, into which to pupate and turn into a moth.

707. How is it possible to untangle the threads of a cocoon? *Bombyx mori*'s cocoon is different from all other moth cocoons in that its thread is very strong, and is spun with astonishing regularity. At first the thread is attached to nearby twigs irregularly, but after a base net or web is made, the spinning becomes symmetrical. (The instinct of the worm which guides it in such precise spinning can be compared to that of the orb spider which can divide a circle into equal angles as though it possessed draftsman's instruments.) At the end of three days the silkworm has immured itself in a thick, firm, shapely cocoon composed of a single continuous thread over a thousand feet long. It takes special skill to clean away the irregular fluffy silk threads on the outside, find the beginning of the long thread which makes the cocoon, and with a clever little reel unwind the whole cocoon without breaking its thousand feet of silk floss.

708. Is white mulberry the only tree silkworms can feed on to make silk?
They have been tried on red mulberry, native in the northeastern part of the United States, and on osage orange which is a member of the mulberry family. The worms will feed on those leaves but the quality of their silk is poor. Silkworms have been bred on white mulberry for thousands of years and there is no necessity to find another diet—that tree and silkworms know how to produce silk together.

709. What is the routine of the silkworm and the mulberry tree?
The behavior of the silk moth is like that of all other moths. It leads a double life—as a caterpillar it eats voraciously, then spins a cocoon in which it is imprisoned while it turns into a winged moth. Finally it emerges to lay eggs that hatch caterpillars. But *Bombyx mori* is not a wild insect like others; it is carefully cultivated by man, and is not known in the wild. The moth is heavy bodied and creamy white, with a 1¾-inch wing spread. It never eats, and, although its wings are well developed, it does not fly. Thousands of years in captivity have evidently made the wing muscles useless.

The one thing the moth does in its short life is to lay about three hundred eggs before it dies. They are yellow eggs at first, then turn gray, and rest over the winter until the mulberry leaves come out in spring. The moment a worm hatches it starts to eat and keeps this up for forty-five days, growing fast and throwing off its old skin (moulting) every nine days. The last moult is scheduled by nature to occur inside the cocoon. Then, after about two weeks, it tears a hole, climbs out, and unfolds its wings.

The moths are trained to lay their eggs on clean white paper. These are kept cool until the mulberry leaves are out and then put in the warm sun to hatch, when the worms are transferred to the leaves. The silk man does not let the moth emerge because the hole it makes in coming out breaks the thread, and makes the cocoon worthless for unraveling. He kills thousands of moths by dropping the cocoon into boiling water for a few minutes before unreeling its silk, saving only enough specimens to give him moths for his production.

710. When did man start cultivating mulberry trees and silk-worms?   About 2800 B.C., in the reign of Huang-ti, the Yellow Emperor, who had one of the most creative brains of all time, comparable to Leonardo da Vinci. He was the maker of Chinese civilization, extended the boundaries of his empire, taught his people to build beautiful temples, regulated the calendar, invented wheeled carts drawn by oxen, and transport boats to navigate the big rivers of China. It was in this alert, creative, and imaginative atmosphere that a grub of a moth was discovered which exuded an extremely fine, soft thread of remarkable strength. At first the worm was torn open and the thread pulled out and used, not for weaving cloth, but for strings of musical instruments and fishlines. The legend says that the Emperor's consort was an exquisitely beautiful girl who made a hobby of training the worms to feed on mulberry leaves, and then proceeded to invent a loom for spinning the silk to make herself attractive. This was the first use on record of the marvelous material which, many centuries later in Rome, Pliny wrote about: *ut in publico matrona transluceat, ut denudet faeminas vestis.*

711. How did the *Bombyx mori* secret reach the rest of the world? For centuries caravans brought their loads of silk across Asia to the coast of Syria. In the fifth century, A.D., Roman Emperor Justinian wanted to halt the flow of wealth to China to pay for the silk so he got in touch with two Persian merchants who had spent some time in China, and commissioned them to steal the secret. This they did, and smuggled out mulberry seeds and silkworm eggs in a hollow cane. They established a colony of trees and worms at Byzantium,

and trained Greeks in the culture of silk production. It was retained
as an imperial monopoly, as in China.

The new silk culture was the cornerstone of the splendor of the
Byzantine court. Then it became identified with the Peloponnesians—
silkmaking and weaving was a fine art in Corinth, Thebes, and
Argos. Greece held the monopoly until around the 12th century
when the Arabs learned the secret and set up the industry in Lisbon.
When Roger the Norman sacked Corinth, Thebes and Argos, he
treated the silk growers and weavers with great respect, but carried
them off as a present to the King of Sicily, where a stately edifice was
erected for them. From there the worms and their mulberry trees
spread into Italy, where Lucca became the center in A.D. 1314.
Wars and revolutions kept driving the silk culture northward and
by 1620 it was established in England, brought there by the Hugue-
not refugees, who settled in the Spitalfields district of London.

WOOD PRODUCTS

712. What are the three major uses of wood? (1) Fuel. (2)
Lumber. (3) Paper. In that order according to the volume of wood
used. This says in three words that trees are the greatest natural
resource for human life on earth, especially with their plus value
of good food products.

713. What percentage of all wood cut is used for fuel? About
50 percent, on a worldwide basis.

714. What are the two general classifications of all wood cut?
Fuel and industrial. Industrial wood, in turn, has three subclassifica-
tions: saw wood, round wood, pulp wood.

**715. How is it that in an age of oil, coal and water power, such a
big percentage of trees is cut for fuel?** The farmers' own consumption accounts for about two-thirds of all fuel wood used. But
the percentage varies greatly among countries. For example, in the
United States four times more industrial wood is felled than fuel
wood; in Europe one-and-one-half times more industrial wood; in

Latin America seven times more fuel wood is felled than industrial wood; Africa and Asia use far more fuel wood than industrial wood.

716. What two countries depend most completely on fuel wood? Finland and Brazil have the highest per capita consumption of fuel wood.

717. What two countries are least dependent on fuel wood? Great Britain and Holland; almost all the wood they use is industrial.

718. Are the gleanings of forests valuable as fuel wood? That depends on the amount of timber in a region and the cost of labor. In well forested United States, Canada and some Baltic areas, great quantities of standing and felled wood are left unused, which in southern Europe and much of Asia would be highly prized and have a ready fuel market.

719. Where is wood used almost exclusively for fuel? In parts of India and Brazil the age-long destruction of forests for fuel wood still goes on. In Latin American countries 75 million people depend on trees for all their firewood, and on charcoal for cooking and heating; but clear-cutting on a large scale has deprived many of wood, and they are using anything—such as grass and brush—that will burn. Much fine heavy mahogany and rosewood is being brought down out of the interior on river steamers for firewood. In southeast Asia the chief cause of forest destruction is cutting for firewood. Low-altitude forests are shrinking steadily before the pressure of rising populations, plus industrial developments such as brick kilns and pottery ovens.

720. Are the countries suffering the loss of firewood doing anything about it? In Brazil eucalyptus plantations planted in 1904 are helping to fire the locomotives of the Paulista Railroad. India is encouraging fuel wood plantations, but these are only local efforts.

721. What can be done about the threatened fuel wood famine? Tree growing on a large scale requires education, strong local government backing, and federal laws that can be enforced. These conditions are lacking in tropical countries. There is no likelihood that coal, oil, gas or electricity will be available economically for the mounting populations in time to offset calamity. The only ray of hope is to shift from logs to sticks and to grow wood by the coppice method —that is, young sprouts from stumps.

722. Do coppices produce a volume of wood faster than ordinary trees? Yes; especially in regions where lush forests have grown, trees coppice vigorously. If this method for producing firewood is pursued systematically, it will make wood faster and can also restore the forest. In one case in southern India, an average annual increment of 500 cubic feet of wood per acre is reported. Young sprouts grow faster and can be replaced faster than older wood.

723. Is charcoal an important form of fuel wood? Yes; many industrial users like charcoal because it makes a very hot fire with the least weight of fuel. In this country charcoal briquettes are increasing in favor for home fuel because charcoal is smokeless, easy to burn, and makes an easily controlled fire. In Japan, charcoal is used extensively for bus and truck fuel. India is a large user of charcoal.

724. How is charcoal made? Wood supplied with plenty of air burns freely; deprived of air it gives off gas and turns to charcoal. Charcoal can be made simply by stacking wood together, covering with earth, igniting in several places, and maintaining a slow burn by admitting small amounts of air. When the temperature reaches 500° F. a chemical reaction occurs which makes it very hot, reduces the air to a minimum and turns the wood to carbon (charcoal). The charring process takes a few days or a couple of weeks, according to the size of the charge. This includes time for slow cooling to a point when the charcoal can be exposed to the air and removed without bursting into flame. A standard five-cord, concrete block kiln can complete the job in about eight days.

725. Is the gas, released when charcoal is made, of any use? Yes, this has a number of interesting by-products. Although mostly it consists of water, it also includes acetic acid, methyl alcohol, some oils and tars. The recovery of these is known as the wood distillation industry.

726. What are the worldwide relative uses of industrial wood?
(1) Saw logs, 68 percent. (2) Pulpwood and pit props, 23 percent.
(3) Other industrial, 8 percent.

727. What do saw logs become in our daily lives? *Timber:*
Barges, bridges, foundations, dams, derricks, docks, mine timbers, ships, stringers, barn sills, heavy-duty trailers and logging vehicles. *Lumber:* Beams, boards, boat hulls, decks and deckhouses, dimension cuts, concrete forms, flooring, framing, joists, planks, posts, rafters, sheathing, sills, studding, subfloors, walls, corncribs. *Milled Lumber:* Battens, baseboards, casing, paneling, railing, fencing, siding, stepping, millwork, doors, windows, frames, bins. *Converted lumber:* Tool handles and parts, baseball bats, skiis, tennis racquets, golf clubs, hockey sticks, clocks, furniture, balusters, bowling alleys and pins, clothespins, matches, toothpicks, brush handles, bobbins, boxes, butchers' blocks; cabinets for radio, television, phonograph, sewing machine; caskets, conduits, crates, crossarms, displays, dowels, fixtures, gunstocks, gutters, ladders, lattice, pegs, mouldings, musical instruments, artists' pallets, patterns, pencils, window shade rollers, aircraft parts, shoe heels, shuttles, signs, skewers, picture frames, tanks, toys, trim, trunks, valises, venetian blinds, wooden wares, shingles. *Railroad ties:* After fuel and lumber, this takes the largest volume of felled trees, in the United States. Originally ties were hand-hewn from round wood; today the majority come from the saw mill cut to size. When railroads were booming, they needed 75 million ties per year. Today the demand is still enormous but far below the early figure, due to preservatives. Ties that lasted five to eight years untreated, now last twenty to thirty years when treated. More than a billion ties are in use today by American railroads. *Cooperage:* Barrels, buckets, cooling towers, kegs, conduits, silos, tanks, tubs. *Plywood and veneer:* Box-car lining, cabinets, boxes, panels, prefabricated houses, siding, signboards, tabletops, wainscoting, canoes, sail boats, motor boats, racing shells, airplane propellers, bearings, utensil handles, crates, furniture, pullman-car lining, show window displays, cigar boxes, luggage, square stick matches, tongue depressors, toys, battery separators, scroll work.

728. What does pulpwood become in our daily lives? Ninety-five percent of pulpwood goes into paper and paperboard, 5 percent into dissolving pulp for plastics, cellophane, and rayon nitrocellulose. Of the 95 percent 49 percent is paper, 51 percent is paperboard. Half of the board is used for corrugated containers, one-third for boxes, 10 percent for building boards, 10 percent for all other uses.

729. What are pit props? Pit props are heavy round wood, used in great numbers in mining and tunneling. They are delivered from the forest to users unsawed, as is pulpwood. Thus they are included in statistics with pulpwood.

730. What are the "other industrial" uses of wood in Question 726 that take 8 percent of felled trees? The bulk goes into round wood for poles, piles and posts. Some three million tall poles per year are needed for replacements of telephone poles. Pilings for docks, wharves, piers, highway and railroad trestles across shallow bodies of water take an immense volume of tree felling. Masts and spars take a lot of fine trees, although much less than formerly. It is estimated that fences in the United States use 600 million posts annually along fifteen million miles of fencing. Then, too, there are Christmas trees.

731. Why doesn't the steel industry instead of the forest supply railroad ties? Metal cannot compete with wood in cost, strength, elasticity, shock-resistance, displacement ease, and durability when ties are given modern preservative treatment. The electric insulating quality of wood is important for automatic signal systems. Where steel ties have been used, especially in Germany and Switzerland, they have to be insulated for use on electric railways, they are noisy, and in the long run cost more than wood because rolling stock has to be repaired more often. The elasticity of wooden ties lends vitality to a good railroad track compounded of ballast, ties, tie plates and spikes. A track must give before the terrific impact of a rushing train, and yet safely bear the load of tonnage.

732. What kind of wood is used for railroad ties? In order of importance: oak, southern pine, gum, Douglas fir, beech, maple. In countries other than the United States, scotch pine, larch, and eucalyptus are used depending on the availability of a size large enough for the purpose, as well as the preserving treatment.

733. How is wood preserved?   Coal tar creosote, made by distilling coal tar, is the chief wood preservative against destroying organisms. For land and fresh-water use, this is diluted with petroleum oil, but for salt water, creosote is diluted with coal tar that protects indefinitely against marine borers.

734. How is the preservative applied?   The log is run into a steel cylinder and the preservative is forced into the wood under pressure of 100 to 200 pounds per square inch. Preservatives only penetrate a small fraction of an inch, but that is enough. A nonpressure treatment uses a hot and cold bath. Millwork for window sashes and doors can be treated by putting the wood in a vacuum, then flooding it with a volatile petroleum solvent of pentachlorophenol, and suddenly releasing the vacuum. The point is that modern chemistry and wood technology are developing fine methods of giving wood long life under adverse conditions.

735. Can wood be made fireproof?   Nothing is fireproof against a hot conflagration that can melt glass, but wood can be made remarkably fire-resistant if soaked in preservative solutions of waterborne, fire-retarding salts. This treatment is only for special situations. It is too expensive for general protection against fungi, insects, and decay bacteria.

736. How is wood pulp made?   Three basic methods are used, depending on the kind of paper or other products for which the pulp is to be used:

1. *Mechanical pulp*. Wood blocks are pressed against huge grindstones while bathed in hot water. About one-third of all pulp is made this way. Most of it goes into newsprint, but it is also converted into other kinds of cheap paper. Ground wood pulp mills usually locate where wood and water power are plentiful. Ground wood pulp makes a paper too weak for most purposes, so newsprint has 15 percent to 20 percent chemical pulp mixed with it.

2. *Chemical pulp*. This cooks wood chips under pressure in chemi-

cal solutions to dissolve out the lignin and some soluble sugars. Lignin is the cement which holds together the wood fibers, so this process leaves the white fluffy fiber that was the building material of the tree almost pure cellulose wood pulp. In general, three kinds of chemical solutions are used, depending on the kind of trees being processed and the quality of paper desired:

a. Sulfite process uses a liquor of calcium, magnesium, ammonium, or sodium bisulfite plus sulfurous acid. This makes a strong light-colored pulp with the widest variety of uses of a wood pulp. One of these uses is for mixing with ground wood pulp in newsprint. With special treatment, sulfite pulp is used for rayon and other cellulose products. It calls for light-colored wood, with long fibers and little resin—spruce, hemlock, balsam.

b. Sulfate process uses sodium sulfide and sodium hydroxide, highly alkaline cooking liquors. This can be used with almost any kind of wood, including those with much resin. Pine of all different species is the chief tree used. Sulfate pulp is for wrapping paper, bags, shipping containers. It makes the familiar tough brown paper called "kraft." Also, it can be bleached and used for high-quality writing and printing papers.

c. Soda process uses a solution of caustic soda to process the cellulose of hardwood trees. Mixed with long-fiber sulfite pulps, it can be used in fine-quality printing papers.

3. *Semichemical pulp.* This is a newer method which softens the chips by cooking briefly in chemicals and then pulps them mechanically by passing them between revolving discs. Contrasted with the purely chemical process, this leaves some of the lignin in. It is especially suitable for hardwoods, enabling them to make excellent paper because of their short fibers. Semichemical pulps are used chiefly in corrugated papers, but they may also be bleached and turned into high-quality white paper—glassine, bond, book, magazine.

737. How long has wood pulp paper been made? Alkaline cooking with soda was established in the United States in 1863. The acid, or sulfite process, was invented by an American, Benjamin C. Tilghmann in 1866, but it was first used in Sweden. It was introduced into our country in 1884. The sulfate process came here from Germany in 1900. The common use of wood as a raw material for paper got under way in this country in the late 1880s.

738. How much paper and paperboard do we consume in this country every year? Around 430 pounds for every man, woman and child.

739. What is the proportional use, by weight, of each kind of paper? Container and box paperboard, 39 percent; newsprint, 19 percent; wrapping paper and bags, 11 percent; book and printing paper, 12 percent; writing paper, 4 percent; tissues, 5 percent; building paper and paperboard, 8 percent; miscellaneous, 2 percent.

740. What paper products are "miscellaneous"? Trees have bestowed on us some nine thousand different products made from paper pulp. Some of those in which the paper is more or less concealed are: ammunition, artificial flowers, artificial leather, straws, baskets, blankets, bottles, bottle caps, combs, cups, doilies, dolls, felts, forks and spoons, game counters, hats, lamp shades, pails, pencils, plates, ribbons and confetti, shoe insoles, spools, suitcases, plastics laminated with paper bases and used for tabletops, electric parts and printed circuits, tubing, rods, molded products, and decorative panels.

741. What is a cellulose acetate product? This is derived from pulp in which wood fibers are first treated by the sulfate process as in paper making. The best known cellulose product is rayon. This is produced by one of four chemical processes, all of which use cellulose: (1) *Cellulose nitrate,* using nitric and sulphuric acids; (2) *Viscose,* using caustic soda and carbon bisulphide; (3) *Cuprammonium,* using copper hydroxide and ammonia; (4) *Cellulose acetate,* using acetic anhydride and sulphuric acid. Nylon, Dacron, Orlon, Acrilan are not cellulose products.

742. What is the basic difference between cellulose acetate and paper? In paper, the wood fibers are not destroyed but intertwine to make a sheet. In cellulose acetate, the original cellulose fibers are changed into a thick syrup. When this is to be used in a fabric, it is squeezed through very fine holes and emerges as thread. This is fundamentally the same operation as that of a silkworm which presses viscid cellulose stuff from the mulberry tree through fine holes in its spinnerettes.

743. How long has rayon been used? Synthetic fibers from wood were made in our country in 1911; their consumption exceeded silk in 1926; and by 1941 the use of rayon was six times the use of silk, and about equal to the use of wool. Today rayon consumption is over a billion pounds in the United States, about four times that of wool.

744. What else is made of yarn spun from tree wood? Today the cellulose acetate thread competes with wool and cotton in dresses, sweaters, underwear, gloves, scarves, neckties, bathrobes, summer suits, bedspreads, draperies, tablecloths and umbrellas. Rayon tire cord is one of the major uses of synthetic fiber from wood.

745. How long has cellulose been used for plastics? As far back as 1870, cellulose nitrate appeared as celluloid. In 1912 cellulose acetate was first used in photographic film. It was made into rods and tubes in 1927. Extended sheets of cellophane were first marketed in 1934.

746. What percentage of a log is wood fiber that can be made into pulp? This varies with the kind of wood. About half the volume of a spruce log is wood fiber or cellulose. The rest is lignin cement which holds the fibers together, and various sugars which the tree has stored for food energy.

747. What is tall oil? Tall oil is the foamy, yellow-brown, soapy substance skimmed from the cooking liquor left in the vat after wood chips have been cooked by the sulphate process. Tall oil is refined and used in soaps, sizes, and in the preparations of emulsions and cold water paints.

748. How did the name tall oil originate? Many Swedes were employed in forestry and papermaking in Minnesota and the Northwest, and their Swedish word for the waste liquor sounds like tall oil. This was echoed by the others, and has become a standard word in the paper industry.

749. Is there any commercial use for sulphite waste liquor? This is largely a wasted by-product of the giant paper industry. Of the lignin content, perhaps 1½ million tons are thrown away annually. But paper company chemists, lured by great potentials (not to mention the problem of disposal when neighbors complain that their streams are being polluted), are getting results that promise the use of more and more of the contents. The hexose sugars are used to make alcohol, especially in Sweden, and yeast. A compound of lignin is used to bind highway "blacktops." Waste liquor boiled down to a paste is used for laying linoleum. In electroplating it is added to the chemical bath to give tougher, longer-lasting metal platings. For some reason lignin acts as an expander of lead in the negative plates of storage batteries, increasing the life of the batteries. Also vanillin is made from lignin for flavoring candy, ice cream, and cake. This is as pure and fragrant a vanilla extract as any turned out by the unripe fruits of the orchids of Central America.

750. What is lignin? A chemical enigma of wood cells (as much as 20 to 30 percent of the volume of wood), the nature of which has baffled chemists until very recently, and which is still one of the big challenges of the wood-products laboratories. Papermakers think of lignin as the brown binder holding together the white cellulose fibers in the log. This brown binder (lignin) is dissolved to separate the wood fibers for paper making. Chemists describe lignin as a carbohydrate, aromatic in nature, made of benzene rings with a three-carbon chain attached. This is a recent assertion, for as late as 1948 they could not agree on the nature of lignin. The difficulty is that there are different kinds of lignin in hardwoods and softwoods, perhaps even between species. Drastic chemicals used to dissolve lignin change its nature.

751. What are silvichemicals? This term refers to the new chemicals from trees. The cellulose acetates and derivatives from tall oil are good examples. Tall oil offers the biggest potential and the greatest challenge in silvichemicals. (See Question 747.)

752. How long are the cellulose fibers used in paper making? They are tiny. The *long* fibers from pine, spruce and hemlock are 2.3 to 3.5 millimeters in length, or roughly ⅒ of an inch. The short fibers of hardwoods are around ¹⁄₂₅ of an inch, barely visible to the sharpest eyesight. Yet they intertwine to make paper.

753. How can paper be made from hardwood fibers only ⅟₂₅ of an inch long? Formerly paper making was limited to the long-fibered softwoods, but then it was found that what mattered was not the actual length but the ratio of length to diameter. If the microscopically short fibers of hardwoods have the same ratios as softwoods, they will interlock. With the improvement of processing —using semichemical methods of pulp making instead of the basic sulfite process—almost any hardwood tree can be used. One of the most important is aspen, formerly considered a weed tree, but today one of the most important paper trees in the Lake states. Oak, birch, and gum are also used for paper today.

754. Are willow, poplar, mulberry and hackberry trees usable for pulp? They are theoretically usable, but not always marketable because a mill may be set up to use a certain type of tree for certain kinds of papers. Pulp mill requirements differ from state to state. The pulp market is pretty much a local market.

755. What are important paper making trees in foreign countries? Bamboo, really a giant clump of grass, is cut for paper making in India. India is developing plantations of the fast-growing paper mulberry, *Broussonetia papyrifera*. This native tree of Polynesia can be grown in our southern states. It is prominent in Williamsburg, Virginia. Australia has few softwoods native to the country and until recent years no wood pulp industry. Today Australian research has found how to use at least nine species of eucalyptus (the superior one is *Eucalyptus regnans*) in paper making, and paper mills are operating both in Australia and Tasmania. To make kraft paper they are mixing the long fibers of Monterey pine with eucalyptus pulp. Monterey pine brought from the California coast is growing much faster "down under" than in its native place.

756. Who made the first paper from wood pulp? The wasp. During Washington's administration paper was so scarce that Congress asked housewives to save every bit of rag. Men had worked on the problem of a paper substitute for rags for almost a century. Then in the early 1700s a French lover of nature, who was also a physicist, René de Réaumur, watched wasps chewing wood, pulping it with wasp saliva, spreading it on their nest where it hardened to crisp paper when it dried, exposed to air. Réaumur was struck with the brilliant idea that something in wood could make paper! It was 1852 before the first wood grinding machine for pulverizing wood while wet was in operation, invented by Frederic Keller, a German weaver. The wood pulp was mixed with 40 percent rag stock to make the first newsprint.

757. What is a Fourdrinier machine?　The word is pronounced *for-dri-neer* in the paper trade, with accent on the last syllable. The invention of this machine revolutionized paper making by converting it from a handmade operation that was slow and called for special skills (although there are no finer papers than handmade ones), into a large scale continuous production. Thus this machine is one of the greatest assets of our civilization, bringing results that complement Gutenberg's invention of printing with movable type.

758. What does the Fourdrinier machine look like?　It is like a procession of machinery, starting with a horizontal strip of wire mesh and then a series of big drums. These are set on a long steel table. The wire mesh quivers and shakes, the drums revolve with a humming and clatter of many bearings from end to end. The machine may be one foot wide and a hundred feet long—experimental size—or it may be twenty-two feet wide and hundreds of feet long, one of the modern giants of the paper mill.

759. How does the Fourdrinier machine work?　At the starting point a tall tank, called the head box, is raised above the steel mesh that travels beneath it. A solution of 99 percent water and 1 percent wood pulp is kept at a constant level in the head box by a system of controls that let it flow out at the bottom at a constant rate, depending on the weight and type of paper that is being made. This spreads a sheet of pulp over the wire mesh. The 1 percent solution insures that it will be smooth and even, seeking a level as does water. The wire mesh is endless and may run at the rate of 2500 feet per minute, while it vibrates violently from side to side to make the wood fibers interlock. The water drains through the fine holes of the mesh and is sucked out by a vacuum underneath. At the end of the wire mesh the sheet of pulp is picked up by a traveling blanket and rolls over drying cylinders, and when it is dry enough to hold together on its own, it travels around on cylinders while rapidly turning into paper. Thus the Fourdrinier machine has taken some thin soup of pulp wood and turned it into a reel of paper in one continuous operation.

760. What types of paper does this machine turn out? The Fourdrinier is used to make all types of wood pulp paper and most types of paperboard.

761. How is a watermark put into paper? This is an insignia, a trademark, or a texture pattern impressed in paper by inserting a special cylinder, called a dandy roll, near the head of the procession where the pulp is still soft and watery.

762. On what kind of paper is United States paper money printed? Paper currency is made by wet printing from a finely etched plate known as an engraving, on stock that is 50 percent linen and 50 percent cotton. This distinctive paper has been made for the Bureau of Engraving and Printing by the same contractor since 1879.

763. Has wood pulp ever been used in our currency? There is no record of its having been used for this purpose.

764. What class of products takes far more of the annual forest harvest than the wood pulp industries? The lumber industry, including plywood, veneer, and synthetic structural lumber, takes almost five times as much as the pulp and paper industries.

765. When did the lumber industry start in this country? The records of the Jamestown Colony say that in 1608 there arrived from England "eight Poles and Dutchman for the purpose of erecting saw mills." The first record of exports of products of the lumber industry is also in 1608 when a Captain Newport set sail for England with a cargo of "pitch, tarre, clapboard, and waynscot."

766. How much lumber has our country's lumber industries yielded to the world? Since Independence Day, 1776, until 1956, a reliable estimate says three million million board feet. This amount of lumber would build three hundred million five-room houses, or a boardwalk six feet wide to the sun.

767. How much is a board foot?   It is a standard unit of measure that equals a square board one foot on each side and one inch thick. The term is used only in North America.

768. What is the size of the lumber industry in the United States today?   About fifty thousand saw mills; four thousand lumber wholesalers; and thirty thousand retailers.

769. What are the five great lumber producing forests of our country?   (1) *Southern forest:* chiefly southern pines, bald cypress, coast white cedar, white and red oak, gum, ash, yellow poplar (tulip tree), hickory. (2) *Central hardwood forest:* oak, hickory, ash, elm, black walnut, beech, maple. (3) *Northern forest:* eastern white pine, spruce, red and jack pine, Canadian hemlock, beech, maple, birch. (4) *Western forest:* western white pine, ponderosa, sugar, Idaho and lodgepole pine, Douglas fir, western larch, Engelmann spruce, white fir, incense and red cedar. (5) *West coast forest:* most important are California redwood and Douglas fir.

770. How much lumber does our country now produce each year? Around forty billion board feet.

771. What is the proportion of softwoods and hardwoods?   81 percent softwood lumber; 19 percent hardwood lumber.

772. What are the chief American hardwoods and their areas? (1) *Northern hardwoods:* sugar maple, yellow birch, basswood (linden), beech. (2) *Appalachian hardwoods:* black cherry, rock elm, yellow poplar (tulip tree). (3) *Southern bottomland:* southern red oak, cottonwood, gum (tupelo). (4) *Delta hardwoods:* red gum (sweet gum), cherry oak, black willow. (5) *Central hardwoods:* white oak, red maple, shagbark hickory, American elm, black walnut, white ash, sugar maple.

773. What woods shrink and swell the most?   Measuring between green wood and dried, all hardwoods shrink and swell more than softwoods. The greatest expanders and contractors among hardwoods, around 20 percent of volume, are dogwood, hop hornbeam, shellbark hickory, and persimmon. The most stable hardwoods, around 10 percent and less, are teakwood, catalpa, mahogany, osage orange. Among softwoods the biggest change in volume, around 12 percent, comes in larch, fir, southern yellow pines. The least, around 8 percent, is northern white cedar, redwood, eastern red cedar, sugar pine.

774. How are grades of lumber described? Building lumber is graded A, B, C, D, for finish. A is practically clear wood used in high-class construction in trim and flooring. Often not segregated, but combined with B and sold as "B and Better." B allows small imperfections, meets requirements for large-size, almost clear, stock that will take natural finish. C allows imperfections that can easily be covered with paint. Used for cornice, porch flooring, bedroom and kitchen trim, where a high-class paint job is needed. Also used for natural finishes in medium-priced jobs. D allows any number of imperfections which do not detract from a finished paint job. Board averages up to five times more knots than Grade B and Better. Used in lower-priced homes for casing cornice, shelving, and low-priced fixtures that will be painted. In general, A and B are natural-finish lumber, C and D are paint-finish lumber.

Common grades of lumber used in construction are numbered from 1 to 5. Numbers 1 and 2 are for use without waste. Numbers 3, 4, and 5 permit waste. 1 is watertight lumber with knots limited in size. Used mostly in doors and window frames. 2 has more and larger knots and occasionally one may shake through, but its general aspect is a fairly clear board with grain-tight knots. 3 has larger and coarser knots, perhaps an occasional knothole, a touch of decay, or saw imperfections. It is used for concrete forms, subfloors, barns. 4 is low quality with decay and holes, and is used for cheaper sheathing, subfloors, roof boards, and mostly for boxes and crates. 5 is imperfect lumber for temporary and coarse jobs near the lumber mill; it is not often found in self-respecting lumber yards.

775. Is lumber from trees already dead less desirable than that from living trees? The inherent quality of the wood is just as good. Chief defects are visible, such as decay, if the tree has been dead long, or cracks, if it was destroyed by a wind storm or lightning.

776. How can one know what kind of lumber he is buying? Send for Agricultural Handbook No. 101, entitled *Wood: Colors and*

Kinds (Washington 25, D.C.: U.S. Government Printing Office). This describes the visible features which distinguish woods from each other as they come from the sawmill, with color plates showing color and graining of the untreated wood. Eighteen American hardwoods and fourteen softwoods most commonly found in retail lumber yards are covered.

777. Where can information be obtained about the identification of woods? The Forest Products Laboratory (Madison, Wisconsin) is the official wood identification agency of the United States government. Their identification service is used in business transactions, lawsuits, criminal evidence, building codes industrial standards, and purchase specifications. They have also been called on to identify wood from Egyptian tombs, sunken ships, petrified forests, and the beam that supports the Liberty Bell.

778. What are the heaviest American hardwoods? Osage orange, hickory, beech, and black locust may weigh 56 pounds per cubic foot of seasoned wood.

779. What are the lightest American hardwoods? Willow and poplar may weigh only 20 pounds per cubic foot of seasoned wood; butternut, basswood, and yellow poplar (tulip tree) may be as light as 25 pounds.

780. What are the heaviest American softwoods? Longleaf pine is the heaviest and strongest of the pines, with shortleaf as runner-up. Both are southern yellow pines in the language of the lumberman. Western larch is the heaviest tree of the big softwood forests of the Northwest, weighing up to 53 pounds per cubic foot of seasoned wood.

781. Is weight the criterion of strength in wood? In general, heavier wood is stronger, and lighter wood is weaker. But weight is not always an accurate index of strength. Weight depends on compactness of wood fibers, content of resins, ratio of heartwood to sapwood. Strength depends on character of grain, whether it interlocks or tends to split.

782. What is seasoned wood?　Seasoning is the process of taking water out of the wood pores. In green (freshly cut) wood half the weight is water, sometimes water is 1½ times the weight of the wood. The drying must be carefully done or the wood will crack, warp, and split.

783. Is seasoned wood stronger than green wood?　Yes. Proper seasoning greatly increases the strength, hardness and stiffness of wood. (See Question 52.)

784. How much moisture is left in good lumber?　That depends on the purpose for which it is to be used. For boxes and crating—expendable uses—wood does not have to be thoroughly dried. For furniture and fixtures it must be well seasoned and dry. The standard weights of lumber are based on a cubic foot of wood air-seasoned to 12 percent moisture content.

785. How is lumber seasoned?　By two methods. (1) Air drying (outdoors or in a shed with plenty of ventilation) consists of stacking the lumber so that air can circulate throughout the pile. This requires many months, possibly a year, depending on weather and the way the lumber is stacked. (2) Kiln drying, in which there is a precise schedule for temperature and humidity control for the kind of wood and for the purpose it will be used for.

786. Can lumber be seasoned from trees on one's own place?　Yes, by using the air-drying method. Prepare a base for good drainage so that air can pass freely underneath and around the pile. Boards are laid in rows with air space between them, and narrow strips of wood, two to four feet apart support and separate each layer. Give the layers a pitch of one inch per foot to spill rain water, and place the pile to take full advantage of prevailing winds. A rough roof, using some of the boards being seasoned, should be placed crosswise—a double layer overlapping—and raised by narrow strips five or six inches above the top layer. The rate of drying is controlled by using thicker or thinner interlayed strips. Lumber dried too fast will warp and crack. If only a small amount of wood for home woodworking is to be seasoned, air dry it in an airy, unheated building or open shed.

787. What is happening to the lumber standing on end around lumber yards? Some lumber companies air dry by standing the boards on end, especially where rainfall is apt to be light. On end piling is also used for certain kinds of lumber in the Northwest.

788. How can a small section of log be seasoned without slicing it into lumber? Cover each cut end with a good coating of paraffin, or with nurseryman's sealer, and store in a dry place where air can circulate around it. This will take months or over a year, but it will be in fine condition for woodworking.

789. Does seasoning kill the diseases and insects in wood? Yes, the wood-destroying fungi spores must have more than 20 percent moisture content to grow. Dryness and heat destroy insects, especially in kiln drying.

790. What causes wood to shrink and swell even after it has been seasoned? Wood cells (cellulose fibers) swell and shrink as their walls absorb or lose moisture. This characteristic of stretching in the presence of water is retained to a moderate degree after they have lost their protoplasm and are dead and hardened. A very slight change in one cell is multiplied by billions of cells in a piece of lumber.

791. How much does wood swell or shrink? That depends on the kind of tree. From oven-dry to a moisture content of 30 percent a board will become 4 to 14 percent wider, or vice versa. Shrinking and expansion occur across the grain with almost no change lengthwise.

792. Does paper, which is made out of wood fibers, shrink and swell like lumber? No, the fibers are intertwined and point in all directions, while in wood they are more or less parallel.

793. What is the advantage of bonding kraft paper to a board? The paper was bonded to mask knots and defects and make a smooth surface for painting so as to upgrade lumber that was hard to sell; then it was discovered that the paper reduced the swelling and shrinking of the board by 50 percent.

794. What causes warping or twisting? The uneven shrinking of wood cells in different parts of the same piece of lumber. This is why good seasoning must be done very slowly, with air circulation across all parts of the lumber, or under carefully controlled temperature and moisture in kiln drying.

795. Is it true that wood shatters like glass when exposed to extremely cold temperatures? This is Arctic fiction. The Forest Products Laboratory has tested wood down to —300° F. and every type of strength, including toughness and elasticity was greater at the low temperatures than at 70° F.

796. What is the compression strength of wood? An average piece of wood 12 inches long, 2 by 2 inches in cross-section, set vertically, can hold up forty thousand pounds. This gives an idea of the great strength of mine timbers, dock piling and posts when the pressure is parallel to the direction of the grain of the wood.

797. What is the strongest timber in the world? When pressure is applied across the grain, strength varies enormously with each kind of wood. The standard measure is a piece 30 inches long and 2 by 2 inches in cross-section, with one inch allowed at each end for support; this bridges a gap of 28 inches. On this basis kaneelhart of Surinam and British Colombia supports 6,300 pounds, which rates it as the strongest timber in the world. Kaneelhart is so heavy that it sinks in water with a specific gravity of 1.15.

798. What is superlatively strong timber like kaneelhart used for? General construction, but there is not enough kaneelhart available to give it much commercial use or value. In this class the great commercial timber is lignum-vitae, *Guaiacum officinale,* with plenty growing around the West Indies and the coastal regions of the Caribbean. This has not only strength and amazing resistance to wear but also a self-lubricating quality due to resin. Thus, lignum-vitae is used for bearing or bushing blocks lining the stern tubes of propeller shafts of steamships, and for mallets, pulley sheaves, caster wheels, bowling balls, masthead trucks, chisel blocks, cable dressers. It is replacing brass and babbitt metal bearings in steel rolling mills and in pumps. The cost is less than steel, the life several times longer, and lubricating is not necessary.

799. What is the hardest timber in the world? Black ironwood, *Krugiodendron ferreum,* from the West Indies, the southern tip of Florida, Yucatan, and British Honduras. It has a specific gravity, air dried, of 1.34 to 1.42—much heavier than water. However, hardness is not measured by weight but by the amount of pressure it takes to sink an iron ball weighing 25 pounds halfway into the wood. For black ironwood this takes a pressure of over two tons—4,080 pounds.

800. What is the weakest timber in the world? Balsa wood, *Ochroma lagopus,* can support only 149 pounds. Balsa takes the blue ribbon for the lightest, only six or eight pounds per cubic foot. It is also the softest, taking only 25 pounds to imbed the iron ball halfway.

801. What is the most important timber tree in the world? Douglas fir is the highest expression of timber tree greatness in our day. A Douglas-fir forest is amazingly uniform; tall, straight trunks stand so closely together that from a distance they may be likened to a wheat field in density. This is not a true fir, whose cones stand erect on branches like big Christmas candles, but is in a class by itself, with cones that dangle and which have peculiar three-pronged tongues sticking out of them.

Two-thirds of the lumber from the Northwest is Douglas fir. In the lumber industry it is often called "Oregon pine." The strength of its streamlined grain is revealed by its use as tall masts. The giant flagpole at Kew Gardens, England, is cut from Douglas fir. It stands 214 feet high.

802. What is the most important hardwood timber tree? Traditionally oak is the great hardwood timber tree. The white oak was the dominant hardwood of the eastern United States in colonial times and was the main timber for ships and the framing and finishing of houses. English colonists knew how to work oak because in England it was the mainstay of the Navy and built the oldest manor houses.

Today oak has top priority as a timber tree but the supply of the big old oaks is almost gone.

803. What are shingles made of? Most of them from western red cedar; bald cypress and redwood are also used. The best shingles are all clear of knots and decay blemishes, are all heartwood, and cut-edge grained. Heartwood is important as it makes them resistant to decay.

804. What are heavy wagon wheels made of? Hub: elm; spokes: oak; felloes: oak, ash, elm or beech. For wood used in stylish carriages see Oliver W. Holmes' *The Wonderful One Hoss Shay*.

805. What is a good baseball bat made of? Ash, which is springy and tough. But the finest straight-grain ash is hard to get today and so a tough, unbreakable bat made of laminated hickory and ash is being tried out. This has met the specifications of the major leagues, but it has not completely been accepted as a substitute for the good old ash bat.

806. Why do batters hold the bat with the label up? Manufacturers place the label on the horizontal side of the grain so that the ball will strike the edge of the grain. This makes the blow more springy—and sends the ball faster and farther.

807. What were the wassail bowls of old England made of that "never wore out"? Lignum-vitae. Often they held boiling hot liquids and received banging against stone—the remarkable lignum-vitae was not hurt or dented.

808. How does ebony compare with lignum-vitae in durability? True ebony is the heartwood of *Diospyrus ebenum* from the dry monsoon forest of Ceylon, turned black by gum resins and a process like fossilization. This makes it very brittle, although the blackness has made it valued since the days of the early Egyptians. Even though it is about as hard and heavy as lignum-vitae, it would never stand up to the beating of a wassail bowl, and does not have the self-lubricating qualities needed for bushing blocks in propeller shafts. Ebony is best used as small pieces of black beauty in handles of light cutlery, finger boards of violins, inlays, backs of brushes, etc.

809. What kind of tree produces the perfect resonance of a fine violin?   The silver fir, *Abies alba,* of Europe is used for the top of the instrument; European sycamore, *Acer pseudoplatanus,* is used for back.

810. What is the wood of a violin bow?   This comes from brazil-wood, which gave its name to the country of Brazil. The tree is chiefly valuable for a red dye which was once very important to European textile industries. The greatest demand today is for violin bows, for which the wood must be "freshly cut, of strictly straight grain, in faultless round pieces of sap wood, forty inches long, four to eight inches in diameter." (See Question 93.)

811. What kinds of woods are used in making pianos?   The function of the wood in a piano is more that of a beautiful cabinet wood than of a sensitive sounding board. It is not an inherent part of the instrument like the wood of a violin. It does have a secondary role to play in transmitting the resonance. For pianos the following woods are generally used: mahogany, walnut, poplar, rosewood, sugar pine, maple.

812. What tree produces the fragrant wood of cigar boxes?   Spanish cedar (*Cedrela odorata*) made the traditional cigar boxes which were hand cut and nailed together. The volatile oil gave a pleasant aroma to the tobacco. Most cigar boxes today are a combination of cardboard and redwood.

813. What are racing shells made of?   The light, strong wood that shoots with little friction through the water, and has a golden luster was Spanish cedar until 1927. Then builders of racing shells tried the giant arbor vitae or western red cedar (*Thuya plicata*) for the skin of the shell, $5/32$ of an inch thick, decked it with Alaska cedar (*Chamaecyparis nootkatensis*), on a frame of sitka spruce (*Picea sitchensis*). This shell is 61 feet long, and weighs around 200 pounds.

814. What makes wood decay?   Only one thing, the attack of wood-destroying fungi. These may appear as fluffy or cottony bodies, or fan-shaped patches, or white or brown root-like strands. The microscopic strands permeate the wood, destroying it by eating the cellulose. Some fungi destroy both the cellulose and the lignin. The bacteria of decay are also classified as fungi, but instead of strands they form enormous colonies of separate microscopic cells.

815. Does not all wood naturally decay in the course of time? No, wood decays only under conditions of moisture and mild temperature which enable the fungi to live and "devour," that is, oxidize, the cellulose and lignin in the wood. Wood that is continuously soaked or continuously dry will not decay. The temperature for decay is between 50° and 90° F. Wood that is seasoned to 20 percent moisture or less will not decay unless it absorbs more moisture.

816. Are molds and stains a kind of decay? No, because their fungi do not attack the substance of the wood to a damaging extent. Molds can be distinguished from decay by their powdery appearance, but they are usually superficial and can be brushed off. Stains penetrate the sapwood, never heartwood, with blue, bluish black, brown (sometimes shades of yellow, orange, purple, and red) patches. Wood affected by molds and stains is generally unimpaired for many uses where appearance is not important.

817. What is dry rot? This is a misleading word used where crumbly spots of decay appear in apparently dry wood. Either the fungi have used long threads of their bodies to conduct water from the ground or some other source of water into otherwise dry wood, or the fungi have been dormant in the wood for months or years, only to wake up when water is temporarily available.

818. Are some kinds of wood more resistant to decay than others? Sapwood (the outer part of the trunk) of all trees is most easily destroyed by the wood-eating fungi because the cells contain water and are porous, with galleries for the fungi to expand in quickly. Heartwood is more resistant in some species, but even that will decay eventually if conditions are right. Certain fungi enjoy the robust fare of heavy gum and resin-filled heartwood.

819. What American trees have heartwood most resistant to decay? Cedar, catalpa, chestnut, bald cypress, juniper, black locust, Osage orange, and redwood. If these are used for fence posts, untreated, the sapwood will soon decay away but the fence may be held up for years by the core, that is, the heartwood.

820. What temperature and moisture conditions permit decay? Temperature above freezing to the point where it is so hot that moisture evaporates. When moisture falls below 20 percent, the fungi die. This is the percentage used as a standard for kiln-dried lumber. Wood-destroying fungi are drowned (lack of oxygen) when the wood is saturated.

821. Does the moisture-temperature formula apply equally to all kinds of woods? Yes. When the White House was remodeled in 1949, many sound timbers were found that had been there since 1816. They were protected from water getting into the wood. A Roman emperor's boat sunk in Lake Nemi, Italy, was raised two thousand years later and could be identified as made of spruce. It remained saturated under still water. A house in Dedham, Massachusetts, has stood intact for three hundred years, protected by paint and circulation of dry air. A log recovered from 150 feet under a river bed when a tunnel was dug, proved to be an extinct kind of sequoia that had been there for some twelve million years, saturated in mud which cut off oxygen so that the bacteria of decay could not operate. A wooden sewer pipe buried under New Orleans for over a hundred years was found as serviceable as the day it was installed in wet mud.

822. Is it then true that piling standing in water needs no protection against decay? Piling completely submerged in fresh water or mud, or below the water table in land use, will not decay. But the part that extends in the soil above the water table must be treated or it will quickly decay. Piles standing in salt water are subject to decay where damp just above the water, or to the attack of marine worms in wet areas between the tides. They are positively threatened by destruction from marine borers in the water unless treated. For this salt-water protection against marine borers, be sure that the coal-tar creosote is not diluted with petroleum as is often done for treatment against fungi and wood-eating insects.

823. What are wise precautions to prevent decay when building a frame house? The Forest Products Laboratory (Madison, Wisconsin) says that a dry, well built house is in practically no danger from decay if these precautions are observed: (1) A well drained site where moisture does not accumulate in joints and pockets. (2) Well seasoned lumber (with 20 percent or less moisture). (3) Lumber not allowed to lie around on damp ground after it is delivered to job. (4) Untreated lumber not allowed to come in contact with soil, and if imbedded in concrete or other masonry, should have ventilation around ends of timbers. (5) Untreated wood flooring never laid on soil or on concrete in contact with soil. Dry wood never decays.

824. Can an expert tell how old a piece of wood is by looking at it?
No. The only way to tell the age of wood is to count the rings on the stump where a tree is felled. A genuine Stradivarius cannot be identified by the age of the wood.

825. Do trees exposed to buffeting by wind, rain, and snow form stronger wood than sheltered trees?   No. Straight, regular grain makes the strongest and best timber. Gnarled, storm-tossed trees make good firewood.

826. Do some kinds of wood breed pests, such as bedbugs and cockroaches, more than others?   No. These pests do not eat wood. They like dirty cracks in any wood at all.

827. How can frame buildings be protected from termites?   Termites are greedy wood eaters, that must always live in the dark. The trouble is not visible (as you might see decay) until a floor, bookshelf, or table collapses. Termites are mostly found in warm climates but have been coming northward at the invitation of central heating. They start nesting in decayed wood, so precautions are similar to those listed above for preventing decay in frame houses. In warm termite country it is important that all wood be lifted above ground on steel or concrete with metal shields between foundation top and beams. All wood foundations should be treated with creosote. If things are getting out of hand, send for Bulletin No. A1. 9: 1911/3, *Preventing Damage to Buildings by Subterranean Termites and Their Control* (Washington 25, D.C.: Superintendent of Documents, U.S. Govt. Printing Office).

828. What is cooperage wood? High-grade hardwood that can be formed and bent into barrels, pails, kegs, casks. Famous is the white oak used in aging whiskey. Containers for dry produce are called slack cooperate; those for liquids, tight cooperage. A shortage of good hardwood and the substitution of metal, burlap, and fiber for barrels and pails have reduced the demand for cooperage wood, but this is still a big business with some 650 million board feet of saw timber going into it.

829. What is cabinet wood? Wood from a hardwood tree resistant to abrasion, which does not warp, and features color, grain, markings. It is used in furniture, panels, radio and TV cabinets. It should be easy to work and take a fine finish.

830. What are some outstanding cabinet woods? Most famous are mahogany and rosewood, hardwoods from the American tropics and West Indies, and teakwood of southeast Asia, also used for boat decks. (Teak *Tectona grandis,* is cultivated in India, Thailand and Pakistan where some plantations are over 75 years old.) Teak is the outstanding cabinet wood used in Danish furniture. Curly grain walnut is a beautiful specialized type and Danish oak is often used in the structural parts of furniture. Palisander (member of the rosewood family) from Africa is elegant. The Belgian Congo is supplying exquisite cabinet woods for plywood veneer, the most beautiful having the worst name, stinkwood, *Ocotea bullata.*

831. What are the chief American cabinet woods? Black walnut, maple, cherry and, for the new styles of blond wood, birch and holly are popular. Oak has been used as both construction timber and cabinet wood throughout English and American history. Softwoods (pine, Douglas fir, and redwood) are often used for furniture and paneling, but this does not classify them as cabinet woods.

832. What is the cabinet wood that lines the Captain's cabin on the steamship Queen Elizabeth? English elm from piles driven in the Thames to support the original Waterloo Bridge in 1811. When the bridge was torn down in 1936, it was found that the bleaching action of the swirling water for 125 years had turned the elm wood to a rare shade of gray which is now preserved in the Captain's cabin on the *Queen Elizabeth.*

833. What effect do changing styles have on the demand for cabinet woods? Two generations ago rosewood was the de luxe furniture wood; today it is blond woods. Mahogany, because of the rare beauty of its grain and fine qualities of working and durability, has held its popularity. However, interest in antiques and reproductions is turning attention again to rosewood. Mahogany is often bleached now, or darkened, to make it almost white or black.

834. What is rosewood and its secret of success? True rosewood belongs to the genus *Dalbergia,* seven species of which, from tropical America, differ only in the way gums and resins have infiltrated the heartwood, lending different markings and colors. Brazilian rosewood, *Dalbergia nigra,* also called jacaranda, has been used for 300 years. This is the rosewood of the superb pianos and furniture of the Old South, seen in New Orleans and Natchez, and of mid-Victorian days. Only heartwood is used; the surrounding sapwood is commercially worthless, although a doubtful market has been made for the sapwood of second-growth jacaranda under the name of "white rosewood." As the heartwood takes a long time to acquire its colors, only old trees, outwardly defective, supply the fragrant, rich purplish and black wood. Heartwood varies through shades of chocolate and violet with irregular black streaks, and a rose-like odor, mild and lasting. The available supply is limited, although plenty of Brazilian rosewood stands are found in the interior. One of the chief uses for this rosewood today is for carpenters' spirit levels and plane handles.

835. What is bird's-eye or curly maple? This usually comes from sugar maple, *Acer saccharum.* It is a rare and freakish growth of grain that is normally straight. One explanation is that the outer sapwood forms many extra, abnormal buds which do not break through the bark but cause little whirlpools in the grain. This accidental grain is not detected until the tree is cut. It may occur over the whole tree, or only on one side of the trunk, or in patches. As it occurs only in the outer sapwood (which lends credence to the bud origin theory) it is available only as veneer $\frac{1}{28}$ inch thick, from a rotary cut log.

836. What is pecky cypress? This is from the sapwood of bald cypress, *Taxodium distichum,* that has been attacked by a fungus. The resulting decay is contained in small pockets and is arrested when the lumber is cut and dried. This localization does not hurt the durability and use of the lumber where watertight wood is not required. It does add a peculiar distinction for interior finish.

837. What is the most important wood in the cutlery trade? Another rosewood species, *Dalbergia retusa,* from Central America, has beautiful color and grain, is very dense, yet easy to work; an inherent oil makes it smooth to the touch and waterproof; when rubbed with a cloth it takes on a waxy finish without any added wax. Soapy water has no affect except to darken the wood. This is the chief wood for knife handles, small-tool handles, brush backs, musical and scientific instruments, steering wheels on yachts and cars, jewelry boxes, rosary beads, buttons, chessmen.

838. What are special uses of the woods of some of our American hardwoods?

1　*Ash:* baseball bats, boat oars and paddles, ladders, bent parts of chairs
2　*Basswood (linden):* Venetian blinds, picture frames, boxes, shade rollers
3　*Beech:* food containers, bent parts of furniture
4　*Black locust:* insulator pins on telegraph pole crossarms; fence posts
5　*Black walnut:* gun stocks; best wood for woodworking shop
6　*Buckeye:* artificial limbs and splints. Earlier uses, for log cabins, baby cribs and water troughs
7　*Butternut:* wood carvings; church altars
8　*Cherry:* most valuable American cabinet wood, burls for figures in veneer, quarter-sawed for solid beauty
9　*Dogwood:* shuttles in textile mills, golf club and mallet heads, small pulleys, woodcuts
10　*Elm:* wheel hubs, cooperage, interior finish
11　*Holly:* piano, organ, and accordion keys, wood engravings and carving
12　*Maple:* fine furniture, athletic equipment
13　*Oregon myrtle:* beautiful lamps, bookends

14 *Osage orange:* policemen's clubs, archery bows, wagonwheel rims

15 *Paper birch:* toys, toothpicks, spools, batons

16 *Persimmon:* carpenters' planes, bobbins, shuttles, shoe lasts, heads of golf clubs

Possum in persimmon tree

17 *Poplar:* cheese boxes, excelsior, matches, fruit crates, butter tubs

18 *Sassafras:* small boats

19 *Shagbark hickory:* axe, hammer, hatchet, and scythe handles; sled runners

20 *Sweetgum:* radio and television veneer, substituting under the names of "satin walnut," "hazelwood," or "hazel pine"

21 *Sycamore:* Butchers' blocks, thin veneer for berry and fruit baskets

22 *Tulip tree:* center wood for plywood sandwich; inside bureau drawers, drawing boards

23 *Tupelo:* rollers for window shades, hatters' blocks

24 *White oak:* tight cooperage, floors, heavy construction, fine furniture

25 *Willow:* excelsior, charcoal, baskets

26 *Yellow birch:* important for home woodworking shop

839. Does the word mahogany designate a certain kind of wood?

Different kinds of wood today claim the prestige of the mahogany label. One coat-tail rider, Philippine mahogany, *Shorea sp.,* is valuable timber but does not compare with true mahogany. The African mahoganies, *Khaya* and *Entandrophragma,* are not true mahoganies but they are beautiful cabinet woods. Mountain mahogany, *Cerco-carpus ledifolius,* from our western mountains, has hard, strong heartwood of cherry red or chocolate, with a play of light and dark shades which gives the mahogany name; but the small size of the tree and its tortured trunk make it useful for small tuns and carving, or firewood.

Genuine mahogany, *Swietenia mahagoni,* the world's prime cabinet wood, comes from tropical America. It grows from the upper Amazon valley to the Florida keys. Its popularity with Europeans dates back to the early 16th century. It was used in England for shipbuilding long before it became fashionable for furniture. It was used to make tables from 1715 onward. The impetus came with the huge diameters of mahogany logs which made fine tabletops as compared with the difficulty of walnut. The earliest surviving record of the use of mahogany is a rough-hewn cross in the Cathedral of St. Domingo (West Indies), bearing this inscription: "This is the first sign planted in the center of this field to mark the beginning of this magnificent temple in the year 1514." Samuel Record, in his book *Timbers of the New World,* states that the cathedral was completed in 1550 and contains much carved mahogany which some consider the finest in the world, and still in splendid condition after four centuries in the tropics.

840. What makes the figures in wood? These are caused by irregular graining as when the grain of the wood swirls at a place where a branch grew off the trunk; by the pigments and the way they infiltrate the wood; by the annual rings of the trunk; and (particularly in oak) by silvery ribbons called rays that run from the center to the outer edge of the log. These are characteristics of the way each kind of tree grows. In addition, the style of markings depends on the way the log is cut.

841. Does each kind of tree have its own kind of graining? In a general way, yes. The kind of tree can be identified by its grain patterns. But in details there are no two trees with the same grain pattern, just as there are no two people with the same fingerprints.

842. What are the different ways of cutting the log?
1. *End grained* cuts across the log at right angles to its axis. This

makes a wheel-shaped piece, patterned by the annual rings. This is not a lumber cut, as sections are limited in size by the diameter. Trees that have the most vivid annual rings, such as elm, oak, fir, and pine have the most interesting markings.

2. *Quarter-sawed* is hardwood sawed parallel to the radius of the log, across the annual rings from bark to center. This more or less parallels the ribbons (rays) which wave back and forth, appearing as interesting silvery or dark splashes according to the way the light hits them. The hardwoods with the most prominent rays are the most beautiful when cut this way—oak, maple, sycamore. This cut is called *edge-grain* when used for softwood lumber. Here there are no rays, and the beauty comes mostly from pigment variations from resins infiltrating as the face of the board passes from light sapwood to darker heartwood. The annual rings make a pattern of parallel lines.

3. *Plain-sawed* is hardwood lumber cut down the length of log with the face of the saw tangent to the annual rings, cutting across the rays at right angles. The rays now appear as discontinuous straight lines suggesting a rain storm, and the annual rings make outlines of steep mountains. When softwood is cut this way it is called *flat-grain.* This is the most economical way of sawing logs and it makes the wood grain produce the most interesting figures. It is an especially beautiful cutting for ash, chestnut, elm, pine, redwood, and cedar.

843. What is veneer wood? Wood sliced very thin, usually used in plywood, and in baskets, fruit crates and trunks. Veneer wood is glued to doors, furniture, cabinets, but this traditional use has been supplanted to a large extent by improved plywood.

844. How is veneer wood cut?

1. *Rotary cutting.* The log held on a lathe is pushed up to a stationary horizontal knife, and as it revolves it is peeled. Wide, thin sheets of wood come off as though unwinding a roll of paper. This is the way most veneer wood is cut. Lathes are able to hold and revolve, with precise accuracy, logs up to ten tons in the northwestern part of our country where Douglas fir giants are an important source of veneer wood for plywood.

2. *Slicing.* A block of hewn wood, called a flitch, is moved past a veneer knife at any diagonal to produce beautiful grain figures.

This is the usual method where highly figured wood is desired, especially hardwood veneers. The slices from a particular log are usually reassembled in the same relative positions that they had in the flitch and are sold as a unit. This enables the plywood manufacturers of fine paneling to produce "matching wood" designs.

3. *Sawing.* For some woods that tend to crack when cut by veneer knives, the wood can be passed by a rotary saw. This is slow compared to the other methods, but it is highly precise, and sawing can be used for both green and seasoned logs, while cutting and slicing can only be used on green logs. The wood is seasoned afterward.

845. How thin is veneer wood? The standard is $\frac{1}{28}$ inch. With certain kinds of wood and special equipment, it is possible to produce veneer as thin as $\frac{1}{100}$ inch. The thinnest sawed veneer is $\frac{1}{20}$ inch. Veneer that is $\frac{1}{4}$ or $\frac{1}{2}$ inch thick is not true veneer; it is called Shook.

846. What is the difference between veneer and plywood? Veneers glued to the front and back of a heavier core classed as lumber are called plywood. The standard veneer is used on furniture. Much cabinet plywood and architectural plywood are of the lumber core variety.

847. How many sheets of veneer are used to make a sheet of plywood? At least three, assembled with the grain of the center layer running at right angles to the grain of the outside veneers. For special purposes any number, but always an odd number, of sheets may be used. A five-ply board is common for extra strength. The outside layers are called *faces,* and the center layer is called the *core.* When more plies are used, those intervening between the core and the faces are called *cross bands.*

848. How does plywood compare with solid wood? For walls and sidings it offers advantages. For heavy structural work using trusses and arches, laminated timber (which is a kind of plywood) is now specified by engineers and architects. Chief advantages are greater strength in smaller volume and weight; equalizing strength between length and breadth, by orienting the grains of the plies at right angles, or any angle desired; less shrinkage, swelling, and splitting; the handling of plywood sheets is easier for the amateur carpenter and this advantage has led to much do-it-yourself work on finishing walls and making tables and cabinets.

849. What kind of glue is used in plywood? Synthetic resins, which established the prodigious plastics industry, are the glues which have created the towering plywood industry. The key was a glue which would not soften after soaking with water and would retain strength for years. The scientific labels for the synthetic resin glues are phenol-formaldehyde and urea-formaldehyde. The plies are glued under pressure of about 150 pounds per square inch. With some formulas, the press may be heated up to 200° F., while by other formulas in which urea-formaldehyde glue is mixed with other materials such as blood albumin or flour made of walnut shells, the binding is made durable at 70° F.

850. How old is the plywood industry? Early Egyptians invented plywood by combining planks and timbers with grains running in different directions to equalize strength. The Romans and the vikings used the principle of plywood in building their galleys and wherries. But the craftsmen who built the high roofs of the cathedrals of Europe centuries ago had to rely on marvelous arches and trusses, for they had no glue that would bind wood together with a material stronger than the wood itself. Glue of this type was not developed until after World War I. The volume of Douglas fir plywood expanded twenty fold between 1925 and 1937.

851. What is the proportion of softwood versus hardwood used in plywood? Before 1937 most plywood was hardwood, but today more than twice as much softwood is used, and most of this is Douglas fir.

852. What hardwoods are most commonly used for the facing of plywood? Walnut, cherry, mahogany, Korina, oak, birch, and Samara.

853. What are some good reference books on plywood? The Forest Products Laboratory (Madison, Wisconsin) has pamphlets on all phases of plywood manufacturing. Their pamphlet *Wood as an Engineering Material* by L. J. Markwardt has much basic information. A more complete work is *Plywoods: Their Development and Manufacture* by Wood and Linn Edinburgh and London: W. & A. K. Johnston, Ltd.

854. What tools are needed to start a home woodworking shop?
The first step is a set of good carpenter tools. With these tools learn the working qualities of various kinds of wood—their splitting characteristics; how well they hold nails; how they glue and stain; how they work with, against, and across, the grain; which are tough and which are easy; their changes of color; warping; fragrance; smoothness to touch; whittling peculiarities. The best woodworker must know his materials and call them by name. Wood is fascinating material with infinite possibilities of becoming things of utility and beauty.

Woodworking machines will not take the place of hand tools, but they will provide greater scope and make the work faster and easier. In recent years much woodworking machinery for home use has become available. Key machines are circular saw, band saw, jig saw, lathe, planer, shaper, jointer, drill press, sander.

855. What are some of the best woods for home woodworking?
Birch, maple, white pine, and spruce lend themselves most easily to woodworking. These have *even grain,* which means that the annual rings are small, inconspicuous, and have uniform widths.

After that the next easiest to work is *straight grain* wood, which means that the fibers (elongated wood cells) are parallel to the center axis of the log, though widths of annual rings may be uneven. Such trees are redwood, bald cypress and white cedar. White pine is the wood supreme for easy working because it has both even grain and straight grain.

For more advanced work, tougher to handle but leading to more striking patterns in the wood, are the *uneven grain* woods such as hackberry, Osage orange, chestnut. In these the annual rings are variable, wavy and irregular.

Medium fine wood which does not cut as easily as the straight grain but which is wonderful for turning and finishing is the *close grain* type. Some examples are beech, sycamore, black cherry, holly, yellow birch, persimmon, and magnolia. In their case the pores are small and inconspicuous (one can hardly see annual rings in holly).

Sugar maple has this fine texture although it is classed with the other maples as even grain.

856. What are some books about home woodworking? Rockwell Manufacturing Company (Pittsburgh 8, Pennsylvania) publishes a number of paperbound books including *Things to Make, Band Saw and Scroll Saw, Shaper, Finishing Methods*. Porter-Cable Machine Company (Syracuse 8, New York) publishes *How to Use Power Tools* by M. H. Reid.

857. What is the best wood for whittling? Whittling wood must be very dry and without knots. The best is white pine, but spruce and birch are good, in that order.

858. How should a beginner start serious whittling? Some beginners start with a turtle two inches long and stain him to his natural dark tone with roofing tar and kerosene. Then they try a bear four inches long. It is important that the grain runs lengthwise so that the toes which are an important feature of the bear will not break off. More difficult is a slender doe and in this case the grain should be vertical because of the doe's long, slender legs.

The beginner will never enjoy greater ease and fragrance than with white pine and spruce, but whittlers promote themselves rapidly, and will soon be whittling on apple, pear, and cherry. When the time comes to search the country for a dry chunk of hawthorn or a piece of satiny almost white holly, the craftsman is out of the whittling class and has become a wood carver.

859. What is the first rule for good whittling? Always a sharp knife. Keep a whetstone handy and hone the blade on the sole of your shoe. You must cut across the grain as effortlessly as with it.

860. Has whittling ever produced a famous artist? John W. Hill was a creative whittler in Waterbury, Connecticut, some 75 years ago. He was also postmaster in days when the government did not supply the design of cancellation to be used on stamps. Hill, therefore, whittled his own cancellations. There were not many letters, and no parcel post, so he could spend most of the time whittling in the back of the post office. Even today, scores of Hill cancellations

have survived. They are called "Waterburys" and are highly valued
by stamp collectors. His ingenuity knew no bounds—Stars and
Stripes, geometric figures, the town bum smoking his pipe, Civil War
soldier, skull and bones, birds, fish, elephants, trees, insects, clover
leaves, acorns, a valentine heart, padlock, shoe, and beer mug. They
expressed the artist's mood of the moment. Perhaps Hill would can-
cel letters with a fresh design and then throw it away. That is one
reason why his art is so rare and valuable.

861. What, then, is the philosophy of whittling? It relaxes, with
rhythm, contemplation, and the satisfaction of creating something.
One can whittle alone or socially—like smoking a pipe. One may
simply shape a stick to roast marshmallows, or form a paddle out of
straight grain spruce board (use maple or ash where there are rapids
and danger of hitting rocks).

862. What are some good books on whittling and woodcarving?
Whittlings and Woodcarving, by E. J. Tangerman, 1936; *Design and
Figure Carving,* by E. J. Tangerman, 1940. Both books are published
by McGraw-Hill, New York.

V. TREE PESTS AND DISEASES

863. What is the difference between tree pests and tree diseases?
Tree pests are insects and their larvae, which eat and destroy leaves
and wood. Tree diseases are caused by bacteria, viruses and fungi
which invade and upset the tissues of the tree.

864. How do insects damage trees? They eat leaves, sometimes
defoliating the tree. They bore into the trunk, admitting the bacteria of decay. They spread disease by carrying the spores of fungi.

865. Does defoliating by insects hurt a tree? It reduces the food-
making powers which weakens the tree for a season. It does not
kill the tree unless defoliation occurs for several years running.

866. What stimulates pests and diseases? Windstorms break
limbs and open the way to decay. Drought reduces resistance. Too
much water cuts down oxygen for roots. Impoverished soil, lacking
nutrients, weakens resistance.

867. How are tree diseases contagious? By wind or insects carrying the germs from tree to tree; and by organisms causing Dutch elm
disease, oak wilt, and so on, moving from tree to tree through root
grafts. This kind of underground communication has recently been
found to be of common occurrence. In one test of a stand of pine,
red dyes and radioactive chemicals introduced into freshly cut stumps
turned up a day or two later in the sap of nearby trees. It was found
that about half of the pines had established natural root grafts with
other trees.

868. How are tree pests and diseases prevented? By knowledge of the disease and the means of spread. Direct-control methods include the use of sprays, dusts and soil treatments; the removal
and destruction of diseased trees or parts; removal of alternate hosts
and vectors. (See Questions 870 and 877.)

869. How are established pests and diseases controlled? Indirect methods are used, such as, sound timber management prac-

tices; fire prevention (decay fungi enter trees through fire wounds); proper timing of cutting; control of stand composition for the mixture of trees; development and use of disease-resistant varieties.

870. What is a vector? Insects or other organisms transporting germs or other agents of disease are called vectors. Eliminating vectors is one good way to save our trees from the common diseases spread by them.

871. Are fungi ever beneficial to trees? Yes. Despite causing deadly diseases, their help to trees outweighs their harm. The underground cottony threads of many of our common mushrooms unite with the roots of important trees (including beech, oak, pine) causing them to grow faster, more healthy. This is called mycorrhiza, meaning "fungus-root." The fungus substitutes for some of the tree roots and works more efficiently. It is said that the flourishing southern yellow pines depend on mycorrhiza for their existence. (See Question 1041.)

872. Does Florida moss harm the tree it grows on? Florida moss is not a parasite. It is an air plant which derives it nourishment from the atmosphere. But it cuts off sunlight from leaves, thus reducing the food-making power of a tree. Moreover, it is a heavy plant, and in time its weight breaks branches. It likes oaks, especially the live oaks, and also fruit trees. In the South, orange growers consider Florida moss an economic hazard, and hire boys to pull it off the orange tree which otherwise could not fruit or grow normally because of cutting off sun from leaves. If kept under control so as not to get too dense or too heavy, it can be retained as a unique symbol of the South without destroying its trees.

873. How can a mushroom kill a tree? The most lethal tree disease results from a parasitic fungus, a kind of mushroom plant with no chlorophyll. Since it cannot cook its own food from air and water, the fungus must live on food made by green plants. It gets inside a tree and become a parasite.

A mushroom is best known for the temporary umbrella which it raises to throw out spores (microscopic cells that reproduce the plant) while the body of the plant consists of cottony threads. For the common mushroom these are hidden in the ground. The parasitic fungus we are thinking about has a body of soft, flexing threads which grow inside the pores of the wood or in the tree's food canals (phloem) of leaf and bark. The fungus permeates them, choking them so that the water or sap contained in the tree's food cannot flow.

874. What is "root girdling"? This is simply a phrase used when trees are transplanted without giving the roots plenty of breathing space. The result is that one root will entwine another, thus strangling both roots.

875. Do plants other than fungi injure trees? Yes. Parasites such as the mistletoe are common on shade trees of the South and West. They develop witches-brooms which divert food from the growing top of trees, thus reducing vigor and causing premature death. Dodders or climbing vines become so tightly wound around trunks and branches that they strangle trees.

Boomrapes or root parasites are found under beach trees. They make contact with the fibrous root of the host tree, form a nodule of tissue which fuses with the tissues of the host, until the entire root system is intertwined.

In southern Florida the strangling fig climbs large trees, encases them, and cuts off light from the tree's leaves by projecting higher. At length the victim tree is destroyed and a fig tree with a hollow trunk is growing in its place.

876. What causes trees to rot and how can rotting in tree trunks be controlled? Rot or decay in wood is caused by the action of nongreen, simple plants known as fungi, or bacteria of decay. The fungi cannot manufacture food as green plants do, but obtain nutrition by dissolving and devouring wood structures produced by the green plants. The use of chemicals to poison wood-rotting fungi may be helpful in small cavities left after fungus-infected wood has been excavated. In valuable trees, professional arborists fill and seal cavities with appropriate materials and insert drains to reduce moisture. Bacteria of decay only operate in wood that is damp.

877. What are alternate hosts?   Some fungi lead double lives, living in one form on a certain kind of plant and in another form on a different plant. An example is the white pine blister rust which grows destructively on white pines at one time while another form of the same fungus grows on gooseberry bushes at another time. In this case, gooseberry is the alternate host of white pine blister rust.

878. What is the greatest single cause of commercial losses by disease in forest stands?   Heart rot caused by fungi is the chief destroyer of valuable standing timber. Infected trees may sometimes be detected by cankers of fruiting bodies which appear on the outside.

879. Does U.S. quarantine against foreign plant diseases prevent the import of many trees?   The quarantine is strict. Even valuable bonsai trees from Japan cannot be imported without baring the roots and this may destroy them. But many trees and their seeds can easily pass inspection, and certain authorized imports can get permits. For full information write: Plant Quarantine Division, Agricultural Research Service, U.S. Department of Agriculture, Washington, D.C.

880. Does pruning help fight tree diseases?   Pruning is the shortening of branches and twigs, cutting out old worn stems and weak shoots, and thinning out where the trees are crowded with many small branches and twigs. All this provides light and air throughout the branches, making a healthier tree, less subject to disease; improving the quantity and quality of the flowers.

881. Are antibiotics used to combat tree disease?   Antibiotics are organic chemicals produced by living organisms (primarily bacteria and fungi) which are capable of inhibiting the growth of, or destroying, other organisms.

Recently several antibiotics were made available for farm and garden use, but they are so powerful that only minute quantities are needed. The first antibiotic made available to the public was *Cycloheximide* (trade name Actidione), effective against leaf-spot fungus of cherry trees. It can destroy the cherry leaf-spot fungus even after it has been established in the leaf for periods of up to four days. It is never applied when the tree is in bloom because it may cause the blossoms to drop off. Cycloheximide has also been found helpful in combating the rust fungus galls on red cedar and for healing trunk wounds of western white pine after blister rust cankers have been removed. It must be used exactly as recommended because overdosing will cause injury to plants. It is compatible with insecticides such as DDT. Streptomycin and terramycin are being used mainly to control fire blight, the disease of apples, pears and other rose-family plants. Sprays for fire blight control may be used in early-bloom and full-bloom stages, when the bacteria causing the disease are most active. These antibiotics are also useful in controlling walnut blight.

The antibiotics available for plant disease control have been declared safe for people to use. Pears and apples harvested from trees sprayed with these chemicals have been found to contain no trace of the antibiotic activity. The use of these antibiotics is a milestone in plant-disease control, and research workers in this field are finding more and more trees and plants that may be protected from disease by these chemicals.

882. What is gibberellin? A chemical that stimulates growth, derived from a fungus identified in Japan in 1926, named *Gibberella fujikuroi*. It is now produced commercially by growing on special food under laboratory conditions the way penicillin is produced. A minute quantity works marvels. Tulip tree, oak, maple grow much taller when treated with gibberellin; others, such as pine and spruce, are stimulated very little. Gibberellin can also be used to break the dormancy of peach trees and thus quicken crop production.

883. What tree epidemics are rampant over our country today?
The white pine blister rust that attacks all 5-needle pines has caused serious damage to white pine forests in the East and West, but now appears to be under control. The Dutch elm disease is still rampant wherever elms grow, and threatens to wipe out that species. No satisfactory control method has yet been found. The oak wilt is threatening oaks in several states.

Spruce budworm is dangerously active in New England and parts of the West. Bark beetles are causing considerable damage in some spots in the Rocky Mountains and in the South. There are many insect infestations in several areas that are kept under constant watch because a combination of the right conditions could turn them into epidemics.

884. Are there many kinds of tree pests? Tree pests are countless. New ones turn up whenever natural balance is disturbed. There are over 300 kinds of fruit pests alone.

885. Were the trees of the virgin forests in America suffering from the same pests and diseases before the white man came? Many of the same insects were damaging and killing, but their operations were localized. The felling of the trees, the opening of the glades of the forest to sunlight and more air currents caused the insects to spread and to multiply faster, and carried the spores of the diseases farther and faster. Thus there are epidemics today that were unknown in colonial days.

886. Have pests and diseases been introduced from overseas? Imported diseases are an important cause of the great war being waged against insect and disease destruction of trees today. The gypsy moth started from a moth imported for a biological experiment. The moth escaped from a laboratory in Massachusetts. The gypsy moth is now feasting on trees over 36 thousand square miles, including all of New England and parts of adjacent states. The chestnut blight, a fungus disease, came in logs from Asia around 1900—in a few years it had killed almost all the American chestnut trees in the country.

887. What is the nature of the disease that deforms the saguaro cactus? The weird disease that has killed and deformed the symbol of the desert is carried in the intestines of a tiny caterpillar, the larva of a small moth named *Cactobrosis fernaldialis*. There is some fear that this disease may eventually kill all the picturesque, time-honored monarchs of the desert. It causes them to melt away into a black putrescent paste. But science is hard on its heels. For progress report and present status write to: University of Arizona, Department of Botany, Phoenix, Arizona. An authority on the saguaro disease says that research has progressed to a point where the moth can be prevented from laying eggs where they will infest the cactus. The disease is caused by a bacterium *Erquinia carnegieana*.

888. Are any insects good for trees? Many insects such as bees and moths are essential to the life of a tree by helping pollination. The linden and locust with honey-fragrant flowers to attract insects are important examples. Most trees with conspicuous flowers are dependent on insects and birds for pollination. The apple-orchard industry is aided by the rental of beehives when blossoms are opening. Countless insects are harmless and attract birds. The praying mantis, wasp, and others keep harmful insects under control by eating them.

889. What kind of insect attacks are the most harmful? The attacks of leaf eaters and bark beetles which destroy vital plant organs are often fatal to trees. Sucking insects, such as scales and aphids, attack foliage and stems but only gradually weaken or slow down growth. Insects which attack flowers, seed and cones retard the reproduction of the forest by destroying much of the seed crop, but do not damage existing trees.

890. What insects are defoliators and how do they kill trees? Larvae of some moths and sawflies, and adults and larvae of some beetles eat the foliage, stopping the manufacture of food so that the tree slowly starves. Recent examples of widespread defoliating epidemics are outbreaks of the spruce budworm in New England and of the fir tussock moth in the West.

891. What are the most destructive insects? Bark beetles. The Forest Service charges this group with 90 percent of the tree deaths caused by insects.

892. What is a bark beetle? A name for a group of beetles which attack the bark of many different types of trees, such as western pine beetle, or the Douglas fir beetle. Other descriptive names are the fir engraver, turpentine and eastern spruce beetle.

893. How do bark beetles kill trees? They bore into the inner bark and lay eggs in the criss-crossed tunnels. When the eggs hatch, the larvae feed on the bark. When there are many beetles, the bark may be girdled and the tree will die.

894. Does the woodpecker injure the tree he pecks on? This is possible by opening a way through bark for the entrance of fungus spores which initiate rot. But the good this bird does outweighs the bad. The woodpecker likes wood borers, May beetles, weevils, and other insects and larvae. His favorite tree is the one where he thinks these pests are lurking under the bark. Many an old apple tree, for instance, is a haven for beetles and a great attraction to the woodpecker.

895. How great is the damage caused to trees by pests and diseases? Insects and diseases kill more timber than fire. Between 1909 and 1918 they killed about 2½ billion board feet of saw timber annually. By 1945 destruction averaged nearly 3½ billion board feet a year—more than 3 times the fire loss. Today the damage is around 7 billion board feet a year—more than 9 times the fire loss.

896. Has the federal government made any coordinated attack on the insect-disease problem? In 1947 forest industries urged Congress to take action and the Forest Pest Control Act was passed. This act provides means for state and federal governments and private owners to pool their money and work together to discover and attack disease and insect outbreaks. It prescribes broad policies and grants federal aid to control projects on nonfederal lands. It provides leadership in conducting surveys on insect outbreaks and provides for planning, organizing and directing control projects.

897. How does grazing harm a forest? Locally, overgrazing may be more destructive than fire. It is particularly harmful to hardwood forests, where trampling destroys the leafy protective covering of the forest floor, exposing the soil to erosion and trampling. Tree seedlings which renew the vitality of the woods are eaten by the grazing animals.

898. How are sucking insects controlled? Sucking insects get their food by inserting their mouth parts through the surface of the plant and drawing the sap into their bodies. Contact poisons such as nicotine sulfate or lime-sulfur usually kill insects by clogging their spiracles, suffocating them or by affecting their nervous systems. Aphids, leafhoppers, treehoppers, scale insects, mealybugs, thrips, lacebugs, psyllids, plant bugs, spittlebugs, chermids and spider mites belong to this group. For spray and dust treatments of these different kinds of sucking insects see Yearbook of Agriculture, 1952, *Insects* (pages 642 ff.).

899. What kind of poison is used for leaf-chewing insects? Stomach poison is used to control leaf-chewing insects such as caterpillars, sawflies and beetles which bite off the foliage and chew and swallow plant tissue. Some leaf-chewing insects harmful to trees are bagworm, juniper webworm, eastern tent caterpillar, catalpa sphinx, Japanese beetle, and imported willow-leaf beetle. Lead arsenate has been a popular stomach poison but it is dangerous to man. DDT is both a stomach and a contact poison and is replacing the older sprays for all kinds of pests, both sucking and chewing.

900. How is a contact poison different from a stomach poison? The contact insecticides must touch the insects at the time of spraying. Pests such as aphids and scale insects cannot move about, and many insecticides lose their effectiveness in a short time. In contrast, many leaf-feeding insects do move about. Larvae or caterpillars may travel from leaf to leaf; flying insects travel from plant to plant. Killing them at the earliest possible time may be unimportant. An application of stomach poison that reaches only a part of the foliage may be enough.

901. What is DDT? DDT is a name for a commercial solution usually used as a spray to kill insect pests. The letters DDT are abbreviations for dichloro—diphenyl—trichloroethane, a chemical compound made of chlorine, benzine and alcohol. It has been used in this country as an insecticide since 1942.

902. How is DDT applied? It can be applied by hand, by aerosol bomb and by broadcast methods in powders used for dusting, or solutions and emulsions for spraying (usually dissolved in various oils, in xylene and solutions other than water).

903. How does DDT affect insects? It causes death by its effects on nerve centers. It produces a paralysis which usually starts in the hind legs, progressing to death within a few minutes or several hours.

904. Can DDT be used to protect shade and ornamental trees? Despite conflicting views among laymen, entomologists have advised the use of DDT in limited applications to protect trees against most leaf-eating insects. A $\frac{1}{10}$ percent DDT emulsion is particularly effective against tent caterpillers but is also used against locust-leaf miner, boxwood-leaf miner, cankerworms, gypsy moths, sawflies, elm-leaf beetles, the catalpho sphinx, evergreen bagworm, mimosa webworms and most defoliators.

Trunk-climbing insects such as gypsy moth caterpillars can be controlled by spraying a broad band of DDT emulsion around the trunk a few feet from the ground. However, helicopter spraying of DDT has destroyed the natural enemies of red spiders, certain sucking insects and sawfly larvae, and encouraged these pests on arbor vitae, honey locusts, oaks and other trees.

905. When is broadcast spraying used?   There are two major kinds—spraying from trucks to keep down weeds along roadsides and from helicopters and airplanes to cover an extensive area, such as is used in gypsy moth and Japanese beetle control operations.

906. Is DDT spraying safe?   How much beneficial life DDT kills as it is applied to check damage by one type of pest is almost impossible to determine. Damage has been reported in scattered areas and only limited tests have been made, with varying results. In tests reported by the National Audubon Society, bird mortality exceeded 50 percent up to 34 days after spraying. The maximum woodland use of DDT is 2 pounds per acre for safeguarding birds. But less than 1 pound per acre is considered dangerous to bees and other pollinating insects. Honey bees are harmed only when they come in direct contact with DDT in the field because it is not carried into the hive. It is less dangerous to the bee colony when applied with caution than arsenical insecticides.

The problem is not only a matter of how much life is directly killed on an immediate or delayed basis by the insect sprays, but how the natural relations of field and forest or prey and predators are affected. For example, bird populations may decline after one or two years because the prey readily available for fledgling birds is difficult to find. Adult birds know how to search for new food supplies, but the young, who learn their food by stumbling on an abundant supply may not survive the impoverished conditions caused by spraying.

Another problem of broadcast spraying is the destruction of biological control of insect pests and the proportion of insect predators. This happens when a pest starts up again to prey in an area in which most of its predators have been killed. This was the case with gypsy moths which nearly vanished after World War II but which are now a greater pest than before the original spraying. Now annual sprayings are necessary if such areas are not to be overrun, since natural controlling agents are gone.

907. Is there a sound public policy on DDT?   Dr. William H. Drury, Jr., Director of the Hatheway School of Conservation Education in Lincoln, Massachusetts, has made the following recommendations for a sensible policy on aerial insect spraying:

What we must demand is that aerial spraying be restricted to areas where man has entirely altered the natural community. Spraying, like terracing, or damming a stream, should only be entered upon where man intends to take over complete control of the biological balance, and this under the advice of biologists, not chemists or businessmen. We should keep our virulent control measures under close supervision, and this control should be restricted to certain built-up areas. We must avoid ignorant spraying which will destroy biological population control in natural communities. Such widespread spraying is seriously damaging to birds, to all insects, and ultimately seems to defeat the fundamental purpose of insect control.

Specifically, spraying should be done by license under town or state supervision. All spraying should be required to pass the town's local conservation committee, and this supervision should include biologists such as some of the conscientious workers in mosquito control districts. These men should know something about natural communities. Furthermore, a land owner must retain his property rights and give his permission before any spraying be done on his land.

Above all, it is clear that before wholesale insect spraying is expanded further, reason and common sense call for a vigorous program of research on its effects.

908. What is the gypsy moth?   Gypsy moth is a leaf-eating insect that defoliates and kills many fruit, shade, forest and ornamental trees. Caterpillars of the gypsy moth cause several million dollars worth of damage each year over a 38-million-acre area of the northeastern states. They mainly attack oak, poplar, willow, birch, and apple trees and, to a lesser degree, cherry, hickory, gum and evergreen trees.

909. What is the history of the gypsy moth in the United States? In 1869 a French scientist imported the gypsy moth into Medford, Massachusetts, from Europe to interbreed it with silkworms. Larvae of the moth escaped from his home and spread through nearby residential wooded areas. The spread was slow at first, so it was many years before any unusual insect population was noticed. But by 1890 the woods around Medford were so defoliated by the moth that a law was passed appropriating money to fight the pest. It spread rapidly through many states, however, and has persisted despite many efforts at control.

910. What methods are used to control gypsy moths? DDT has been used exclusively against the insect since 1946. Spray operations are preceded by surveys to delimit infested areas. Fall and winter surveys test the physical set-up of the forest to see if there is sufficient danger of further spread to warrant treatment. Spraying is done in the spring with economical aircraft and blower equipment, by federal government workers. Small commercial spraying operations still use hydraulic equipment, which is costlier and more time-consuming.

For many years New England states have been under a federal quarantine to prevent the spread of gypsy moth. Products that might carry the gypsy moth cannot be moved into a sprayed area unless they are certified free of infestation. The largest single aerial spray job ever conducted in the United States to eliminate a pest was started in 1957. The U.S. Agricultural Department cooperated with the middle atlantic states to spray nearly three billion acres of forest land in those states.

911. Does defoliating by tent caterpillars hurt the tree? For many years forest tent caterpillars in Wisconsin were defoliating aspen trees but were not regarded as a serious pest. However, aspen is used commercially for pulp wood and the tent caterpillar seriously interferes with the bark peeling of this wood. Defoliation reduces transpiration, slows down the flow of sap, and peeling stops. This is costly to the pulp wood industry. After repeated infestations of tent caterpillars many trees are now dying, having become susceptible to tree disease.

912. How can tent caterpillars on shade and ornamental trees be controlled? The best control lies in collecting and destroying the egg masses during the winter months when they are easily seen on the twigs. When the caterpillars are about ½ inch long in the spring, spraying the foliage with DDT is highly effective.

913. What is Dutch elm disease? Dutch elm disease (or DED) is caused by the fungus *Ceratostomella ulmi* which develops in living trees as a parasite and in dead elm wood as a saprophyte. In living trees the fungus occurs in water-conducting vessels of the wood. It produces yeast-like spores that are carried through these vessels in the flow of the sap. The toxins the fungus produces and the brown, gum-like deposits in the water-conducting vessels cause wilt and the death of the tree or its branches. After the tree dies, the fungus, still growing on the wood as a saprophyte, produces spores under the loosened bark and in insect galleries formed between the bark and wood.

914. Over what areas is DED found today? The eastern seaboard as far north as Vermont and upper New York and south as far as Virginia, to the Mississippi and beyond. It has spread as far west as Denver, Colorado, and it is likely to occur wherever elms are grown.

915. How does DED spread? The fungus is carried from diseased to healthy trees by two kinds of bark beetles: the native elm, and the smaller European bark beetle—the more important of the two. When the Dutch elm disease fungus occurs in elms in which beetles breed, the fungus may stick to the backs of the beetles which transport the disease to healthy elms in other localities.

916. What is the chief vector of DED? *Scolytus multistriatus,* the smaller European bark beetle.

917. How can one tell if elms have DED? If elm leaves begin to wilt, turn yellow, dry or thin out and fall, the elm may be affected by the disease. It usually appears on one or two branches before spreading to other top parts.

918. Are all elms affected by DED?   All species of elm native in the United States are susceptible to Dutch elm disease fungus.

919. Are any elms resistant to DED?   The Chinese and Siberian elms have a high degree of resistance to the disease, and these species are rarely damaged. One European elm, the Christine Buisman elm, has been found to be highly resistant to the disease and is being propagated and distributed by several nurseries.

920. Where was DED first identified as a fatal disease?   It was first identified as a fatal disease in the Netherlands about 1920. The disease had been known in Europe for many years. Reports concerning dying elms, which was probably due to this disease, were made in 1917–1918.

921. How did DED reach infested areas in the United States? Agents of the Plant Industry Bureau traced the entry and trails of imported elm burl logs (bearing both the disease and its vector, the European elm bark beetle) from old records kept by customs officials, lumber dealers, and railroads. After two years of research they found that the trail started with one infected log at Baltimore and led to records on more than 500 logs shipped into this country between 1925 and 1934. They came in at four ports and sixteen railroads carried them thirteen thousand miles through 21 states. Some of the logs went straight to their destination; some were unloaded, and reloaded after long time lapses. But these logs spread the disease wherever they were shipped.

922. When and where was DED first detected in the United States? At Cleveland, Ohio, in 1930. Samples from dying elms were sent to Dr. Neil Liming, pathologist at the Ohio Agricultural Experiment Station (Wooster, Ohio). He identified the disease which was first recognized in the Netherlands in 1920.

923. Is there any best prevention for DED?   The best way to prevent the disease is to destroy its insect carriers, the elm bark beetles.

924. How may the elm bark beetle be destroyed? Spraying healthy elms with DDT sprays, followed up by a good sanitation program is the most effective method of combating the bark beetles which spread the disease. Elm trees should be sprayed before the spring when the elm leaves appear, with a dormant spray of DDT, using either a hydraulic sprayer or a mist blower. A foliar spray may be used 90 days later. A number of elm disease sprays are available commercially based on the formula given below. It is important that xylene be used in the solvent.

To make 100 gallons of a dormant spray, use 5½ gallons of concentrated DDT (294 pounds of DDT dissolved in 74 gallons of xylene, adding 19 pints of Tuton X-100) for the hydraulic sprayer, or 32 gallons of concentrate for the mist blower, adding 12 gallons of white oil.

A foliar spray is made with only half as much concentrate and white oil. Agitate constantly while diluting the solutions.

925. Can I save my elm after it is affected by DED? There is no known cure today for elm trees once they become badly infected with Dutch elm disease. However, the disease can sometimes be pruned from the tree if found in early stages before it reaches the tree trunk.

926. Do the native and the European-type bark beetles act the same way in spreading DED? No. Both bark beetles feed in living elms and breed in recently cut, dead or dying elms. But the adults of the smaller European elm bark beetle will fly from infested wood to living trees and feed in the smaller twig crotches, while the native elm bark beetles will hibernate in the outer bark of living elms. In spring the native beetle will bore into the bark to feed, introducing the disease into the vascular system of a healthy elm when feeding, and it thus penetrates to the wood of the tree.

927. How can DED be diagnosed? It can be diagnosed correctly only in a laboratory equipped for identifying the fungus. If an elm tree shows the foliage symptoms described, cut off a few small branches, with wilted, dry or discolored leaves. If there is a brown discoloration in one or more annual rings of the wood—as spots, a stippling for a partial or complete ring—take these branches (4 or more, about ½ inch in diameter and 6 inches long) for laboratory diagnosis to the nearest state agricultural experiment station. The elm is not affected by DED unless this discoloration appears.

928. Does the elm bark beetle live only in live elms? Dead elm material of all sorts may be the home of the beetles.

929. How can diseased elm wood be destroyed? By burning, by removing all the bark and by thoroughly wetting all bark surfaces with an emulsion or solution spray containing 8 pounds of DDT in each 100 gallons. For solutions, the solvent should be No. 2 fuel oil.

930. Is the Augustine ascending elm resistant to disease? In 1946 the Augustine Ascending Elm Research Association was formed in Chicago to distribute a new type of elm—propagated by graft on American elm roots. However, Dr. Swingle of the U.S. Bureau of Plant Industry reported that the Augustine ascending elm is susceptible to Dutch elm disease.

931. What is a good sanitation program against elm bark beetles? The U.S. Department of Agriculture Forest Service makes the following recommendations in the leaflet *Dutch Elm Disease Control,* by Russell R. Whitten: (1) Destroy, no later than April 15, all elm material infested or likely to be infested with elm bark beetles found during the dormant period. (2) Destroy within 30 days similar material found between April and September. (3) Carry on sanitation in stands of low-value elms as conscientiously as in stands of high-value elms. (4) Search regularly for breeding places. (5) Destroy elm material containing larvae of smaller European elm bark beetle before you destroy elm material classed as potential breeding places. Trees infected with DED are potential breeding material.

932. What is elm phloem necrosis? PN is another elm disease as deadly as the Dutch elm disease. It is caused by a virus instead of a fungus.

933. How are elm trees attacked by PN? A leafhopper carries the infection from diseased to healthy elms. It may also be spread from diseased root grafts. The disease usually affects the entire top of the tree instead of a few branches as in DED.

934. What species of elm are attacked by PN? American and winged elms are the only elms damaged by this disease, although resistant trees of both kinds have been found.

935. How can PN be recognized in elms? Cut through the bark at several places around the lower trunk on buttress roots and pry the bark from the wood to see the inner bark. If the inner bark next to the wood is yellow, butterscotch-colored or flecked with brown or black, the elm probably has the disease.

936. Is there any sure test for PN? Remove a piece of bark from the tree, strip the discolored inner layer and put it in a stoppered vial or close the hand around it for a few minutes. If the elm has phloem necrosis, it will give a faint odor of wintergreen.

937. How is PN controlled? Like DED, phloem necrosis can be controlled by spraying. The sprays are applied to protect healthy trees from a small leafhopper called *Scaphiodeus luteolus* which spreads the disease. Use a foliar spray when elm leaves are fully grown—usually in June and before July 1. Apply a second foliar spray about mid-August.

938. Over what area has elm PN spread? Phloem necrosis attacked elms in the mid-West, West Virginia, Ohio to Nebraska and Kansas and south to Mississippi when it was first identified. Today it is believed to be wherever elms are found, although no systematic survey has been made.

939. What is oak wilt? Oak wilt is caused by a fungus, *Ceratocytis fagaearum,* which is related to *Graphium ulmi,* the fungus causing Dutch elm disease. The fungus penetrates into the cambium through wounds, and spreads rapidly through the entire tree. The effects appear in discolored leaves. The upper portion of the crown is usually affected first, but it quickly spreads downward. The white threads and spores of the fungus develop in the sapwood. No spores appear on the exterior surface of the bark.

940. Over what area of the United States has oak wilt spread? Single oaks died of the disease at least 30 years ago in Iowa, Minnesota, and Wisconsin, but since 1942, when the disease was definitely recognized, 18 states from Nebraska, in the west, to Pennsylvania have become affected with oak wilt. The disease escaped notice because wilting and dying was attributed to drought, but as rainfall returned, the disease became apparent.

941. How does the oak wilt fungus get into a tree? The fungus enters the tree through the roots or wounds in the trunk or branches. It spreads through the tree by way of the sapwood; as it grows, strands of the fungus and a gummy secretion clog the tree's water-conducting vessels, making the leaves wilt and die.

942. Are any species of oak resistant to oak wilt? So far, every species tested is susceptible to the disease. Red and black oaks will die if infected with oak wilt, but the effect on white oaks is usually not fatal.

943. How does the disease of oak wilt spread? There are two ways: underground through the roots from tree to tree in a stand where the roots of neighboring trees become grafted to one another; overland by insect carriers that are attracted to the mats of fungus spores in diseased trees. A single dead tree has been said to leave as many as 200 such mats, some as big as a man's hand. The growth of mats cracks open the bark. Beetles, squirrels and possibly birds invade the cracks, eat the mats and spread the disease.

944. What are some of the methods now being used to combat oak wilt? Since the fungus grows best at temperatures between 65° and 75° and the insects become active at 70°, spring and early summer are the dangerous times for the disease to spread. A tree that has no wounds in its bark is protected from vectors. One control measure is to avoid injuring or cutting oak trees in the spring.

Another method is to spot the centers of infection early by airplane surveys and isolate the centers of infection. If the disease is spreading underground via the roots, the center may be isolated by cutting the roots in a circle around it with trenching machines.

For slowing the overland spread of the disease, the simplest method is to girdle infected trees, cutting deep into the heartwood.

Burning bark, branches and twigs of dead trees while sawing the lumber is a sanitation method that is highly recommended to timber-men. No infection can spread from dried oak wood and the wood is not damaged by the wilt disease.

A costlier and thus far not generally used method is control through antibiotics. This method has shown effectiveness in the laboratory but is not in general use.

945. What happened to the native American chestnut tree? Today chestnut blight has almost entirely destroyed the American chestnut. The disease was first discovered in the New York City Zoological Park in 1904. Later it was discovered that a fungus from northeast Asia was the cause of the disease, and had probably entered this country on Asiatic chestnut nursery trees. The infection spread from New York City to New England. Less than fifty years after the blight was discovered, it had reached every part of the natural range of the American chestnut.

946. How did the chestnut disease spread? American birds, insects, and winds carried the spores of the deadly fungus areas to healthy ones, while shipments of infected nursery stock, seed, and logs also widened the infected area.

947. About how many chestnut trees were killed? Chestnut trees killed are estimated at more than 9 million acres of chestnut forest stands. Today, living, old chestnut trees are very rare. But the wood of the dead chestnuts is sound and in demand for poles to hold up the nets of tobacco plantations.

948. Where does the United States get its chestnuts today? About 20 million pounds of European chestnuts are imported each year, chiefly from Italy. As the blight continues to spread in Europe, however, fewer chestnuts will be available.

949. Are native chestnut trees making a comeback in New England? We find chestnut sprouts in the woods growing large enough to bear burs. Sprouts from native chestnut stumps may achieve considerable size in areas where the living trees have been absent for twenty or more years. But native chestnut sprouts or seedlings are only temporarily resistant to the chestnut blight. This disease has destroyed them during the past 50 years almost to the point of extinction, primarily because of host vulnerability to the wind-blown spores of the fungus which germinate readily and penetrate into tiny bark injuries. This windblown spread without vectors, such as bark beetles which carry the Dutch elm disease fungus, is an important distinction between the two great tree diseases. As the number of diseased chestnut trees left standing decreases, the prevalence of the fungus likewise decreases. In this sequence, the occurrence of individual trees which escape exposure to the disease fungus may appear to suggest disease resistance. In reality, this is escape survival since the trees succumb to the disease when finally exposed later to the spores of the fungus.

950. What is white pine blister rust? White pine blister rust is a disease of white pines caused by a fungus *Cronartium ribicola,* which grows alternately on white pines and on current and gooseberry bushes, both of which belong to the genus *Ribes* and are popularly referred to as "ribes."

951. Where is white pine blister rust distributed in the United States? It is present in most of our white pine forests in over 30 states from Maine to California and is advancing slowly into remaining white pine areas of California and the Central Rocky Mountains.

952. How did blister rust get started? It was introduced into this country in nursery stock imported from Europe about 1900, but was not discovered in North America until 1906. Since its accidental introduction it has spread naturally through most white pine forest of the United States.

953. Is blister rust always fatal to the tree? Blister rust kills white pines of all ages. Young trees die within a few years; older trees may die before reaching maturity. Death occurs when cankers completely girdle several branches, the main stem, or trunk. Unless infected limbs are removed before the disease spreads to the trunk, the tree will die.

954. How can white pine blister rust be recognized? The fungus enters the needles of white pine and grows into the bark, where it forms diseased areas called cankers. In the spring from April to June orange-yellow blisters push through the diseased bark and release spores.

Since saving infected trees means finding and removing all cankers, they must be recognized in different stages of maturity. Immature cankers appear as an orange-yellow spot on the bark about 1/4 inch in diameter around the base of diseased needle clusters. As the fungus grows, the cankers grow larger and appear as spindle-shaped swellings on branches and young stems. The edge of the canker is outlined by a narrow yellowish rim of bark. Inside the rim the bark is discolored light green or bronze. During the summer and fall a yellowish fluid appears and dark reddish-brown spots called pycnial scars appear.

When the blisters push through the pycnial area in spring the cankers are mature. Each blister consists of a white membrane containing the powdery spores. When the membrane bursts, small holes or pits are left in the bark, which dies, becoming rough and cracked. Where cankers girdle a branch or stem green needles grow yellow and die.

955. Can cankers on white pine be removed? Yes, while high costs are a factor in determining whether the canker-removal work is justified, satisfactory results have been obtained on diseased trees, from young plantation to old ornamental home pines. Infected large limbs are often removed by sawing and the smaller ones are removed with pruning shears. When the bark of the trunk is infected, the infected areas may be removed if caution is exercised. For advice on tools and procedures on canker removal see U.S. Dept. of Agriculture Circular No. 948, *Saving White Pines by Removing Blister Rust Cankers.*

956. How does blister rust spread to healthy pines? The powder-like *aeciospores* of the blister rust fungus cannot infect other pine trees. They spread by wind and infect the leaves of ribes. Pustules appear on the undersurface of the diseased leaves and release *uredospores* to leaves of the same or nearby bushes. These are followed by columns of brown, hairlike *teliospores* which germinate and infect the pines. For more information about this weird life cycle through different kinds of spores see page 389 in *Botany, Principles and Problems* by Sinnott and Wilson (McGraw-Hill).

957. Can blister rust be prevented from spreading to healthy trees?
Loss of pines can be prevented by destroying the wild and cultivated ribes bushes growing within infecting distance of the trees (usually a few hundred feet). Trained workers systematically locate and destroy bushes on hundreds of acres annually. While hand pulling and grubbing have been and still are the principal methods of killing ribes, bushes difficult to find have been effectively controlled by chemicals. 2,4-D and 2,4,5-T are outstanding because of their safety and the ease in transporting their smaller bulk over rough terrain and areas not accessible by truck roads. They may be applied by heavy-duty ground rigs or sprayed from the air.

The U.S. Department of Agriculture is carrying on a carefully coordinated program to establish and maintain control of the rust in several parts of the country. The Department has suggested that forest owners can help rid their white pine woodlands of ribes by following approved forestry methods. Well-stocked stands provide shade, which help suppress ribes. Logging practices that disturb the soil and admit full sunshine should also be avoided.

Owners of white pine forests should consult the state forester or official in charge of blister rust control in their locality.

958. What is the littleleaf of pine?   Littleleaf is the most serious disease of short leaf and, to a lesser extent, of loblolly pine in the Piedmont region of the Southeast. Its incidence is highest in Alabama and stands infected with the disease can be found from central Virginia to northeastern Mississippi.

959. What are the symptoms of littleleaf disease?   Because of similarity to mineral deficiencies of soil, littleleaf has been hard to diagnose. In the early stages of the disease foliage may be slightly yellow and the current year's needles shorter than normal. In the advanced stages the foliage appears in tufts at the twig tips due to progressive reduction in needle and shoot length. The foliage becomes yellowed and branches begin to die. Small cones containing sterile seed are another common symptom of the disease.

960. What is the cause of littleleaf disease? No single cause of littleleaf is known, but after years of research, it is considered the result of a combination of causes. Destruction of the growing tips of the roots by the soil fungus *Phylophthora cinnamomi* is primary, but adverse soil conditions such as poor aeration, low fertility and periodic moisture stress reduce growth and prevent recuperation of the damaged roots. Since the absorbing surfaces of roots have been reduced, less nitrogen is taken in, causing the conditions that may lead to the tree's death.

961. Is there a way to control littleleaf disease of pine? There is no practical control of littleleaf in forest stands, but yard and park trees have benefited by applications of 5-10-5 commercial fertilizer rich in nitrogen at the rate of 1 ton per acre, together with ½ ton of ammonium sulfate. This will prevent symptom development in healthy trees and improve trees in early stages of the disease.

Indirect controls suggested to foresters by the U.S. Department of Agriculture include programs of selecting and breeding shortleaf pines for disease resistance. Soil rehabilitation is another long-term control measure. Increasing the proportion of soil-building species of hardwoods is beneficial since littleleaf rarely develops in superior forest soils. Recent research indicates that adding nutrient zinc to the soil may promote growth with great effectiveness.

Losses from littleleaf may be reduced by the following rules: (1) In stands having few diseased trees, cuts may be light and spaced at 10-year intervals. (2) In stands with 10 to 25 percent of the trees showing littleleaf, cut on a 6-year cycle, removing all diseased trees. (3) In stands with over 25 percent of the trees showing littleleaf, cut all shortleaf pine as soon as merchantable. Areas severely eroded in the past and subject to renewed erosion if the present cover is removed may best be left undisturbed.

962. What is dwarf mistletoe? Dwarf mistletoe is a seed-plant parasite consisting of flowering shoots and a modified root or absorbing system inside the host's tissues. It is found only on conifers and is most common in the far West.

963. Does dwarf mistletoe hurt trees? It causes heavy losses to black spruce, ponderosa, jack and lodgepole pine. It is found on white spruce, knobcone pine, piñon, limber pine and Jeffrey pine, but is not considered as dangerous to these species. Recent surveys in Colorado and Wyoming show that the parasite caused about one-third reduction in growth and a great increase in deaths of lodgepole pine.

964. How does the dwarf mistletoe parasite hurt the host tree? It causes premature death of the host. Young trees die quickly. Older, hardy trees may show almost no effects for years. As the parasite spreads through the crown, the growth of the tree is slowed down by extension of absorbing strands in the bark and reinfection from new seeds. Eventually the top of the tree weakens and dies, diameter growth stops and death of the tree follows. It also results in degrading the tree with pitch-soaked cankers.

965. Can dwarf mistletoe be controlled? Clear cutting as a sanitation measure and proper forest management is the best way to control dwarf mistletoe as no effective chemicals have been found.

966. What is nematode infestation? Nematodes are soil worms that weaken trees by biting or chewing roots and root hairs.

967. What does a nematode look like? A nematode is a tiny roundworm—akin to, but much smaller than, the common earthworm. Nematodes whip around and are very active. They can adapt themselves to many situations in soil, in hot or cold water. Some are equipped with a hollow needle which pierces plant cells and sucks in the protoplasm.

968. Where and when do nematodes attack? The worst damage is done to young seedlings in fruit-tree nurseries where root stocks are frequently shipped in from other areas. If seedlings are grown in infested soil, the nursery practice of lining out new rootstocks may result in a heavy buildup of plant parasitic nematodes in the soil.

969. What control measures are effective against nematodes? Recently soil fumigation in the fall has been found to improve the growth in formerly infested fruit-tree nursery soil. Commercial preparations containing ethylene dibromide are recommended to nurserymen with a nematode problem for fumigating areas used year after year for growing plants received from various parts of the country.

970. What causes the popular Southern mimosa tree to yellow and wilt?   Wilting and yellowing of the leaves are signs that the mimosa tree may be affected with a fungus disease called mimosa wilt. A fungus from the *Fusarium* family lives in the soil and enters mimosa through the roots. It spreads upward in the water-conducting tubes of the wood, causing wilting and quick death to the tree.

971. How does the mimosa wilt fungus spread from place to place?   The fungus spreads rapidly by the movement of infested soil or infected trees. In Morgantown, North Carolina, the disease had affected a few trees in one city block, when it was discovered there in 1943. By 1949 thousands of trees on 559 city blocks had died from mimosa wilt. This problem exists in seven states from New Jersey to Alabama.

972. What is the best solution of the mimosa wilt problem?   Because the wilt fungus attacks through the roots, it is difficult to control through ordinary sprays and fertilizers. Soil treatments with fungicides such as Ferbam have been successful with seedlings. But the best solution is the development of wilt-resistant varieties of mimosa. After much experimentation, The United States Department of Agriculture began distribution of two selections named Tyron and Charlotte. They are available as root cuttings for propagation, as not all seedlings proved resistant. Although present trees are still in danger, planting wilt-resistant varieties promises future safety.

973. What is fireblight?   Fireblight is a disease of apples, pears and other members of the rose family that makes the tree look as if it had been through a fire with blossoms, leaves, shoots and branches brown and withered. It is caused by bacteria that hibernate in the tree in winter and come to life and multiply in the spring. The disease is spread to other trees by insects, but even a heavy rain can splash ooze to a nearby tree and infect it. Fireblight is costing fruit-growers millions of dollars.

974. Can fruit trees be protected against fireblight?   Only a few years ago farmers and fruit plantation owners could not combat fire-

blight with ordinary sprays. Only pear trees were sometimes protected by copper-lime sprays, but then the fruit turned brown. Today
scientists have worked on new antibiotic sprays, such as a spray
containing 100 parts of streptomycin and 10 parts of terramycin per
1,000,000 parts of solution. Chemicals called "wetting agents" are
put into the spray to make the antibiotics soak into the leaves. These
sprays have been used with great success in control experiments,
and results indicate that these disease-fighting drugs will save millions
of dollars worth of fruit in the future.

**975. Is "apple scab" another name for the fireblight disease of
apples?**   No. Fireblight is a bacterial diseases that infects the whole
tree. Apple scab is a fungus disease that attacks the foliage, and
leaves a shallow, black corky spot on the fruit. The scabs not only
detract from the appearance of the apple, but they allow more rapid
loss of moisture than through intact skin. Scabs may also open the
way for disease-producing bacteria and disease-spreading insects.

976. How can apple trees be protected from apple scab?   Several
commercial fungicides and insecticides such as Cap Tan and Ferbam
have appeared on the market for owners of apple trees to use with
home-spray equipment. Sulfur dust and mercury compounds have
also been commonly and successfully used to protect home apple
trees. Orchard owners, however, must adhere to a costly spraying
schedule, especially in the humid parts of the United States. Growers
may consult their state agricultural extension service for details about
these spraying programs.

977. How serious is birch dieback?   This mysterious disease has
devastated paper birches in our northern states and Canada. It affects
older trees so there is hope that younger trees will survive and restore
the birch forests.

978. Does the spruce budworm attack only spruce trees?   No.
The spruce budworm is a small caterpillar that eats the foliage of
spruce and balsam fir in the eastern states and Canada; but it is also
a serious pest to jack pine in the Midwest and to Douglas fir, alpine
fir, white fir, Engelmann spruce, blue spruce, lodgepole and ponderosa pine in the West. It has become such a threat to the pulp and

paper industry that Congress was asked to set aside funds for studying the problem and developing a plan of attack.

979. How does spruce budworm harm a tree? Young caterpillar larvae hatching from eggs deposited on fir-tree foliage become active in the spring. They mine the old needles first. Then they enter the opening buds, where they feed on the tender young needles. They also eat pollen. Although some trees die from heavy defoliations, lasting several years, by thousands of caterpillars, other trees may be so weakened by the budworm that they die from secondary attacks of other insects and fungi.

980. Is there a solution to the spruce budworm problem? Aerial spraying with DDT during the short period when the caterpillars are actively feeding on the foliage has produced immediate and satisfactory results. But studies made by entomologists and foresters indicate that the best way to prevent epidemics of the budworm is by increasing the resistance of the forest to attack. These studies have recommended procedures aimed at restoring a high proportion of spruce to balsam fir and at keeping the balsam in the stands young and vigorous. By clear cutting of mature balsam stands and operating stands on a short rotation, the more vigorous trees left will be able to survive severe defoliation and reduce tree deaths.

981. How does the fir engraver beetle damage trees? This pest of our western fir forests is a beetle that kills trees by cutting transverse egg galleries along the cambium layer, girdling the trunk or killing patches of cambium. Its larvae cause further damage by mining separate channels at right angles to the egg gallery. The beetle introduces a fungus stain into the tree which weakens its resistance. When trees are vigorous, injured patches of cambium heal over; but during epidemics many trees are killed in a single season, either by the fir engraver or by secondary insects.

982. Can the fir engraver of our western true firs be held in check? Since beetles attack both old and weakened firs and new leaders that replace the old tops, there is a wide variation in tree injury which makes control difficult. Insecticides have been used with moderate success, such as ethylene dibromide (2 pounds to 5 gallons of fuel oil), or orthodichlorobenzene (8 pounds to 5 gallons of fuel oil). Hope for control may lie in removing dead and weakened firs while improving the growth and strength of the remaining stand.

983. How does the Poria Weirii root rot destroy Douglas fir?

Poria Weirii is a common fungus of the Douglas fir, the most important lumber tree of western North America. It spreads from tree to tree through the roots and kills many or all trees in small patches of infection. The disease persists in dead-root systems, sometimes for over a century, and infects succeeding young firs.

One type of control calls for replacement of Douglas fir by brush or other conifers which are less susceptible to the fungus. This disease is becoming more dangerous with continuous production of Douglas fir, and no direct or indirect control method is completely successful. Recommendations lie in new forest-management practices which take *Poria Weirii* into consideration in planting and cutting.

984. How can ornamental evergreens be protected from winter injury?

Winter injury, or the discoloration of needle tips or leaf margins on broadleaf evergreens, is caused by drying out of the leaf tissue because of overevaporation of water from the leaves. Evaporation follows periods of high temperatures with intense sunlight and drying winds. When the soil is frozen or when roots do not absorb enough water for replacement the leaves dry out.

The best treatment for winter injury is to provide good growing conditions during the following spring and summer, cultivating and fertilizing the soil. For roots near the surface of the ground, only shallow cultivation should be practiced. Dead parts should be pruned. Prevention lies in the use of windbreaks and mulches of leaf mold, straw or well-rotted manure around the bases of trees during the winter months.

985. How can shade and ornamental trees be protected from avoidable injury?

Man-made wounds are often the result of lack of knowledge, indifference or carelessness. The greatest number of wounds are caused by fires. Man-powered machines such as automobiles and lawn mowers bark many lawn trees, while careless contractors have injured countless street trees with blasting materials and power tools. The installation of sewer, water and gas lines has also resulted in tree injury. Much damage has been done by owners who give the wrong kind of care to their trees: careless pruning, badly filled cavities, scorching the bark when burning out caterpillar nests. Exercise of care, and understanding the proper treatments for damage and disease are the best ways to preserve invaluable home trees.

986. How do tree wounds heal?   According to the Farmers' Bulletin, No. 1896, *Care of Damaged Shade Trees* (U.S. Department of Agriculture), normal healing of wounds is closely related to the growth of woody parts. Increases in the diameter of these parts is brought about by growth that takes place directly under the bark. Increases in length are indicated by the spacing between the ringlike scars left by the terminal buds during successive years of growth. Essentially the same growth processes that enable the tree to increase the length and diameter of its woody parts also function to heal its wounds. If the end of a branch is broken off, the branch does not necessarily cease to grow in length because it has lost the terminal bud. A shoot from a lateral bud may shortly outgrow its companions and form a new terminal so that the branch continues to grow in length. In like manner, growth processes may heal a wound on the trunk or branch. Living cells around the margin of such a wound may form a rim of callus that closes up a little each growing season until the wound is completely covered and healed over. Accompanying this healing there are generally internal protective changes that close the vessels in the wood with tiny bladderlike sacs and by the deposition of wound gums. (See Question 1037.)

987. How can one aid in the healing of tree wounds?   A tree must be vigorous to callus over wounds. The homeowner must maintain the vigor of healing trees by soil treatments that will supply adequate water, air and food-building materials for normal growth. The unnatural conditions under which many shade trees are grown are responsible for unfavorable soil conditions. Sidewalks, roads and buildings restrict normal root development. Decomposing leaves which provide valuable minerals are usually discouraged. Manure, compost and peat will improve the structure of compacted soils and fertilizing ingredients may be supplied to deficient areas. Suitable drainage for excess soil water is another remedy for poor vigor that hinders healing.

988. What are some recommended tree-wound dressings? Asphalt paint, obtainable at most paint stores, may be used as a tree-wound dressing to stimulate wound healing. It may be made antiseptic by mixing into gilsonite, a natural asphalt, a 0.2 percent phenylmercury nitrate solution. Phenylmercury nitrate is very poisonous and must be handled with great care. Pine tar, zinc oxide with linseed oil, and Bordeaux mixture (copper sulfate) in linseed oil are good for preventing decay. Lanolin and lanolin-base mixtures which prevent drying are also good wound dressings.

989. What is slime flux? Slime flux is a bacterial infection. Sour sap oozes from injuries or from pruning wounds and flows down the trunk over the bark. High pressures in the wood force out a bad-smelling fluid which may become viscous and sticky. This happens most often in spring but may continue through the growing season.

990. What can be done for trees affected by slime flux? Drying up wounds by surface sterilization may relieve pressure. Water-soaked trunks can be drained by tapping near the base of the trunk directly under the fluxing part. Bore a hole to the center of the trunk with a ⅜ inch auger. It should be sloped slightly upward for better drainage. If water-logged tissue is tapped the sour sap will discharge under pressure and can be forced out through a piece of galvanized pipe. The pipe should be long enough to carry the fluid free of the trunk and root crown, so that it does not kill the bark. Relieving the pressure and drying up the wounds will effectively treat many cases of slime flux.

VI. THE TREE AS A LIVING THING

991. How much of a tree is composed of living cells? Very little of the volume of the tree's body, perhaps 1 percent or less.

992. What part of the tree is alive? A thin film of cells just beneath the bark enclosing trunk, branches and roots. This sheathing, called cambium, is only one or a few cells thick, and is invisible to the naked eye. Other living cells are at the tips of roots, and in leaves and buds.

993. How does a tree grow? Increasing in height and lengthening of branches begins inside a bud at the moment it starts to open. Then cells at the base of the bud divide vigorously, multiplying their numbers. These miraculous cells have soft, thin walls; they are distended with protoplasm and contain a nucleus with inheritance genes and enzymes (proteins that control growth). As these cells increase in number, the apex of the twig is pushed up or out, leaving behind cells formed by the division. Then the cells which had multiplied by division absorb water. The water enters into the center of each cell, pushing the protoplasm to the outside where it is held just beneath the cell wall. This causes the cell to expand in all directions but chiefly by elongation. Most growth comes from the elongation of cells. The enzymes exert a mysterious control which results in the growing tree taking the form (top growth will go farther than growth to the side, making it tall and tapering) of its species and keeping it always in balance.

Growth in diameter of trunk is coordinated with the increase of height and width. Each of the living cells in the cambium is long and slender, rectangular in cross-section, and arranged parallel to the axis of the trunk. Like the cells squashed down at the base of buds, these are thin walled, vital with flowing protoplasm including enzymes. When buds are opening and twigs are elongating, trunk and limbs receive a signal to increase in girth. Their cells are split crosswise by a partition across the middle, and one half glides alongside the other. In some cases two cells of trunk and limbs split down their length, leaving one half beside the other. This builds the width of the annual ring when the two halves swell to full-sized cells. At the same time, they elongate, keeping up with the increasing height of the tree or the increasing length of its branches.

994. How does a tree create wood? When growth slows down, the walls of the cells on the inside of the cambium film harden with the addition of lignin (see Question 750) and other chemicals, their protoplasm disappears, and they turn into dead wood cells. At the same time a marvelous job of conversion takes place in the cells on the outside of the cambium film. Here most of the cells are thickening their walls with cellulose, but not with lignin; they are keeping their protoplasm but nuclei disappear. They are alive but not dynamic. These cells are lined up end to end. Where they touch, the ends form plates set at diagonals, as though mortised by a carpenter. These are perforated so that strands of protoplasm flow between them. They are called sieve tubes and they serve as supply lines of food: a continuous course from the leaves, where food is manufactured, all the way to the roots.

995. Do the sieve tubes later turn into wood? No, all wood is made on the inner face of the cambium sheath, and all food-conveying cells are on the outside face. Six to eight times more wood cells than sieve-tube cells are added each growing season. Thus the trunk is built mostly of wood. The food cells are active only for about a year, and then their places are taken by freshly made sieve tubes. The old ones lose their protoplasm, and being soft, they are crushed by the force of the expanding wood and lost sight of.

996. Why do lower branches of trees gradually die? Normally because of lack of light. Without light, buds do not open. When buds die there are no leaves, and the cambium the length of the branch also dies. Other reasons for the death of branches are breaking by storms and attacks by fungi or insects.

997. What are the chief causes of the death of trees? Violent destruction by man, insects, fire, erosion, wind, lightning, flooding. Slow destruction by parasite attack, especially that of fungus decay, and starvation through years of bad weather or change of environment (for example, real estate development) which weakens resistance to disease.

998. In the absence of fatal events, would trees live forever? The philosophical answer to this could be yes, based on the fact that all the living cells are renewed each year, fresh and young. The bristlecone pines are over 4,000 years old and who can say how long they will live if spared destruction by the things that usually deal death to trees?

The practical answer is that trees do suffer the infirmities of old age leading to death. The rate of food-making by the leaves is much slower in older trees than in younger ones. Older trees do not produce new and vigorous shoots. Wood-making cells slow down. Dead branches increase as growth decreases. Wounds do not heal as easily as on young trees.

999. What are the life spans of some important American trees? Bigger trees with harder wood mature slowly. An oak takes twenty years to mature its seed, and its average life is two to three hundred years. This is also true of hickory and walnut. An apple tree fruits after five to eight years and it is often old and feeble in forty years. Maple is intermediate, seeding in twelve to fifteen years, and old in fifty to seventy-five years. Birches are old at forty. Maximum ages far exceed these limits. Some oaks may live 1,500 years.

Softwoods (or evergreens) are longer lived than hardwoods because of resin and turpentine substances in the wood which help them resist decay and insect attack. (See Question 37.) Sequoia appears immune to pests and the bark is fire-resistant—so it normally lives five hundred years or more. The General Sherman is over 3,000 years. (See Question 63.) Some junipers may live 2,000 years. Pines as a group live from 100 to 600 years.

An individual tree's life span is not scheduled like that of an animal which can run around and find conditions to preserve life. A tree must stand and take it, and is therefore more vulnerable to changes in climate, moisture, soil, and temperature.

1000. How have trees moved around to reach their sites on the face of the earth? Seeds have enabled trees to march around the world through the ages. Inside the seed is the miniature of its parent—

a tiny leaf, stem and root. This is packed with food on which it can live while traveling, and wrapped in a package easily transported by wind, water, birds and other animals.

Pine, maple, elm, ash, ailanthus and birch seeds have wings to ride the winds. Acorns and nuts are transported by squirrels. Birds eat berries and disperse their seeds. Floating coconut and mangrove seeds ride the seas.

1001. If heartwood is the most indestructible part of a tree trunk, why are there so many hollow trees?   In an undamaged live tree, heartwood is well protected from fungi and wood-boring insects. Damage by lightning, or where branches break off, may give entrance to the bacteria of decay. In the moisture of the interior, decay may go on for years and cause a hollow tree. This happens chiefly to trees like apple, willow and linden the heartwood of which does not contain resin and tannin. Evergreens like red cedar, bald cypress and redwood do not become hollow.

1002. How can hollow apple trees produce blooms and apples?
In a mature tree the whole central region is dead. As the trunk expands, this heartwood region expands and the sapwood becomes narrower around the outside; and all the food transporting part of the tree is just under the bark; thus, the center is useful only as a mechanical support. The life of the tree can flourish as long as the tree can stand.

1003. Do trees have nervous system?   Not in the sense of a network of nerve fibers. But all protoplasm of animals and trees is sensitive, and may communicate impulses from cell to cell without nerves. The best example among trees is the way the leaves of mimosa, when touched by a browsing animal or peppered by raindrops, will promptly crease lengthwise, then move together like closing fingers of an extended hand, and then turn downward. People who try to find a purpose in everything say that mimosa has learned how to get protection in a tropical downpour and from a browsing animal which turns aside when a delicious green leaf disappears before its nose.

1004. What makes leaves and branches turn toward sunlight?
This is primarily a chemical action, occurring when enzymes that

stimulate growth are inhibited by light. This causes more cell elongation and division on the dark side of the twig and leaf stem than on the bright side. The growing cells push the twig or stem so as to bend it toward the light. In the same way a stem coming out of the seed will elongate in darkness. This operation can also be seen in potato runners that emerge from potato eyes in a dark cellar and seem to run after light. (See Question 1036.)

1005. Are leaf veins nerves? In botanical language they are called nerves, but in the sense that they carry vital fluids of the tree body, they are analogous to veins and arteries of an animal body.

1006. Does a tree have anything like circulation of blood? No. Its vital fluids are sap which is mostly water, in which minerals from the soil are dissolved along with plant sugar in solution. The sap moves upward from the roots through the wood of the trunk and limbs and into the leaves. The sugar in solution moves down from the leaves and circulates through the tree *via* the sieve tubes just beneath the bark. But this is not blood or a circulation pumped by any organ like a heart.

1007. Without a pump, what makes sap flow up through a tree? Sap flows up through wood cells end to end (the grain of the wood). These are microscopically slender, so the column of water is divided into practically weightless threads, yet continuous from roots to leaves. The cohesion of water molecules on the surface of water is very strong, and in such minute threads all molecules are surface. These amazing pipelines terminate in leaves where water evaporates rapidly into the air. This sets up a tension in the water threads which pulls up more water. The tensile strength of sap—that is, the ability to pull on it lengthwise without breaking it—has been found to be as great as 2,250 pounds to the square inch. This is 150 times greater than the pressure of the atmosphere and enough to lift sap many times higher than the tallest trees, merely by the gentle tug of evaporation at the top.

1008. How does a tree get the materials for its structure? The tree breathes from the tips of its highest leaves to the tips of its deepest roots. The material used in the structure of its wood is 95 percent taken out of the air. This includes the water which it picks up in the ground but which fell out of the air.

The 95 percent consists of carbon, hydrogen, and oxygen. This is the body of the tree, its material mass, strength, toughness. Strangely this is wrought out of air and water. The remaining 5 percent is the chemical magic of the tree. This consists of minute amounts, mere traces of some 15 other elements. The amazing thing is that these are not mixed haphazardly in the tree but are precisely put together with a little of this and a touch of that, making things happen in a predestined way. The delicate combinations are far beyond the ability of man's chemical laboratory.

Phosphorus creates seeds and promotes root growth. Calcium develops leaves, protoplasm, and fresh cells. Magnesium gives the mysterious power to chlorophyll and spurs on phosphorus. Potassium makes the life blood of the tree, filling the sap of growing tips, giving power to pollen, helping nitrogen to form proteins. Sulfur is the building material of protein, and it makes root hairs. Iron acts as a sparkplug for chlorophyll. Silicon, the element of glass, enters into the manufacture of the bark of the tree.

1009. What force causes food to flow down through the tree? Food-supply lines are made of elongated living cells, with beveled ends fitted together. These ends are perforated so that threads of protoplasm flow from cell to cell. Tree food travels through this system by diffusion, a phenomenon by which solutions move from greater concentration to less concentration. (A drop of ink in a glass of water spreads, or diffuses, through all the water.) With living cells this happens through cell walls known as permeable membranes. This is the famous process of osmosis by which living cells are in communication. Thus, sugar in solution made in leaves flows along the threads of protoplasm that communicate through the perforations of the sieve tubes, as well as by osmosis.

1010. Is sugar the only food a tree lives on? Sugar is the first stable food made by leaves. This type of sugar is called glucose, dextrose, or grape sugar—chemical formula: $C_6H_{12}O_6$. It is about $\frac{3}{5}$ as sweet as the sugar in our sugar bowls. In the sense that this is the basic food made by leaves it may be said that it is the only food a tree lives on. However, it is quickly converted into other forms of food such as starches, fats, oils and proteins. To make protein, nitrates, sulfates and sometimes phosphates must be added to the sugar.

1011. How does a leaf make sugar? By photosynthesis, a fundamental process of nature, the sole source of food in the world for all plants and animals. It consists of combining elements of water and air by means of the power of light, producing glucose. First the hydrogen and oxygen in the water molecule are split apart. Then the free hydrogen is combined with a molecule of carbon dioxide from the air. This combination of hydrogen and carbon dioxide is worked over until it turns into glucose. The extra oxygen from the water may be used to oxidize sugar already made to give energy for building cell walls—or else it is thrown away into the air where it may later be breathed by animals. Of the air (which enters the leaf factory through perforations mostly on the underside of a leaf) 80 percent is nitrogen. But free nitrogen in the air cannot be used to make sugar by the tree. When the carbon dioxide is extracted and put into sugar, the nitrogen is thrown away, going out through the pores of the leaf—the way it came in.

1012. What part does chlorophyll play in food making? Chlorophyll selects certain light rays. This unique chemical compound absorbs the orange and red rays of sunlight and uses them directly in combining hydrogen from water and carbon dioxide from air. Chlorophyll reflects or transmits the yellow and blue rays (that is, throws them off while absorbing the red and orange). The yellow and blue rays are combined when our eyes see the leaves as green in color.

1013. Can modern chemistry make chlorophyll and in so doing produce food at will? Chemists have claimed that they can make chlorophyll in small amounts and at great expense. But it is so complicated chemically that its exact structural formula is not definitely known, and it cannot be produced easily and repeatedly. A formula for chlorophyll is $C_{55}H_{72}N_4O_5Mg$. The atom of magnesium at the end of this formula is remarkable because elsewhere magnesium plays little or no part in living things. How such a complicated molecule is formed quickly in the first tiny leaf that peeps out of the opening seed is a mystery.

1014. Does chlorophyll have any counterpart in an animal? Its chemical formula is the same as blood—with one tiny difference. Instead of the atom of magnesium, blood has an atom of iron.

1015. If sugar is the only basic food of trees, how is it that fertilizers are called tree food? In addition to basic sugar, a tree in order to grow, produce seeds, and prosper, needs small quantities of nitrates, magnesium, iron, phosphorus, potassium, calcium—which are obtained not from photosynthesis, but from the soil. These mineral elements are dissolved in soil water where roots pick them up. Under natural conditions small amounts of these minerals are always available in soil. But where they have been used up or eroded away, the soil is impoverished. That is why fertilizers are used. This is not food in a strict sense because these minerals are not oxidized to supply energy.

1016. Do trees drink rainwater that falls on their leaves? No. Leaves are waterproof. Trees get their water from the ground.

1017. How can a waterproof leaf make food by fluttering in the sun? The leaf is an instrument more delicate and precise than the finest watch. Upper and lower surfaces are made of cells that fit together as hexagons, like the closely packed cells of a beehive. These skins are one cell thick, waxed with tough waterproof cutin, but translucent so that light can pour through. In the dimensions of a cell there is considerable space between ceiling and floor. Although a leaf may look thin to us, it is, in effect, a big factory room for making food. Very long cells (*palisade* cells) hang vertically from the ceiling. Below these is a big collection of cells (*spongy* cells) curved and facing in all directions permitting air to circulate between them.

A leaf is permeated by a fine network of pipes bringing water from the roots, and taking sugar solution away. This pipe system appears in the form of veins in the larger parts, but branches to invisibly fine threads that reach into every part of the leaf so perfectly that no cell is more than two cells away from pipeline service.

Air is admitted to the spaces between cells through openings in the bottom surface. These openings (called *stomata,* meaning "little mouths") are very numerous. An average is 25 to 50 thousand per square centimeter of leaf surface. These are opened and closed by

two fat cells on each side like two curved sausages with ends touching.
Light causes them to take in water and swell up—the stiffening opens
the pore between them. One minute after the sun passes under a
cloud, a valve is closed. They are only open completely when the sun
strikes. The palisade cells are packed with chlorophyll that filters
the sunlight. Thus, when light pours through a leaf, it goes into action
with plenty of air and fluids to work with.

Whereas a watch is run by mechanical power from the tension of a
spring, a leaf is run by light power and its work is photochemical. Man
uses photochemistry in coating photographic films, and in the photo-
electric cell.

**1018. How does a leaf change position so as to present the broad-
est surface to the sun?**   The leaf has two visible parts—the broad
part, which contains the food factory, is called the *blade,* and the
stem, called the *petiole.* The petiole is part of the whole operation. It
may be long or short to hold the leaf clear of its neighbors; and it may
turn, bend, or droop, in giving the leaf the most advantageous position.

1019. How many leaves does it take to create an apple?   It has
been estimated that it takes thirty leaves to make a Jonathan apple,
and fifty leaves to make a big Delicious apple. A large peach takes
thirty leaves, but an average-sized bunch of grapes can be filled with
juicy sugar by twelve to fifteen leaves. Of course, the number of
leaves is not what matters, but the area of the surface. It takes only
a few enormous leaves of the banana tree to pack a huge bunch of
bananas with carbohydrates.

1020. Does a tree breathe?   Not like an animal which breathes
rapidly by means of a lung. But the living cells of trees use respiration, that is, combining food with oxygen to release energy. This
process is basically the same as respiration of animal cells. In the
tree the exchange of gases with the outer air is accomplished by diffusion. It proceeds slowly and quietly compared to the vivid operation of animal breathing, but it never stops. Every living cell is respir-
ing all the time. (See Question 1008.)

**1021. What is the difference between respiration and transpira-
tion?**   Respiration combines oxygen with plant sugar, releasing car-

bon dioxide and energy. (This is exactly the reverse of photosynthesis, in which carbon dioxide is combined with hydrogen in water, and oxygen is released.)

Transpiration has nothing to do with energy storing and releasing in food. It is simply the release of water in the form of invisible vapor from leaves. This comes out through the pores of leaves. The water so released originated in the ground and was carried up to the leaf as sap. (See Question 1007.)

1022. How does a tree use energy?   Some tree energy escapes in the form of heat, as it does in animals. Rapidly opening flower and leaf buds generate heat. Most tree energy is expended in internal activities such as motion in the streaming of protoplasm; the moving of chromosomes in cell division; the converting of food into cell walls and protoplasm; the manufacturing of proteins and essential oils, resins and tannin; the accumulation of mineral solutions from the soil—not to mention the need for energy to grow and produce leaves, flowers, fruits, seeds.

1023. What is the difference between living cells of trees and animals?   One difference is that tree cells (this is true of all plants) surround themselves with a definite wall, whereas animal cells have merely a membrance that is a slightly toughened surface of protoplasm. The tree cell wall is made of cellulose. The wall between two adjacent cells is double, with pectin sandwiched in between as a binding material. As cells mature, their cellulose walls harden to become wood. Thus, the body of a tree with cellulose-walled cells bound together by pectin is a much firmer and enduring body than that of an animal. Also, cell walls provide a skeleton structure, whereas animals must obtain their skeletons with bones, apart from other body cells.

Another difference is that certain tree cells can produce chlorophyll, the green pigment that enables them to make their food out of water and air.

Except for these important differences, the awe-inspiring fact is that the fundamental nature of plant and animal cells is the same. They carry on similar intricate chemical processes, and the principle of cell division and genetic inheritance is the same, tying together the whole biological kingdom!

1024. Do trees have sex? Yes, all seeds are produced sexually—the female egg must be fertilized by the male sperm. The egg is contained in the swollen part at the base of the pistil of a flower. The sperm, contained in pollen, is produced in tiny containers at the top of the stamens. In a typical tree flower these are both in the same flower. In such a case a tree may fertilize its own seeds simply by letting the pollen fall out of the pollen boxes on to the pistil.

Nature has endowed some trees with cross-pollination, that is the pollen from one tree fertilizes the egg of another tree of the same kind. In this case the egg and the sperm of an individual tree ripen on different days or at different hours of the same day. Pollen blows across from one to the other, or is carried by insects. Trees which are wind pollinated have dry pollen and their flowers lack petals and are often in the form of tassels which whip around in the wind. Those which are insect pollinated have sticky pollen, and their flowers have petals and fragrance. The ways and devices of nature in effecting sexual reproduction among trees rooted to the ground have amazing logic and resourcefulness.

1025. What are the principal trees using wind pollination? All the pines; standard hardwoods such as elm, maple, beech, ash, sycamore, gum, persimmon; and those trees with tassel flowers, which are particularly adapted to wind pollination: walnut, hickory, oak, beech, birch, willow, poplar, and alder. (See Question 1029.)

1026. What are the principal trees using insect pollination? Catalpa, horsechestnut, redbud, dogwood, shadblow, hawthorn, apple, cherry, peach. Basswood (American linden) uses insects without having showy petals, but it does have much fragrance.

1027. Do trees ever have separate sex organs in different flowers on the same tree? Yes. All pines do this, with male cones at the tips of high branches throwing pollen to the wind, while female cones are lower down in the angles of twigs ready to be spattered with the yellow pollen. The tassel-flowered trees have stamens and pistils in separate tassels. Sometimes elm and maple separate their male and female flowers, but more often they are combined. Trees with sex organs in different flowers, but on the same tree, are called monoecious.

1028. Are there male and female trees? Yes, a few trees have separate sexes because their male and female flowers grow on separate trees. Some examples are ash, holly, poplar, willow, ailanthus, date palm, and ginkgo. Trees with separate sexes are called dioecious.

1029. How can trees with separate sexes depend on transferring pollen with such a fickle agent as wind? By making astronomical quantities of pollen grains and filling the air with these microscopic parcels of sperm. A single birch tassel may produce more than 10 million. One cluster of flowers on a sycamore maple may produce 25 million; multiply this by 12 for a single branch. Oak's male tassel is small but it can put on the airways over 500 thousand grains. Pine tree pollen is produced in such quantity that it looks like yellow steam against a blue sky. Fabre, the perceptive French naturalist, tells of two female pistachio trees in the Paris Botanical Garden which had flowered abundantly for years, but never produced fruit. Suddenly one year, astonishingly and without any apparent reason, their ovaries turned into nuts which ripened nicely. A search was made to find some unknown male pistachio tree in the neighborhood. At long last one was found in a garden on the other side of Paris, which had flowered that year for the first time. The wind had borne its pollen over the houses of Paris to hit those pinpoint targets miles away.

1030. How long does pollen remain alive? Pollen's working life depends on temperature and moisture, and every kind of pollen is different. Apple will live for several months if prevented from drying out. Date palm pollen with live for several months if kept dry. Dry pollen stands extreme temperatures better than wet pollen. Apple and pear live close to freezing, which would kill peach and apricot pollen. Generally, a day or two after pollen is shed, it is worthless for fertilizing ovaries. Its length of life is not comparable to that of seeds.

1031. What is the nature of a pollen grain? The oldest types of plants such as ferns, mosses and fungi reproduce by spores instead of seeds. These are thin-walled cells shed by the parent plant, apt to fall in a moist spot and sprout immediately. A pollen grain is a kind of spore. Like a spore it is a single cell, invisible to the naked eye, and can travel as blown dust. It is far better able to take a beating because it has a tough coat embossed with knobs, spikes, and ridges that resists acid and alkali attacks and is insoluble in all solvents. Attempts to analyze pollen indicate that it is about 50 percent fat, 8 percent protein; the rest is cellulose and a mystery chemical compound called sporonine. Sporonine (the same substance found in standard spores) is about 65 percent carbon, 26 percent oxygen and 9 percent hydrogen. This is a revelation of how nature—quietly, swiftly, easily, without complex laboratory equipment, and without terrific pressures and extremes of heat and cold—combines common elements to produce a product that is perfectly designed to accomplish a purpose. And these exquisite living jewels turn up at precisely the right place and time, by the billions, on trees.

1032. What is the difference between pollination and fertilization?
Pollination is the delivery of pollen to a pistil. Fertilization is the uniting of the sperm (which was carried by the pollen grain in the form of a nucleus) with the ovary so as to start it turning into a seed.

1033. How does the sperm get from a pollen grain lodged at the top of the pistil, into the ovary buried inside the swelling at the bottom of the pistil? The grain, firmly held by stickiness or by feathery hairs, is moistened by a sugary solution and warmed by sunlight. It opens, a pollen tube emerges, punctures the pistil and grows down its length until it reaches the ovary. It feeds on nourishment supplied by the living cells of the pistil encountered en route, so that it can keep growing to reach the goal—whether a half inch or several inches away. (Corn pollen landing on long corn silk may have to travel eight or ten inches!)

1034. How can a weak tube from a microscopic pollen grain travel through the inside of a pistil? Some pistils have a tunnel, others have a channel of soft cells, and the pollen tube eats its way through these.

1035. Do trees use vitamins? Yes, vitamin B has a good influence on root growth. Vitamins, growth substances, hormones, and auxins are used, and are almost interchangeable words when talking about the life of trees. A slight trace of these substances can have remarkable and subtle effects, sometimes stimulating growth, sometimes inhibiting it. Their chemical nature is that of a complicated carbohydrate; a basic auxin formula is $C_{18}H_{32}O_5$. This means that 18 atoms of carbon, 32 atoms of hydrogen, and 5 atoms of oxygen are combined to make a molecule of auxin. What power or wisdom contrived the exact number and proportions of elements put together for this substance is a question far beyond our comprehension. Equally so, *how* they are assembled and recreated so silently into auxin in a tree, and *how* they go about making cells work faster and twigs elongate.

1036. What happens when auxin elongates twigs? Auxin is made always in the growing tip, just after the bud opens. The substance then travels through living protoplasm of the cambium just beneath the bark to the place where it goes to work. This manufacturing in one place and traveling to a distant spot to help with the growing is interesting. It works best in darkness or low illumination. This is why tree branches turn toward light as the cells are stimulated to grow more on the darker side, and this pushes the branch toward the light. In dim woods saplings will elongate greatly, as though reaching for light. The corollary is that bright illumination makes auxin shy and this inhibits growth. Thus, trees on bright mountain tops tend to be stunted. (See Question 1004.)

1037. How does a tree form a callous that protects a wound? This is the result of another hormone that is similar to the growth substances. But whereas auxin, the elongator, is produced at the tips of growing shoots, wound hormones are created at the site of the injury where they stimulate cell division and develop a special protective layer of tissue. (See Question 986.)

1038. How do enzymes differ from hormones in the life of a tree? Hormones are carbohydrates that stimulate cell division and so promote the body building of a tree. Enzymes are proteins that appear in the protoplasm of any living cell and act as a sort of lubricant for its digestion, that is, they speed up the process of turning food into energy. Chemists would call them a catalyst because the enzyme itself is not used up in the process. Enzymes are nonliving and will do their work in a test tube as well as in a living cell. An enzyme will perform only the operation it is designed for. Hundreds of different kinds of these marvelous proteins have been identified. As one biologist says, enzymes are fashioned to fit a particular process, just as a key is made to fit a particular lock.

1039. What is a mycorrhiza? This awkward word means "fungus root" (*myco,* fungus, and *rhiza,* root, adapted from the Greek). A peculiar kind of root formed by the white threads of a fungus encloses a tree root with a heavy, white hairy mantle. The result is a stubby thick root which looks like a deformity but is actually an efficient root organ that contributes to the health of the tree.

1040. What kind of trees have mycorrhizas? Almost all pines. It is said that the great southern pine forests germinate more seeds and attain the health and size they do as a result of this combining of mushroom threads and roots. A large number of hardwoods, especially birch, oak, and beech develop mycorrhizas. Over 80 percent of all flowering plants enjoy mycorrhizas.

1041. How does mycorrhizal growth differ from destructive attacks of fungi? The threads of the fungus seem to be more efficient than root hairs in imbibing both mineral salts and organic nitrogen from the ground. In return for this service the tree has only to pay with its sugar, which the leaves manufacture so abundantly that there is plenty to spare. Moreover, the fungus does not poison roots or inhibit root hairs. It adds a larger and longer-lasting organ of nourishment-collecting to the normal complement of root hairs.

When A. B. Frank, Professor of Plant Physiology in Berlin, concluded that the mycorrhiza represents a cooperation between mushroom and tree which helps both, and is not the attack of a parasite, a storm of protest arose. This kind of root looks diseased, but the trees on which it is found are the healthiest. Much research has confirmed the early theory. Today soil is inoculated with the mushrooms to improve the crops of trees, as well as many other crops.

1042. What kind of fungi form mycorrhizas with trees? They are the everyday mushrooms of the woodland.

1043. Does each kind of tree prefer a certain kind of mushroom? Trees have preferences. Birch often uses the fly amanita; white pine likes the milky mushroom (*Lactarius*); Scotch pine prefers boletus;

beech and oak seem to prefer a puffball. But there is no positive way in which trees and mushrooms choose partners. Some mushrooms will be found on a number of different trees.

1044. Do the fungi threads penetrate the living cells of the tree root?
There are two kinds of mycorrhizas. The *ectrotrophic* surrounds the root with the felt of living threads, from which a few loose threads reach out. The *endotrophic* mycorrhiza pricks into the living cells of the root, and the tip of the fungal thread forms a ball from which bushy branches fill the inside of the cell (a microscopic event). This type takes more carbohydrates from the tree, but it does not seem to matter, and when the fungus dies the tree enjoys the borrowed food. This kind of mycorrhiza seems just as beneficial as the exterior kind. It is used by redwood and big tree sequoia, and by auracaria, cypress, arbor vitae. Juniper uses both interior and exterior mycorrhizas.

INDEX

References are to question numbers